P9-BIG-542

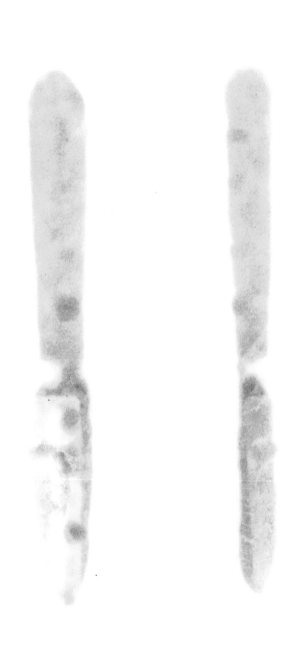

International Library of Psychology
Philosophy and Scientific Method

THE LOGICAL SYNTAX
OF LANGUAGE

THE LOGICAL SYNTAX
OF LANGUAGE

By

RUDOLF CARNAP

LONDON
ROUTLEDGE & KEGAN PAUL LTD
BROADWAY HOUSE: 68-74 CARTER LANE, EC4V 5EL

First published in Great Britain 1937
by Routledge & Kegan Paul Ltd.
Broadway House, 68-74 Carter Lane
London, EC4V 5EL
Reprinted 1949, 1951, 1954, 1959
Reprinted (with corrections) 1964
Reprinted 1967, 1971

Reproduced and Printed in Great Britain by
Redwood Press Limited
Trowbridge & London

ISBN 0 7100 3125 4

Translated by

AMETHE SMEATON (COUNTESS VON ZEPPELIN)

CONTENTS

PART III. THE INDEFINITE LANGUAGE II

A. RULES OF FORMATION FOR LANGUAGE II

B. RULES OF TRANSFORMATION FOR LANGUAGE II

C. RULES OF CONSEQUENCE FOR LANGUAGE II

PART V. PHILOSOPHY AND SYNTAX

PREFACE TO THE ENGLISH EDITION

The present English edition contains some sections which are not found in the German original. These are §§ 16a, 34a–i, 38a–c, 60a–d, 71a–e. These twenty-two sections were included in the manuscript of the German original when it was sent for publication (in December 1933) but had to be taken out because of lack of space. The content of § 34a–i was, in a slightly different formulation, published in German in the paper *Ein Gültigkeitskriterium für die Sätze der klassischen Mathematik*, and the content of §§ 60a–d and 71a–d in *Die Antinomien und die Unvollständigkeit der Mathematik*. § 60 of the original has been omitted here, since it was only a shortened substitute for § 60a–d.

In the Bibliography some less important publications have been deleted, and others, mainly of the last few years, have been added.

Several smaller additions and corrections have been made. The more important of these occur at the following points: § 8, regressive definition; § 12, RI 2 (see footnote); § 14, proofs added to Theorems 3 and 7; § 21, D 29; § 22, two insertions in D 64 (see footnote), D 83; § 29, footnote; § 30, PSII 4 (see footnote to § 12); PSII 19, condition added; § 48 (see footnote); § 51, definition of 'L-consequence'; § 56 (see footnote), Theorems 8 and 9 taken out; § 57, Theorems 2 and 3 corrected, and last paragraph added; § 62, explanation of '$\mathfrak{Q}_2[\mathfrak{S}_2]$'; §§ 65 and 66, definitions of 'extensional' restricted to closed partial expressions, and Theorem 65.8a added; § 67, end of second paragraph. The majority of these corrections and a number of further ones have been suggested by Dr. A. Tarski, others by J. C. C. McKinsey and W. V. Quine, to all of whom I am very much indebted for their most helpful criticisms.

The problem of rendering the German terminology was naturally a most difficult one, in some cases there being no English word in existence which corresponded exactly to the original, in others the obvious equivalent being unavailable because of its special associations in some other system. It was necessary sometimes to appropriate for our purposes words which have not previously borne a technical significance, sometimes to coin entirely new ones. If at first sight some of these seem ill at ease or outlandish, I can only ask the reader to bear in mind the peculiar difficulties involved, and assure him that no term was chosen without most careful consideration and the conviction that it would justify itself in use.

To facilitate discussion and reference, the German symbolic abbreviations have been retained in all the strictly formalized portions of the book. English equivalents have been substituted only where they occur in the non-formal text, as mere convenient abbreviations which are not properly symbolic (e.g. "TN" for "term-number" instead of the German "GZ"), or as incidental symbols introduced simply for purposes of illustration (e.g. "fa" for "father" instead of the German "Va"). Wherever a German abbreviation has been used for the first time, the full German word has been inserted in brackets; and in the case of the terms introduced by formal definitions, a complete key to the symbolization is given in a footnote at the beginning of the respective sections.

I wish to express my best thanks to the Countess von Zeppelin for the accomplishment of the difficult task of translating this book, further to Dr. W. V. Quine for valuable suggestions with regard to terminology, and to Dr. E. C. Graham, Dr. O. Helmer, and Dr. E. Nagel for their assistance in proof-reading.

R. C.

Cambridge, Mass., May 1936

FOREWORD

For nearly a century mathematicians and logicians have been striving hard to make logic an exact science. To a certain extent, their efforts have been crowned with success, inasmuch as the science of logistics has taught people how to manipulate with precision symbols and formulae which are similar in their nature to those used in mathematics. But a book on logic must contain, in addition to the formulae, an expository context which, with the assistance of the words of ordinary language, explains the formulae and the relations between them; and this context often leaves much to be desired in the matter of clarity and exactitude. In recent years, logicians representing widely different tendencies of thought have developed more and more the point of view that in this context is contained the essential part of logic; and that the important thing is to develop an exact method for the construction of these sentences about sentences. The purpose of the present work is to give a systematic exposition of such a method, namely, of the method of "logical syntax". (For further details, see Introduction, pp. 1 and 2.)

In our "Vienna Circle", as well as in kindred groups (in Poland, France, England, U.S.A., and, amongst individuals, even in Germany) the conviction has grown, and is steadily increasing, that metaphysics can make no claim to possessing a scientific character. That part of the work of philosophers which may be held to be scientific in its nature—excluding the empirical questions which can be referred to empirical science—consists of logical analysis. The aim of logical syntax is to provide a system of concepts, a language, by the help of which the results of logical analysis will be exactly formulable. *Philosophy is to be replaced by the logic of science*—that is to say, by the logical analysis of the concepts and sentences of the sciences, for *the logic of science is nothing other than the logical syntax of the language of science*. That is the conclusion to which we are led by the considerations in the last chapter of this book.

The book itself makes an attempt to provide, in the form of an exact syntactical method, the necessary tools for working out the problems of the logic of science. This is done in the first place by the formulation of the syntax of two particularly important types of language which we shall call, respectively, 'Language I' and

'Language II'. Language I is simple in form, and covers a narrow field of concepts. Language II is richer in modes of expression; in it, all the sentences both of classical mathematics and of classical physics can be formulated. In both languages the investigation will not be limited to the mathematico-logical part of language—as is usually the case in logistics—but will be essentially concerned also with synthetic, empirical sentences. The latter, the so-called 'real' sentences, constitute the core of science; the mathematico-logical sentences are analytic, with no real content, and are merely formal auxiliaries.

With Language I as an example, it will be shown, in what follows, how the syntax of a language may be formulated within that language itself (Part II). The usual fear that thereby contradictions—the so-called 'epistemological' or 'linguistic' antinomies—must arise, is not justified.

The treatment of the syntax of Languages I and II will be followed by the outline of a general syntax applicable to any language whatsoever (Part IV); and, although the attempt is very far from attaining the desired goal, yet the task is one of fundamental importance. The range of possible language-forms and, consequently, of the various possible logical systems, is incomparably greater than the very narrow circle to which earlier investigations in modern logic have been limited. Up to the present, there has been only a very slight deviation, in a few points here and there, from the form of language developed by Russell which has already become classical. For instance, certain sentential forms (such as unlimited existential sentences) and rules of inference (such as the Law of Excluded Middle), have been eliminated by certain authors. On the other hand, a number of extensions have been attempted, and several interesting, many-valued calculi analogous to the two-valued calculus of sentences have been evolved, and have resulted finally in a logic of probability. Likewise, so-called intensional sentences have been introduced and, with their aid a logic of modality developed. The fact that no attempts have been made to venture still further from the classical forms is perhaps due to the widely held opinion that any such deviations must be justified—that is, that the new language-form must be proved to be 'correct' and to constitute a faithful rendering of 'the true logic'.

To eliminate this standpoint, together with the pseudo-problems and wearisome controversies which arise as a result of it, is one of the chief tasks of this book. In it, the view will be maintained that we have in every respect complete liberty with regard to the forms of language; that both the forms of construction for sentences and the rules of transformation (the latter are usually designated as "postulates" and "rules of inference") may be chosen quite arbitrarily. Up to now, in constructing a language, the procedure has usually been, first to assign a meaning to the fundamental mathematico-logical symbols, and then to consider what sentences and inferences are seen to be logically correct in accordance with this meaning. Since the assignment of the meaning is expressed in words, and is, in consequence, inexact, no conclusion arrived at in this way can very well be otherwise than inexact and ambiguous. The connection will only become clear when approached from the opposite direction: let any postulates and any rules of inference be chosen arbitrarily; then this choice, whatever it may be, will determine what meaning is to be assigned to the fundamental logical symbols. By this method, also, the conflict between the divergent points of view on the problem of the foundations of mathematics disappears. For language, in its mathematical form, can be constructed according to the preferences of any one of the points of view represented; so that no question of justification arises at all, but only the question of the syntactical consequences to which one or other of the choices leads, including the question of non-contradiction.

The standpoint which we have suggested—we will call it the *Principle of Tolerance* (see p. 51)—relates not only to mathematics, but to all questions of logic. From this point of view, the task of the construction of a general syntax—in other words, of the definition of those syntactical concepts which are applicable to languages of any form whatsoever—is a very important one. In the domain of general syntax, for instance, it is possible to choose a certain form for the language of science as a whole, as well as for that of any branch of science, and to state exactly the characteristic differences between it and the other possible language-forms.

The first attempts to cast the ship of logic off from the *terra firma* of the classical forms were certainly bold ones, considered from the historical point of view. But they were hampered by the striving after 'correctness'. Now, however, that impediment has been overcome, and before us lies the boundless ocean of unlimited possibilities.

In a number of places in the text, reference is made to the most important literature on the subject. A complete list has not, however, been attempted. Further bibliographical information may easily be obtained from the writings specified. The most important references are given on the following pages: pp. 96 ff., comparison of our Language II with other logical systems; pp. 136 ff., on the symbolism of classes; pp. 158 ff., on syntactical designations; pp. 253 f., on the logic of modalities; pp. 280 f. and 320 f. on the logic of science.

For the development of ideas in this book, I owe much to the stimulation I have received from various writings, letters and conversations on logical problems. Mention should here be made of the most important names. Above all, I am indebted to the writings and lectures of Frege. Through him my attention was drawn to the standard work on logistics—namely, the *Principia Mathematica* of Whitehead and Russell. The point of view of the formal theory of language (known as " syntax " in our terminology) was first developed for mathematics by Hilbert in his "metamathematics", to which the Polish logicians, especially Ajdukiewicz, Lesniewski, Lukasiewicz, and Tarski, have added a "metalogic". For this theory, Gödel created his fruitful method of "arithmetization". On the standpoint and method of syntax, I have, in particular, derived valuable suggestions from conversations with Tarski and Gödel. I have much for which to thank Wittgenstein in my reflections concerning the relations between syntax and the logic of science; for the divergences in our points of view, see pp. 282 ff. (Incidentally, *à propos* of the remarks made —especially in § 17 and § 67—in opposition to Wittgenstein's former dogmatic standpoint, Professor Schlick now informs me that for some time past, in writings as yet unpublished, Wittgenstein has agreed that the rules of language may be chosen with complete freedom.) Again, I have learned much from the writings of authors with whom I am not entirely in agreement; these are, in the first place, Weyl, Brouwer, and Lewis. Finally, I wish to express my gratitude to Professor Behmann and Dr. Gödel for having read the manuscript of this book in an earlier draft (1932), and for having made numerous valuable suggestions towards its improvement.   R. C.

Prague, May 1934

INTRODUCTION

§ 1. WHAT IS LOGICAL SYNTAX?

By the **logical syntax** of a language, we mean the formal theory of the linguistic forms of that language—the systematic statement of the formal rules which govern it together with the development of the consequences which follow from these rules.

A theory, a rule, a definition, or the like is to be called *formal* when no reference is made in it either to the meaning of the symbols (for example, the words) or to the sense of the expressions (e.g. the sentences), but simply and solely to the kinds and order of the symbols from which the expressions are constructed.

The prevalent opinion is that syntax and logic, in spite of some points of contact between them, are fundamentally theories of a very different type. The syntax of a language is supposed to lay down rules according to which the linguistic structures (e.g. the sentences) are to be built up from the elements (such as words or parts of words). The chief task of logic, on the other hand, is supposed to be that of formulating rules according to which judgments may be inferred from other judgments; in other words, according to which conclusions may be drawn from premisses.

But the development of logic during the past decades has shown clearly that it can only be studied with any degree of accuracy when it is applied, not to judgments (thoughts, or the content of thoughts) but rather to linguistic expressions, of which sentences are the most important, because only for them is it possible to lay down sharply defined rules. And actually, in practice, every logician since Aristotle, in laying down rules, has dealt mainly with sentences. But even those modern logicians who agree with us in our opinion that logic is concerned with sentences, are yet for the most part convinced that logic is equally concerned with the relations of meaning between sentences. They consider that, in contrast with the rules of syntax, the rules of logic are non-formal. In the following pages, in opposition to this standpoint, the view that logic, too, is concerned with the *formal* treatment of sentences will be presented and developed. We shall see that the logical characteristics of sentences (for instance, whether a sentence is analytic, synthetic, or contradictory; whether it is an existential sentence or not; and so on) and the logical relations between them (for instance, whether two sentences contradict one another or are compatible with one another; whether one is logically deducible from the other or not; and so on) are solely dependent upon the syntactical structure of the sentences. In this way, logic will become a part of syntax, provided that the latter is conceived in a sufficiently wide sense and formulated with exactitude. The difference between syntactical rules in the narrower sense and the logical rules of deduction is only the difference between *formation rules* and *transformation rules*, both of which are completely formulable in syntactical terms. Thus we are justified in designating as 'logical syntax' the system which comprises the rules of formation and transformation.

In consequence of the unsystematic and logically imperfect structure of the natural word-languages (such as German or Latin), the statement of their formal rules of formation and transformation would be so complicated that it would hardly be feasible in practice. And the same difficulty would arise in the case of the artificial word-languages (such as Esperanto); for, even though they avoid certain logical imperfections which characterize the natural word-languages, they must, of necessity, be still very complicated from the logical point of view owing to the fact that they are conversational languages, and hence still dependent upon the natural languages.

For the moment we will leave aside the question of the formal deficiencies of the word-languages, and, by the consideration of examples, proceed to convince ourselves that rules of formation and transformation are of like nature, and that both permit of being formally apprehended. For instance, given an appropriate rule, it can be proved that the word-series "Pirots karulize elatically" is a sentence, provided only that "Pirots" is known to be a substantive (in the plural), "karulize" a verb (in the third person plural), and "elatically" an adverb; all of which, of course, in a well-constructed language—as, for example, in Esperanto—could be gathered from the form of the words alone. The meaning of the words is quite inessential to the purpose, and need not be known. Further, given an appropriate rule, the sentence "A karulizes elatically" can be deduced from the original sentence and the sentence "A is a Pirot"—again provided that the type to which the individual words belong is known. Here also, neither the meaning of the words nor the sense of the three sentences need be known.

Owing to the deficiencies of the word-languages, the logical syntax of a language of this kind will not be developed, but, instead, we shall consider the syntax of two artificially constructed symbolic languages (that is to say, such languages as employ formal symbols instead of words). As a matter of fact, throughout all modern logical investigations, this is the method used; for only in a symbolic language has it proved possible to achieve exact formulation and rigid proofs. And only in relation to a constructed symbolic language of this kind will it be possible to lay down a system of rules at once simple and rigid—which alone will enable us to show clearly the characteristics and range of applicability of logical syntax.

The sentences, definitions, and rules of the syntax of a language are concerned with the forms of that language. But, now, how are these sentences, definitions, and rules themselves to be correctly expressed? Is a kind of super-language necessary for the purpose? And, again, a third language to explain the syntax of this super-language, and so on to infinity? Or is it possible to formulate the syntax of a language within that language itself? The obvious fear will arise that in the latter case, owing to certain reflexive definitions, contradictions of a nature seemingly similar to those which are familiar both in Cantor's theory of transfinite aggregates and in the pre-Russellian logic might make their appearance. But we shall see later that without any danger of contradictions or antinomies emerging it is possible to express the syntax of a language in that language itself, to an extent which is conditioned by the wealth of means of expression of the language in question.

However, we shall not at first concern ourselves with this problem, important though it is. We shall proceed, instead, to construct syntactical concepts relating to the languages we have chosen, and postpone, for a while, the question as to whether we are able or not to express the rules and sentences based on these concepts in that language itself. In the first stages of a theory, such a naïve approach seems always to have proved the most fruitful. For instance, geometry, arithmetic, and the differential calculus all appeared first, and only much later (in some cases, hundreds of years after) did epistemological and logical discussions of the already developed theories ensue. Hence we shall start by constructing the syntax, and then, later on, proceed to formalize its concepts and thereby determine its logical character.

In following this procedure, we are concerned with two languages: in the first place with the language which is the object of our investigation—we shall call this the **object-language**—and, secondly, with the language in which we speak *about* the syntactical forms of the object-language—we shall call this the **syntax-language**. As we have said, we shall take as our object-languages certain symbolic languages; as our syntax-language we shall at first simply use the English language with the help of some additional Gothic symbols.

§ 2. LANGUAGES AS CALCULI

By a **calculus** is understood a system of conventions or rules of the following kind. These rules are concerned with elements—the so-called **symbols**—about the nature and relations of which nothing more is assumed than that they are distributed in various classes. Any finite series of these symbols is called an **expression** of the calculus in question.

The rules of the calculus determine, in the first place, the conditions under which an expression can be said to belong to a certain category of expressions; and, in the second place, under what conditions the transformation of one or more expressions into another or others may be allowed. Thus the system of a language, when only the formal structure in the sense described above is considered, is a calculus. The two different kinds of rules are those which we have previously called the rules of formation and transformation—namely, the syntactical rules in the narrower sense (e.g. "An expression of this language is called a sentence when it consists, in such and such a way, of symbols of such and such a kind, occurring in such and such an order"), and the so-called logical laws of deduction (e.g. "If a sentence is composed of symbols combined in such and such a way, and if another is composed of symbols combined in such and such another way, then the second can be deduced from the first"). Further, every well-determined mathematical discipline is a calculus in this sense. But the system of rules of chess is also a calculus. The chessmen are the symbols (here, as opposed to those of the word-languages, they have no meaning), the rules of formation determine the position of the chessmen (especially the initial positions in the game), and the rules of transformation determine the moves which are permitted—that is to say, the permissible transformations of one position into another.

In the widest sense, logical syntax is the same thing as the construction and manipulation of a calculus; and it is only because languages are the most important examples of calculi that, as a rule, only languages are syntactically investigated. In the majority of calculi (even in those which are not languages in the proper sense of the word), the elements are written characters. The term 'symbol' in what follows will have the same meaning as the word 'character'. It will not be assumed that such a symbol possesses a meaning, or that it designates anything.

When we maintain that logical syntax treats language as a calculus, we do not mean by that statement that language is nothing more than a calculus. We only mean that syntax is concerned with that part of language which has the attributes of a calculus—that is, it is limited to the formal aspect of language. In addition, any particular language has, apart from that aspect, others which may be investigated by other methods. For instance, its words have meaning; this is the object of investigation and study for semantics. Then again, the words and expressions of a language have a close relation to actions and perceptions, and in that connection they are the objects of psychological study. Again, language constitutes an historically given method of communication, and thus of mutual influence, within a particular group of human beings, and as such is the object of sociology. In the widest sense, the science of language investigates languages from every one of these standpoints: from the syntactical (in our sense, the formal), from the semasiological, from the psychological, and from the sociological.

We have already said that syntax is concerned solely with the formal properties of expressions. We shall now make this assertion more explicit. Assume that two languages (*Sprachen*), S_1 and S_2, use different symbols, but in such a way that a one-one correspondence may be established between the symbols of S_1 and those of S_2 so that any syntactical rule about S_1 becomes a syntactical rule about S_2 if, instead of relating it to the symbols of S_1, we relate it to the correlative symbols of S_2; and conversely. Then, although the two languages are not alike, they have the same *formal structure* (we call them isomorphic languages), and syntax is concerned solely with the structure of languages in this sense. From the syntactical point of view it is irrelevant whether one of two symbolical languages makes use, let us say, of the sign '&', where the other uses '•' (in word-languages: whether the one uses 'and' and the other 'und') so long as the rules of formation and transformation are analogous. For instance, it depends entirely on the formal structure of the language and of the sentences involved, whether a certain sentence is analytic or not; or whether one sentence is deducible from another or not. In such cases the *design* (visual form, *Gestalt*) of the individual symbols is a matter of indifference. In an exact syntactical definition, no allusion will be made to this design. Further, it is equally unimportant from the syntactical point of view, that, for instance, the symbol 'and' should be specifically a thing consisting of printers' ink. If we agreed always to place a match upon the paper instead of that particular symbol, the formal structure of the language would remain unchanged.

It should now be clear that any series of any things will equally well serve as terms or expressions in a calculus, or, more particularly, in a language. It is only necessary to distribute the things in question in particular classes, and we can then construct expressions having the form of series of things, put together according to the rules of formation. In the ordinary languages, a series of symbols (an expression) is either a temporal series of sounds, or a spatial series of material bodies produced on paper. An example of a language which uses movable things for its symbols is a card-index system; the cards serve as the object-names for the books of a library, and the riders as predicates designating properties (for instance, 'lent', 'at the book-binders', and such like); a card with a rider makes a sentence.

The *syntax* of a language, or of any other calculus, is concerned, in general, with the *structures of possible serial orders* (of a definite kind) *of any elements whatsoever*. We shall now distinguish between pure and descriptive syntax. *Pure syntax* is concerned with the possible arrangements, without reference either to the nature of the things which constitute the various elements, or to the question as to which of the possible arrangements of these elements are anywhere actually realized (that is to say, with the possible forms of sentences, without regard either to the designs of the words of which the sentences are composed, or to whether any of the sentences exist on paper somewhere in the world). In pure syntax only definitions are formulated and the consequences of such definitions developed. Pure syntax is thus wholly analytic, and is nothing more than *combinatorial analysis*, or, in other words, the *geometry* of finite, discrete, serial structures of a particular kind. *Descriptive syntax* is related to pure syntax as physical geometry to pure mathematical geometry; it is concerned with the syntactical properties and relations of empirically given expressions (for example, with the sentences of a particular book). For this purpose—just as in the application of geometry—it is necessary to introduce so-called correlative definitions, by means of which the kinds of objects corresponding to the different kinds of syntactical elements are determined (for instance, "material bodies consisting of printers' ink of the form 'V' shall serve as disjunction symbols"). Sentences of descriptive syntax may, for instance, state that the fourth and the seventh sentences of a particular treatise contradict one another; or that the second sentence in a treatise is not syntactically correct.

When we say that pure syntax *is concerned with* the forms of sentences, this 'concerned with' is intended in the figurative sense. An analytic sentence is not actually concerned with anything, in the way that an empirical sentence is; for the analytic sentence is without content. The figurative 'concerned with' is intended here in the same sense in which arithmetic is said to be concerned with numbers, or pure geometry to be concerned with geometrical constructions.

We see, therefore, that whenever we investigate or judge a particular scientific theory from the logical standpoint, the results of this *logical analysis* must be formulated as *syntactical sentences*, either of pure or of descriptive syntax. The *logic of science* (logical methodology) is nothing else than the *syntax of the language of science*. This fact will be shown clearly in the concluding chapter of this book. The syntactical problems acquire a greater significance by virtue of the anti-metaphysical attitude represented by the Vienna Circle. According to this view, the sentences of metaphysics are pseudo-sentences which on logical analysis are proved to be either empty phrases or phrases which violate the rules of syntax. Of the so-called philosophical problems, the only questions which have any meaning are those of the logic of science. To share this view is to *substitute logical syntax for philosophy*. The above-mentioned anti-metaphysical attitude will not, however, appear in this book either as an assumption or as a thesis. The inquiries which follow are of a formal nature and do not depend in any way upon what is usually known as philosophical doctrine.

The method of syntax which will be developed in the following pages will not only prove useful in the logical analysis of scientific theories—it will also help in the *logical analysis of the word-languages*. Although here, for the reasons indicated above, we shall be dealing with symbolic languages, the syntactical concepts and rules—not in detail but in their general character—may also be applied to the analysis of the incredibly complicated word-languages. The direct analysis of these, which has been prevalent hitherto, must inevitably fail, just as a physicist would be frustrated were he from the outset to attempt to relate his laws to natural things—trees, stones, and so on. In the first place, the physicist relates his laws to the simplest of constructed forms; to a thin straight lever, to a simple pendulum, to punctiform masses, etc. Then, with the help of the laws relating to these constructed forms, he is later in a position to analyze into suitable elements the complicated behaviour of real bodies, and thus to control them. One more comparison: the complicated configurations of mountain chains, rivers, frontiers, and the like are most easily represented and investigated by the help of geographical co-ordinates—or, in other words, by constructed lines not given in nature. In the same way, the syntactical property of a particular word-language, such as English, or of particular classes of word-languages, or of a particular sub-language of a word-language, is best represented and investigated by comparison with a constructed language which serves as a system of reference. Such a task, however, lies beyond the scope of this book.

TERMINOLOGICAL REMARKS

The reason for the choice of the term '(logical) syntax' is given in the introduction. The adjective 'logical' can be left out where there is no danger of confusion with linguistic syntax (which is not pure in its method, and does not succeed in laying down an exact system of rules), for example, in the text of this book and in logical treatises in general.

As the word itself suggests, the earliest calculi in the sense described above were developed in mathematics. Hilbert was the first to treat mathematics as a calculus in the strict sense—i.e. to lay down a system of rules having mathematical formulae for their objects. This theory he called *metamathematics*, and his original object in developing it was to attain the proof of the freedom from contradiction of classical mathematics. Metamathematics is—when considered in the widest sense and not only from the standpoint of the task just mentioned—the syntax of the mathematical language. In analogy to the Hilbertian designation, the Warsaw logicians (Lukasiewicz and others) have spoken of the 'meta-propositional calculus', of *metalogic*, and so on. Perhaps the word 'metalogic' is a suitable designation for the sub-domain of syntax which deals with logical sentences in the narrower sense (that is, excluding the mathematical ones).

The term *semantics* is used by Chwistek to designate a theory which he has constructed with the same object as our syntax, but which makes use of an entirely different method (of this we shall say more later). But since, in the science of language, this word is usually taken as synonymous with 'semasiology' (or 'theory of meaning') it is perhaps not altogether desirable to transfer it to syntax—that is, to a formal theory which takes no account of meanings. (Compare: Bréal, *Essai de sémantique. Science des significations.* Paris, 1897. 5th edn. 1921, p. 8: "La science, que j'ai proposé d'appeler la Sémantique", with footnote: "Σημαντικὴ τέχνη, la science des significations".)

The designation *sematology* may (following Bühler) be retained for the empirical (psychological, sociological) theory of the application of symbols in the widest sense. The empirical science of language is thus a sub-domain of sematology. But it must be distinguished from *semasiology* which, as a part of the science of language, investigates the meaning of the expressions of the historically given languages.

PART I

THE DEFINITE LANGUAGE I

A. RULES OF FORMATION FOR LANGUAGE I

§ 3. PREDICATES AND FUNCTORS

The syntactical method will here be developed in connection with two particular symbolic languages taken as object-languages. The first of these languages—we shall call it Language I, or, briefly, I—includes, on the mathematical side, the elementary arithmetic of the natural numbers to a certain limited extent, roughly corresponding to those theories which are designated as constructivist, finitist, or intuitionist. The limitation consists primarily in the fact that only definite number-properties occur— that is to say, those of which the possession or non-possession by any number whatsoever can be determined in a finite number of steps according to a fixed method. It is on account of this limitation that we call I a definite language, although it is not a definite language in the narrower sense of containing only definite, that is to say, resoluble (i.e. either demonstrable or refutable) sentences. Later on, we shall be dealing with Language II, which includes Language I within itself as a sub-language. Language II contains in addition indefinite concepts, and embraces both the arithmetic of the real numbers and mathematical analysis to the extent to which it is developed in classical mathematics, and further the theory of aggregates. Languages I and II do not only include mathematics, however; above all, they afford the possibility of constructing empirical sentences concerning any domain of objects. In II, for instance, both classical and relativistic physics can be formulated. We attach special importance to the syntactical treatment of the synthetic (not purely logico-mathematical) sentences, which are usually ignored in modern logic. The mathematical sentences, considered from the point of view of language as a whole, are only aids to operation with empirical, that is to say, non-mathematical, sentences.

In Part I the syntax of Language I will be formulated. Here, the English language, supplemented by a few Gothic symbols, will be used as the syntax-language. In Part II the syntax of Language I will be formalized, that is, it will be expressed in the form of a calculus-language; and this will be done in Language I itself. In Part III the syntax of the richer Language II will be developed, but only by the simpler method of a word-language. In Part IV we shall abandon the object-languages I and II, and create a general syntax which will be applicable to all languages of every kind.

For the understanding of the following chapters, a previous knowledge of the elements of logistics (symbolic logic) is desirable, although not absolutely necessary. Further details supplementing the short explanations given here are to be found in the regular expositions of the sentential calculus and the so-called functional calculus. See: Hilbert [*Logik*]; Carnap [*Logistik*]; Lewis [*Logic*].

A language which is concerned with the objects of any domain may designate these objects either by *proper names* or by systematic positional *co-ordinates*, that is by symbols which show the place of the objects in the system, and, thereby, their positions in relation to one another. Examples of positional symbols are, for instance, house-numbers, in contradistinction to the individual names (such as 'The Red Lion') which were customary in earlier days; Ostwald's designation of colours by means of letters and figures, as opposed to their differentiation by means of colour-names ('blue', etc.); the designation of geographical places by their latitude and longitude, instead of by proper names ('Vienna', 'Cape of Good Hope'); and the customary designation of space-time points by four co-ordinates (space and time co-ordinates, four real numbers) in physics. The method of designation by proper names is the primitive one; that of positional designation corresponds to a more advanced stage of science, and has considerable methodological advantages over the former. We shall call a language (or sub-language) which denotes the objects belonging to the domain with which it is concerned by positional designations, a *co-ordinate-language*, in contradistinction to the *name-languages*.

Up to now it has been usual in symbolic logic to use name-languages, the objects being, for the most part, designated by the names 'a', 'b', etc. (corresponding to the designations 'moon', 'Vienna', 'Napoleon', of the word-languages). Here, we shall take co-ordinate-languages for our object-languages, and, specifically, in Language I, we shall use the natural numbers as co-ordinates. Let us consider, as a domain of positions, a one-dimensional series with a definite direction. If 'a' designates a position in this series, then the next position will be designated by 'aı'. If the initial position is designated by '0', then the succeeding positions will obviously be designated by '0ı', '0ıı', and so on. We call such expressions accented expressions. Since, however, for the representation of higher positions, they entail a certain amount of inconvenience, we shall, for the purpose of abbreviation, introduce the usual number-symbols by definition. Thus: '1' for '0ı', '2' for '0ıı', and so on. If we wish to indicate the positions in a two-, three-, or n-dimensional domain, we use ordered couples or triads or n-ads of number-symbols.

In order to express a property of an object, or of a position, or a relation between several objects or positions, **predicates** are used. *Examples:* (1) Let 'Blue (3)' have the meaning: "the position 3 is blue"; in a name-language: 'Blue (a)' is "the object a is blue". (2) Let 'Wr (3,5)' mean: "the position 3 is warmer than the position 5"; in a name-language 'Wr (a,b)': "the body a is warmer than the body b"; 'Fa (a,b)': "the person a is father of the person b", and so on. (3) Let 'T (0,8,4,3)' mean: "the temperature at the position 0 is as much higher than at the position 8 as the temperature at the position 4 is higher than at the position 3". In the above examples, 'blue' is a one-termed predicate; 'Wr' a two-termed predicate; 'T' a four-termed predicate. In 'Wr (3,5)', '3' is called the first, and '5' the second argument of 'Wr'. We distinguish two classes of predicates: the predicates in the examples cited above express (as we usually say) empirical properties or relations. We call these *descriptive predicates*, and distinguish them from *logical predicates*, which are those which (as we usually say) express logico-mathematical properties or relations. The following are examples of logical predicates: 'Prim (5)' means: "5 is a prime number"; 'Gr (7,5)': "7 is greater than 5", or: "the position 7 is a higher position than the position 5". The exact definition of the syntactical concepts 'descriptive' and 'logical' will be given later, without reference to meaning as in the present inexact explanation. [The designation 'predicate', which was formerly applied only in cases involving one term, will here, following the example of Hilbert, be applied also in cases involving more than one term; the use of a common word to cover both cases has proved itself to be far more practical.]

Predicates are, so to speak, proper names for the properties of positions. We have designated positions by means of systematic order-symbols—namely, number-symbols. In like manner we may also designate their properties by number-symbols. Instead of colour-names, colour-numbers (or triads of such numbers) may be used; instead of the inexact designations 'warm', 'cool', 'cold', and so forth, we can now use temperature-numbers. This has not only the advantage that much more exact information can be given, but, in addition, a further advantage which is of decisive importance for science—namely, that only by means of this "arithmetization" is the formulation of universal laws (for example: that of the relation between temperature and expansion, or between temperature and pressure) rendered possible. In order to express properties or relations of position by means of numbers, we shall use **functors**. For instance: let 'te' be the temperature functor; 'te $(3) = 5$' then means: "the temperature at the position 3 is 5"; if we take the functor 'tdiff' to represent temperature difference, then 'tdiff $(3,4) = 2$' means: "the difference of the temperatures at positions 3 and 4 equals 2". Besides such *descriptive functors*, we make use also of *logical functors*. For example: 'sum $(3,4)$' has the meaning: "3 plus 4"; 'fak (3)' is equivalent to "$3!$". 'sum' is a two-termed logical functor, 'fak' (*Fakultät*) a one-termed logical functor. Here also in the expression 'sum $(3,4)$', '3' and '4' are called *arguments*; in 'te $(3) = 5$', '3' is called the argument for 'te', and '5' is called the value of 'te' for the argument '3'.

An expression which in any way designates a number (determined or undetermined), we call a *numerical expression* (exact definition on p. 26). Examples are: '0', '0^{II}', '3', 'te (3)', 'sum $(3,4)$'. An expression which corresponds to a propositional sentence of a word-language we call a *sentence* (definition on p. 26). Examples are: 'Blue (3)', 'Prim (4)'. An expression is called *descriptive* (definition on p. 25) when either a descriptive predicate or a descriptive functor occurs in it; otherwise it is called *logical* (definition on p. 25).

§ 4. SYNTACTICAL GOTHIC SYMBOLS

The two symbols 'a' and 'a' occur at different places on this page. They are therefore *different* symbols (not the *same* symbol); but they are *equal* (not *unequal*). The syntactical rules of a language must not only determine what things are to be used as symbols, but also under what circumstances these symbols are to be regarded as syntactically equal. Very often, symbols which are unlike in appearance are stated to be syntactically equal: for example, in ordinary language, 'z' and 'ʒ'. [Such a declaration of equality does not always necessarily mean that the two symbols are to be used indiscriminately. There may be differences in usage which depend on non-syntactical factors. For instance, it is customary not to use 'z' and 'ʒ' in the same context: one writes nearly always, either 'zebra' or 'ʒebra', not 'ʒebra'.] As they are used in this book, 'z' and 'ʒ' are syntactically unequal. On the other hand, we shall regard '(', '(', '[', '[' as equal symbols, and likewise the corresponding closing brackets. The differentiation of small and large, round and square brackets in the expressions of our object-language is therefore syntactically irrelevant. Such a differentiation is introduced solely for the convenience of the reader. Further, in our system (in contrast with Russell's) the symbols '≡' and '=' are held to be equal. We could write '=' throughout, but, again for the convenience of the reader, when '=' occurs between sentences (and not between numerical expressions) we usually write '≡' instead.

We shall call two expressions equal expressions when their corresponding symbols are equal symbols. If two symbols, or two expressions, are equal (syntactically), then we say also that they have the same syntactical *design*. But that does not in any way prevent their having different visual shapes, as, for example, in the case of '(' and '[', or '=' and '≡'; or differing in colour, or any other characteristics that are syntactically irrelevant.

Nearly all the investigations carried out in this book are concerned with pure (not descriptive) syntax; and thus have to do, not with expressions as spatially separate things, but only with their syntactical equality or inequality, and hence with their syntactical design. Whatever is stated of any one expression applies at the same time to every other *equal* expression, and may, accordingly, be predicated of the expressional design. Therefore, for the sake of brevity, we shall often speak simply of 'expression' or 'symbol', instead of 'expressional design' or 'symbolic design'. [For instance, instead of saying: "in the expression 'Q(3,5)' (and hence in every equal expression) a symbol like the symbol '3' occurs", we say more briefly: "in every expression of the design 'Q(3,5)' a symbol of the design '3' occurs"; or, still more simply, "in the expression 'Q(3,5)', the symbol '3' occurs".] In the domain of pure syntax, this simplified form of speech cannot lead to ambiguity.

Symbols of the five kinds enumerated below occur in I. (Explanations follow later.)

1. Eleven single *symbols* (symbol-designs):

'(', ')', ',', '|', '$\sim$', '$\vee$', '$\bullet$', '$\supset$', '=', '$\exists$', 'K'.

The following four categories, to each of which an unlimited number of symbols may belong:

2. The (numerical) *variables* ('u', 'v', ... 'z' in the definitions of §§20–24, also 'k', 'l',...'t').

3. The *constant numerals* (e.g. '0', '1', '2', etc.); the symbols belonging to groups (2) and (3) are called *numerals*.

4. The *predicates* (groups of letters with initial capitals, e.g. 'Prim', also 'P', 'Q', 'R').

5. The *functors* (groups of letters with small initial letters, e.g. 'sum').

A symbol which is not a variable is called a **constant**. An **expression** of I consists of an ordered series of symbols of I, of which the number is finite (but which may also be either 0 or 1; that is to say, an expression may either be empty or consist of one symbol only).

By a syntactical *form* (or, shortly: a form) we understand any kind or category of expressions which is syntactically determined (that is to say, determined only with reference to the serial order and the syntactical category of the symbols; and not by any non-syntactical conditions such as place, colour, etc.). The form of a certain expression can be specified more or less exactly: the most accurate specification is that which gives the design of the expression; the most inaccurate, that which merely states that it is an expression.

We shall introduce an abbreviated method for writing down statements about form. For instance, in the language of words, we can make the following statement about the form of the expression 'Prim (x)': "This expression consists of a predicate, an opening bracket, a variable, and a closing bracket, written in this order." Instead of this we shall write more briefly: "this expression has the form $\mathfrak{pr}(\mathfrak{z})$". This method of the use of the Gothic symbols consists in introducing syntactical names to represent symbol-categories; the syntactical description of form is then effected simply by placing these syntactical names one after the other. We shall designate the symbols (of all designs) by '$\mathfrak{a}$'; the variables (numerical) by '$\mathfrak{z}$' (*Zahlvariable*); the symbol (symbol-design) '0' by '$\mathfrak{nu}$' (*null*); the numerals in general by '$\mathfrak{zz}$' (*Zahlzeichen*); the predicates by '$\mathfrak{pr}$' (and, specifically, the one-termed, two-termed, n-termed predicates by '$\mathfrak{pr}^1$', '$\mathfrak{pr}^2$', '$\mathfrak{pr}^n$', respectively); the functors by '$\mathfrak{fu}$' (and, specifically, '$\mathfrak{fu}^1$', etc.). For the syntactical designation of the eleven individual symbols, we shall use the symbols themselves, and in addition for the two-termed *junction-symbols* (*Verknüpfungszeichen*)—'$\vee$', '$\bullet$', '$\supset$', '$=$'—the designation '$\mathfrak{verkn}$'. Thus, for instance, in 'Prim (x)', '(' is a symbol of the object-language; on the other hand, in '$\mathfrak{pr}(\mathfrak{z})$', '(' is a symbol of the syntax-language which serves as a syntactical name for that symbol in the object-language, and is, accordingly, nothing else than an abbreviation for the English words 'opening bracket'. When a symbol is used in this way as a name for itself (or, more precisely, as a name for its own symbol-design), we call it an *autonymous* symbol (see §42). No ambiguity can arise as a result of the double use of the symbols '(', etc., since these symbols only occur autonymously in connection with Gothic letters. Whenever we wish to differentiate different symbols of the same kind by their syntactical designations we use indices. For instance: '$P(x,y,x)$' has the form $\mathfrak{pr}(\mathfrak{z},\mathfrak{z},\mathfrak{z})$, or, more exactly, the form $\mathfrak{pr}^3(\mathfrak{z}_1,\mathfrak{z}_2,\mathfrak{z}_1)$. For the most important kinds of *expressions* we shall also use syntactical symbols (with capital letters). Expressions (of any form) we designate by '$\mathfrak{A}$' (*Ausdruck*), numerical expressions by '$\mathfrak{z}$' (*Zahlausdruck*), sentences by '$\mathfrak{S}$' (*Satz*). Other designations will be introduced later. Here, also, we make use of indices in order to indicate the equality of expressions. In a sentence of the form $(\mathfrak{S}\vee\mathfrak{S})\supset\mathfrak{S}$, the three constituent sentences may be equal or unequal; in a sentence of the form $(\mathfrak{S}_1 \vee \mathfrak{S}_2) \supset \mathfrak{S}_1$, the first and third of the constituent sentences are equal sentences.

By means of the indices '$\mathfrak{b}$' and '$\mathfrak{l}$', it is possible to indicate that a symbol is *descriptive* or *logical* respectively. For instance, '$\mathfrak{fu}_\mathfrak{l}$' designates the logical functors, '$\mathfrak{z}_\mathfrak{b}$' the descriptive numerical expressions. Instead of writing "a symbol (or expression) of the form...", we often write for short: 'a...'; for example, instead of "a two-termed logical functor", we write briefly: 'an $\mathfrak{fu}_\mathfrak{l}{}^2$'; similarly 'a $\mathfrak{z}$', 'an $\mathfrak{A}_\mathfrak{b}$', and so on.

In what follows the Gothic symbols will be used in connection with the English text; in the later construction of the syntax of I, which is not given in a word-language but by means of further symbols, these symbols do not occur.

The chief object of the method of Gothic symbols is to protect us from the incorrect mode of expression, very frequent in both logical and mathematical writings, which makes no distinction between symbols and that which is designated. For instance, we find "in this or in that place, $x = y$ occurs", where the correct form would be "...'$x = y$' occurs", or "...$\mathfrak{z}_1 = \mathfrak{z}_2$ occurs". If an expression of the object-language is being discussed, then either this expression must be written in inverted commas, or its syntactical designation (without inverted commas) must be used. But if the syntactical designation is what we are talking about, then it, in turn, must be put into inverted commas. Later on we shall show how very easily the neglect of this rule, and the failure to differentiate between symbols and the objects designated by them, leads to error and obscurity (§§ 41, 42).

§ 5. THE JUNCTION SYMBOLS

The one-termed or two-termed junction symbols are used to construct a new sentence out of one or two sentences respectively. In a strictly formally constructed system, the meaning of these symbols—as will be discussed more fully later—arises out of the rules of transformation. In order to facilitate the understanding of them, we shall provisionally explain their meaning (and similarly that of other symbols) by less exact methods; first, by an approximate translation into words of the English language, and secondly, with more precision, by means of the so-called truth-value tables.

$\sim(\mathfrak{S}_1)$ is called the negation of $(\mathfrak{S}_1)$; $(\mathfrak{S}_1)\vee(\mathfrak{S}_2)$, $(\mathfrak{S}_1)\cdot(\mathfrak{S}_2)$, $(\mathfrak{S}_1)\supset(\mathfrak{S}_2)$, $(\mathfrak{S}_1)=(\mathfrak{S}_2)$ are called, respectively, the disjunction, conjunction, implication, equivalence (or equation) of $\mathfrak{S}_1$ and $\mathfrak{S}_2$, in which $\mathfrak{S}_1$ and $\mathfrak{S}_2$ are called terms.

The translations of these symbols are as follows: 'not'; 'or' (in the non-exclusive sense); 'and'; 'not...or...' (sometimes also translatable by 'if...then...'); 'either...and..., or not...and not...'. We shall usually write the symbol design ' = ' in the form ' ≡ ' where it occurs between sentences (not between numerical expressions); ' = ' and ' ≡ ' count, therefore, as equal symbols, i.e. as symbols of the same syntactical design.

In the majority of accepted systems, a special symbol of equivalence is used, in addition to the symbol of identity or equality ' = '. (For instance, Russell uses ' ≡ ', Hilbert ' ~ '.) We, on the other hand, both in Language I and in Language II use only one symbolic design (but for the easier comprehension of the reader, we use two kinds of figures). As we shall see later (pp. 244 f.), this method is both admissible and useful for extensional languages such as I and II.

In what follows, for the sake of brevity in writing down any symbolic expressions that occur either in the object- or in the syntax-languages, we shall (as is customary) leave out the brackets surrounding a partial expression $\mathfrak{A}_1$ (which may be either a sentence or the syntactical designation of a sentence) in the following cases:

1. When $\mathfrak{A}_1$ consists of one letter only.
2. In the relation $\sim(\mathfrak{A}_1)$, or $\mathfrak{verin}(\mathfrak{A}_1)$, or $(\mathfrak{A}_1)\mathfrak{verin}$, when $\mathfrak{A}_1$ begins either with ' $\sim$ ', or with a $\mathfrak{pr}$, or with an operator (see below).
3. When $\mathfrak{A}_1$ is a disjunctive term, and is itself a disjunction.
4. When $\mathfrak{A}_1$ is a conjunctive term, and is itself a conjunction.
5. When $\mathfrak{A}_1$ is an operand and itself begins with an operator (of this more later).

Thus instead of '$(\sim(\mathfrak{S}_1))\vee(\mathfrak{S}_2)$' [but not instead of '$\sim((\mathfrak{S}_1)\vee(\mathfrak{S}_2))$'], we write for short: '$\sim\mathfrak{S}_1\vee\mathfrak{S}_2$'; similarly: '$\mathfrak{S}_1\vee\mathfrak{S}_2\vee\mathfrak{S}_3$', '$\mathfrak{S}_1\cdot\mathfrak{S}_2\cdot\mathfrak{S}_3$'.

This simplification will, however, be used here only for the practical purpose of writing down the expressions—the formulation of syntactical definitions and rules will be referred to the expressions with no brackets omitted.

There are, obviously, four possibilities in connection with the truth and falsehood of two sentences, $\mathfrak{S}_1$ and $\mathfrak{S}_2$. These will be represented by the four lines of the *truth-value table* given below. The table shows in which of these four cases the junction sentence is true and in which it is false; for instance, the disjunction is false only in the fourth case, otherwise it is true.

	$\mathfrak{S}_1\ \mathfrak{S}_2$	$\mathfrak{S}_1 \vee \mathfrak{S}_2$	$\mathfrak{S}_1 \cdot \mathfrak{S}_2$	$\mathfrak{S}_1 \supset \mathfrak{S}_2$	$\mathfrak{S}_1 \equiv \mathfrak{S}_2$
(1)	T T	T	T	T	T
(2)	T F	T	F	F	F
(3)	F T	T	F	T	F
(4)	F F	F	F	T	T

The two-line table below is the table for negation.

	$\mathfrak{S}_1$	$\sim \mathfrak{S}_1$
(1)	T	F
(2)	F	T

With the help of the above tables, the truth value of a multiple compound sentence can easily be ascertained for the different cases by first of all determining the values for the component partial-sentences, and then proceeding step by step to the whole sentence. Thus, for instance, it can be determined that for $\sim \mathfrak{S}_1 \vee \mathfrak{S}_2$, the same truth distribution T, F, T, T holds good as for the case of implication; and from this we get the translation into words: 'not...or...', for implication. Further it can also be established that $\mathfrak{S}_1 \supset (\mathfrak{S}_1 \vee \mathfrak{S}_2)$ has the truth-value distribution, T, T, T, T, and is thus unconditionally true whether $\mathfrak{S}_1$ and $\mathfrak{S}_2$ be true or false. Later on we shall call such sentences *analytic sentences*.

§ 6. UNIVERSAL AND EXISTENTIAL SENTENCES

Here we shall again give the meanings of expressions by means first of translation and then of a statement of the truth-conditions. For instance, let 'Red' be a $\mathrm{pr_b}$; 'Red (3)' will then mean: "The position 3 is red." Now, let '$(x)\ \big(\mathrm{Red}\ (x)\big)$' mean: "Every position is red"; and '$(\exists x)\ \big(\mathrm{Red}\ (x)\big)$': "At least one position is red", and therefore: "There is (at least) one position that is red." Besides these ordinary forms of sentence, we shall introduce the following.

'$(x)3$ $(\mathrm{Red}(x))$' will mean the same as: '$\mathrm{Red}(0) \cdot \mathrm{Red}(1) \cdot \mathrm{Red}(2) \cdot$ $\mathrm{Red}(3)$', that is: "Every position up to 3 is red"; '$(\exists x)\,3$ $(\mathrm{Red}(x))$' will mean the same as '$\mathrm{Red}(0) \vee \mathrm{Red}(1) \vee \mathrm{Red}(2) \vee$ $\mathrm{Red}(3)$', or "There is one position up to 3 which is red."

The expressions which occur at the beginning of the sentences above, namely: '(x)', '$(\exists x)$', '$(x)\,3$', '$(\exists x)\,3$', are called the *unlimited* **universal operator**, the *unlimited* **existential operator**, the *limited* universal operator, and the *limited* existential operator respectively. In the two limited operators, '3' is called the *limiting expression* of the operator, and in all four of the operators *x*' is called the *operator-variable*. '$\mathrm{Red}(x)$' is called the **operand** (belonging to the operator). In Language I, *only limited operators* occur; we shall not make use of the unlimited operators till later, in Language II.

If $\mathfrak{A}_1$ and $\mathfrak{A}_2$ are operators, then, instead of writing $\mathfrak{A}_1\left(\mathfrak{A}_2(\mathfrak{S})\right)$, we shall write simply $\mathfrak{A}_1\mathfrak{A}_2(\mathfrak{S})$. (Compare p. 19, condition 5.)

A variable (or the symbol-design of a variable), $\mathfrak{z}_1$, is called **bound** at a certain position in $\mathfrak{A}_1$ (whether a symbol of the design $\mathfrak{z}_1$ occurs at this position or not) when there is a (proper or improper) partial expression of $\mathfrak{A}_1$ which contains this position and has the form $\mathfrak{A}_2(\mathfrak{S})$, where $\mathfrak{A}_2$ is an operator having the operator-variable $\mathfrak{z}_1$.

A variable $\mathfrak{z}_2$ which occurs at a certain position in $\mathfrak{A}_1$ is called **free** at this position in $\mathfrak{A}_1$ when $\mathfrak{z}_2$ is not bound at this position in $\mathfrak{A}_1$. *Example:* Let $\mathfrak{S}_1$ have the form: $\mathfrak{S}_2 \vee \mathfrak{S}_3 \vee \mathfrak{S}_4$; and specifically the design: '$\mathrm{P}_1(x) \vee (x)\,5\left(\mathrm{P}_2(x,y)\right) \vee \mathrm{P}_3(x)$'. At all positions of $\mathfrak{S}_3$, 'x' is bound in $\mathfrak{S}_3$ and therefore also in $\mathfrak{S}_1$; in $\mathfrak{S}_1$ the first and the fourth 'x' and the 'y' are free. If a variable which is free in $\mathfrak{A}_1$ occurs in $\mathfrak{A}_1$, then $\mathfrak{A}_1$ is called **open**; otherwise it is called **closed**.

In order to express *unlimited universality, free variables* will be used in I. For example, let $\mathfrak{S}_5$ be '$\mathrm{sum}(x,y) = \mathrm{sum}(y,x)$'. This will mean: "For any two numbers, the sum of the first and the second is always equal to the sum of the second and first." If $\mathfrak{S}_5$ is true, then so is every sentence arising out of $\mathfrak{S}_5$ as the result of substituting any arbitrary numerical expressions for 'x' and 'y'; for instance, '$\mathrm{sum}(3,7) = \mathrm{sum}(7,3)$' ($\mathfrak{S}_6$). [Thus, in our system, the so-called sentential functions also are ranked as sentences. Our classification into closed and open sentences corresponds to the usual classification into sentences and sentential functions.]

In the use of *free variables* for expressing unlimited universality, our language agrees with that of Russell. But when Russell, in his explanatory text [*Princ. Math.* I] says that a free (real) variable is equivocal, or has an indeterminate meaning, we do not agree with him. 'Red(x)' is a proper sentence with a perfectly unambiguous meaning; it is exactly equivalent in meaning to the sentence (occurring in our Language II and in Russell's language) '(x) (Red (x))'.

The expression which arises out of a given expression $\mathfrak{A}_1$ by the *substitution* of $\mathfrak{Z}_1$ for $\mathfrak{z}_1$ will be designated syntactically by '$\mathfrak{A}_1 \begin{pmatrix} \mathfrak{Z}_1 \\ \mathfrak{z}_1 \end{pmatrix}$'. This can be exactly defined in the following manner. The positions in $\mathfrak{A}_1$ at which $\mathfrak{z}_1$ occurs freely in $\mathfrak{A}_1$ are called the *substitution-positions* for $\mathfrak{z}_1$ in $\mathfrak{A}_1$; $\mathfrak{A}_1 \begin{pmatrix} \mathfrak{Z}_1 \\ \mathfrak{z}_1 \end{pmatrix}$ is that expression which arises out of $\mathfrak{A}_1$ when $\mathfrak{z}_1$ is replaced by $\mathfrak{Z}_1$ at all the substitution-positions in $\mathfrak{A}_1$; here $\mathfrak{Z}_1$ must be so constructed that no variable which is bound at any of the substitution-positions for $\mathfrak{z}_1$ in $\mathfrak{A}_1$ occurs as a free variable in $\mathfrak{Z}_1$. If, in $\mathfrak{A}_1$, $\mathfrak{z}_1$ does not occur as a free variable, then $\mathfrak{A}_1 \begin{pmatrix} \mathfrak{Z}_1 \\ \mathfrak{z}_1 \end{pmatrix}$ is the unchanged expression $\mathfrak{A}_1$.

Example: Let $\mathfrak{S}_1$, $\mathfrak{S}_5$, $\mathfrak{S}_6$ represent the previously mentioned sentences, and let $\mathfrak{z}_1$ be the variable 'x' and $\mathfrak{z}_2$ 'y'. Then $\mathfrak{S}_1 \begin{pmatrix} \mathfrak{z}_1 \\ \mathfrak{nu} \end{pmatrix} \begin{pmatrix} \mathfrak{z}_2 \\ \mathfrak{nu}^! \end{pmatrix}$ represents the sentence: '$P_1(0) \vee (x) 5 (P_2(x, 0^!)) \vee P_3(0)$'. $\mathfrak{S}_5 \begin{pmatrix} \mathfrak{z}_1 \\ {}^{\cdot}3 \end{pmatrix} \begin{pmatrix} \mathfrak{z}_2 \\ {}^{\cdot}7^! \end{pmatrix}$ is $\mathfrak{S}_6$. — '$(\exists x)(x = y^!)$' means: "For every number y, there is a next higher number." Here a $\mathfrak{Z}$, in which 'x' occurs as a free variable, for instance '$x^!$', must not be substituted for 'y'; $(\exists x)(x = x^{!!})$' is obviously false.

§ 7. THE K-OPERATOR

An expression of the form $(K\mathfrak{z}) \mathfrak{z}(\mathfrak{S})$ is not a sentence—as are the corresponding expressions which have a universal or an existential operator—it is a numerical expression. The K-operator, $(K\mathfrak{z}) \mathfrak{z}$, is not a sentential operator but a descriptional operator;

or, more specifically, a numerical operator. $(K_{3_1})\, 3_1\, (S_1)$ means: "the smallest number up to (and including) 3_1 for which S_1 is true, and, when no such number exists, 0". *Examples:* Let 'Gr(a, b)' mean: "a is greater than b"; '$(Kx)_9\, (Gr(x, 7))$' is equivalent in meaning to '8'; '$(Kx)_9\, (Gr(x, 7) \bullet Prim(x))$' is equivalent in meaning to '0'.

In general, it follows from the meaning stated that two sentences of the forms (1) and (2) below mean the same:

$$pr_1\, [(K_{3_1})\, 3_1\, (pr_2(3_1))] \dots\dots\dots\dots\dots\dots(1)$$
$$[\sim (\exists\, 3_1)\, 3_1\, (pr_2(3_1)) \bullet pr_1\, (0)] \vee (\exists\, 3_1)\, 3_1\, [pr_2(3_1) \bullet$$
$$(3_2)\, 3_1 (\sim (3_2 = 3_1) \supset \sim pr_2(3_2)) \bullet pr_1\, (3_1)] \dots\dots(2)$$

The previously mentioned designations: 'operator-variable', 'limiting-expression', 'operand', 'bound' and 'free' variables, are also applied to expressions having K-operators. [In contrast with the usual (Russellian) description, description by means of the K-operator is never either empty or equivocal; it is always univocal; hence in the use of the K-operator no special precautionary rules are necessary in our system.]

§ 8. THE DEFINITIONS

Symbols for which no definitions are framed are called *undefined* or *primitive* symbols. The logical primitive symbols of Language I consist of the eleven individual symbols mentioned already (see p. 16), together with nu and all the 3. As descriptive primitive symbols any pr_b or fu_b may be set up. All other 33, pr, and fu, which it is desired to employ, must be introduced by *definitions*. A 33 or a pr is always explicitly defined; an fu either explicitly or regressively.

An explicit definition consists of one sentence; a regressive definition of two sentences. Each of these sentences will have the form: $3_1 = 3_2$, or: $S_1 \equiv S_2$. The expression 3_1 (or S_1) is called the *definiendum*, and contains the symbol which is to be defined. 3_2 (or S_2) is called the *definiens*.

In an explicit definition, the symbol which is to be defined occurs only in the definiendum; in a regressive definition, on the other hand, it occurs also in the definiens of the second sentence.

For the rest, a definiens may contain only either primitive symbols or such as have previously been defined. Thus the order in which definitions are set up may not be altered arbitrarily. To each defined symbol belongs a *chain of definitions*, by which is meant the shortest series of sentences which contains the definition of that symbol together with the definitions of all defined symbols occurring in the chain. The chain of definitions of a symbol is always finite, and (apart from the order of succession) uniquely determined.

To the *explicit definitions*, in the wider sense in which the word is used here, belong both the explicit definitions in the narrower sense —that is to say those where the definiendum consists only of the new symbol (for instance, the definition of a $\mathfrak{z}\mathfrak{z}$ in I)—and the so-called definitions *in use*—those where the definiendum contains other symbols besides the new symbol (for instance the definition of a $\mathfrak{pr}$ or an $\mathfrak{fu}$ in I).

The definition of a *numeral*, $\mathfrak{z}\mathfrak{z}_1$, has the form: $\mathfrak{z}\mathfrak{z}_1 = 3$.
The definition of a *predicate*, $\mathfrak{pr}_1{}^n$, has the form:

$$\mathfrak{pr}_1{}^n (\mathfrak{z}_1, \mathfrak{z}_2, \cdots \mathfrak{z}_n) \equiv \mathfrak{S}.$$

The explicit definition of a *functor* $\mathfrak{fu}_1{}^n$ has the form: $\mathfrak{fu}_1{}^n (\mathfrak{z}_1, \mathfrak{z}_2, \cdots \mathfrak{z}_n) = 3$. [*Example:* 'nf$(x) = x'$'. Def. 1, p. 59.]
The *regressive definition* of an $\mathfrak{fu}_1{}^n$ has the form: (*a*) $\mathfrak{fu}_1{}^n$ $(\mathfrak{nu}, \mathfrak{z}_2, \cdots \mathfrak{z}_n) = 3_1$; (*b*) $\mathfrak{fu}_1{}^n (\mathfrak{z}_1', \mathfrak{z}_2, \cdots \mathfrak{z}_n) = 3_2$. In 3_2, $\mathfrak{fu}_1{}^n$ is always followed by the argument-expression $\mathfrak{z}_1, \mathfrak{z}_2 \cdots \mathfrak{z}_n$, the variables of which are not bound. [*Example:* Def. 3 for 'prod', p. 59; the first equation serves for the transformation of $\mathfrak{fu}_1 (\mathfrak{nu}, 3)$; the second equation refers $\mathfrak{fu}_1 (\mathfrak{z}_3', \mathfrak{z}_4)$ back to $\mathfrak{fu}_1 (\mathfrak{z}_3, \mathfrak{z}_4)$ so that, for example, in 'prod $(6, y)$', by using the second equation six times and the first equation once, 'prod' may be eliminated.] Further, every definition-sentence must fulfil the following two conditions: (1) in the definiens, no free variable may occur which does not already occur in the definiendum; and (2) two equal variables must not occur in the definiendum.

If *condition* (1) is not made, then it is possible for definitions to be framed by means of which a *contradiction* may be inferred. This may be shown by an example (Lesniewski gives a similar example for the sentential calculus [*Neues System*], pp. 79 f.). We define a $\mathfrak{pr}$ 'P':

$$P(x) \equiv (\mathrm{Gr}(x,y) \cdot \mathrm{Gr}(y,5)) \quad\text{.............................} \quad (1)$$

(1) $\quad (\mathrm{Gr}(7,6) \cdot \mathrm{Gr}(6,5)) \supset P(7) \quad\text{............................} \quad (2)$

$\quad\quad\quad \mathrm{Gr}(7,6) \cdot \mathrm{Gr}(6,5) \quad\text{.....................................} \quad (3)$

(2) (3) $\quad\quad\quad\quad\quad\quad\quad\quad\quad P(7) \quad\text{............................} \quad (4)$

(1) $\quad\quad P(7) \supset (\mathrm{Gr}(7,4) \cdot \mathrm{Gr}(4,5)) \quad\text{............................} \quad (5)$

(5) $\quad\quad P(7) \supset \mathrm{Gr}(4,5) \quad\text{...} \quad (6)$

(6) $\quad\quad {\sim}\mathrm{Gr}(4,5) \supset {\sim}P(7) \quad\text{......................................} \quad (7)$

$\quad\quad\quad {\sim}\mathrm{Gr}(4,5) \quad\text{...} \quad (8)$

(7) (8) $\quad\quad\quad\quad\quad\quad\quad\quad {\sim}P(7) \quad\text{............................} \quad (9)$

(4) and (9) contradict one another.

It is not necessary, on the other hand, to make the *converse condition*; a variable not present in the definiens may be present in the definiendum. (Compare, for instance: Def. 3.1, p. 59.)

Condition (2) is made, not for the purpose of avoiding contradictions, but for the purpose of assuring retranslatability. For instance, if one defined: 'P$(x, x) \equiv$ Q(x)', then 'P' in 'P$(0, 1)$' could not be eliminated.

If we have a sentence of the form $\mathfrak{Z}_1 = \mathfrak{Z}_2$, or $\mathfrak{S}_1 \equiv \mathfrak{S}_2$, then, as we shall see later, $\mathfrak{Z}_1$ may be replaced by $\mathfrak{Z}_2$, or $\mathfrak{S}_1$ by $\mathfrak{S}_2$, and conversely, in every other sentence (p. 36). This means that every explicitly defined symbol, wherever it occurs, may be *eliminated* by the help of its definition. But in the case of a regressively defined symbol, the elimination is not always possible. [*Example*: If 'prod(x,y)' occurs in a sentence in which 'x' is free (e.g. 'prod$(x,y) =$ prod(y,x)'), then 'prod' cannot be eliminated.]

We are now in a position to define more exactly the terms '*descriptive*' and '*logical*', which, up to the present, have only been roughly explained.

If a symbol $\mathfrak{a}_1$ is undefined, then $\mathfrak{a}_1$ is called descriptive $(\mathfrak{a}_\mathfrak{d})$ when $\mathfrak{a}_1$ is a pr or an fu. If $\mathfrak{a}_1$ is defined, then $\mathfrak{a}_1$ is called an $\mathfrak{a}_\mathfrak{d}$ when an undefined $\mathfrak{a}_\mathfrak{d}$ occurs in the definition-chain of $\mathfrak{a}_1$. An *expression* $\mathfrak{A}_1$ is called descriptive $(\mathfrak{A}_\mathfrak{d})$ when an $\mathfrak{a}_\mathfrak{d}$ occurs in $\mathfrak{A}_1$. $\mathfrak{a}_1$ is called logical $(\mathfrak{a}_\mathfrak{l})$ when $\mathfrak{a}_1$ is not an $\mathfrak{a}_\mathfrak{d}$. $\mathfrak{A}_1$ is called logical $(\mathfrak{A}_\mathfrak{l})$ when $\mathfrak{A}_1$ is not an $\mathfrak{A}_\mathfrak{d}$.

§ 9. SENTENCES AND NUMERICAL EXPRESSIONS

We will now name a few kinds of expressions. The most important of these are the sentences $(\mathfrak{S})$, and the numerical expressions $(\mathfrak{Z})$. Hitherto we have given only inexact explanations of them by reference to meanings. Now, however, these kinds must be defined formally and exactly. We have already surveyed all the possible ways of constructing sentences and numerical expressions in Language I, so that we have now only to enumerate the various forms arising out of them.

An $\mathfrak{S}$ may contain other $\mathfrak{S}$ and $\mathfrak{Z}$ as parts; similarly a $\mathfrak{Z}$ may contain other $\mathfrak{Z}$, and also (by means of the K-operator) $\mathfrak{S}$ as well. Hence the definitions which we are about to give of the terms 'sentence' and 'numerical expression', to which we shall add the auxiliary term 'argument-expression', refer to one another, but only in so far as in determining whether a particular expression submitted, $\mathfrak{A}_1$, is an $\mathfrak{S}$ or a $\mathfrak{Z}$, we shall refer to the question whether a certain *proper* partial expression of $\mathfrak{A}_1$ is an $\mathfrak{S}$ or a $\mathfrak{Z}$. Thus it follows that this process of reference comes to an end after a finite number of steps; the definitions are unambiguous and do not contain a vicious circle. [Definitions of a strictly accurate form will be given later within the framework of the symbolically formulated syntax.]

A symbol of I which is either $\mathfrak{nu}$, or a defined numeral, or a $\mathfrak{z}$, is called a **numeral** ($\mathfrak{zz}$). An expression of I is called an **accented expression** ($\mathfrak{St}\,(Strichausdruck)$) when it has one of the following forms: 1. $\mathfrak{nu}$; 2. $\mathfrak{St}^l$. [An $\mathfrak{St}$ is, therefore, either '0' (improper accented expression) or '0' with one or more accents 'I'.]

An expression of I is called a **numerical expression** ($\mathfrak{Z}$) when it has one of the following forms: 1. $\mathfrak{zz}$; 2. $\mathfrak{Z}^l$; 3. $\mathfrak{fu}^n\,(\mathfrak{Arg}^n)$; 4. $(\mathrm{K}\mathfrak{z}_1)$ $\mathfrak{Z}_1\,(\mathfrak{S})$, where $\mathfrak{z}_1$ does not occur in $\mathfrak{Z}_1$. Regressive definition for 'n-termed **argument-expression**' ($\mathfrak{Arg}^n$) in I: an $\mathfrak{Arg}^1$ is a $\mathfrak{Z}$; an $\mathfrak{Arg}^{n+1}$ has the form $\mathfrak{Arg}^n, \mathfrak{Z}$.

An expression of I is called a **sentence** ($\mathfrak{S}$) when it has one of the following forms: 1. $\mathfrak{Z}=\mathfrak{Z}$ ('Equation'); 2. $\mathfrak{pr}^n\,(\mathfrak{Arg}^n)$; 3. $\sim(\mathfrak{S})$; 4. $(\mathfrak{S})\mathfrak{verln}(\mathfrak{S})$; 5. $\mathfrak{A}_1\,(\mathfrak{S})$, where $\mathfrak{A}_1$ has the form $(\mathfrak{z}_1)\,\mathfrak{Z}_1$ or $(\exists\mathfrak{z}_1)\,\mathfrak{Z}_1$, and where $\mathfrak{z}_1$ does not occur in $\mathfrak{Z}_1$. [It is not necessary for the operator-variable to occur in the operand as a free variable; if not, then $\mathfrak{A}_1(\mathfrak{S}_1)$ is equivalent in meaning to $\mathfrak{S}_1$.]

The most important classification of expressions is the classification into sentences and non-sentences. The frequent division of expressions which are not sentences into expressions with 'independent meaning' ("proper names" in the wider sense) and the rest ("incomplete", "unfulfilled", "synsemantic" expressions) may be regarded as more significant from the psychological than from the logical standpoint.

B. RULES OF TRANSFORMATION FOR LANGUAGE I

§ 10. GENERAL REMARKS CONCERNING TRANSFORMATION RULES

For the construction of a calculus the statement of the transformation rules, as well as of the formation rules, as given for Language I, is essential. By means of the former we determine under what conditions a sentence is a *consequence* of another sentence or sentences (the *premisses*). But the fact that $\mathfrak{S}_2$ is a consequence of $\mathfrak{S}_1$ does not mean that the thought of $\mathfrak{S}_1$ will be accompanied by the thought of $\mathfrak{S}_2$. It is not a question of a psychological but of a logical relation between sentences. In the statement of $\mathfrak{S}_1$, the statement of $\mathfrak{S}_2$ is already objectively involved. We shall see that the relationship which is here indicated in a material way can be purely formally conceived. [*Example:* Let $\mathfrak{S}_1$ be '$(x)_5 \left(\text{Red}(x) \right)$', and $\mathfrak{S}_2$ 'Red(3)'; given that all positions up to 5 are red, then it is also given (implicitly) that the position 3 is red. In this particular case, perhaps, $\mathfrak{S}_2$ will have been "thought" simultaneously with $\mathfrak{S}_1$; but in other cases, where the transformation is more complicated, the consequence will not necessarily be thought coincidently with the premisses.]

It is impossible by the aid of simple methods to frame a definition for the term 'consequence' in its full comprehension. Such a definition has never yet been achieved in modern logic (nor, of course, in the older logic). But we shall return to this subject later. At present, we shall determine for Language I, instead of the term 'consequence', the somewhat narrower term '*derivable*'. [In constructing systems of logic, it is generally customary to use only the latter narrower concept, and it is not usually clearly understood that the concept of derivability is not the general concept of consequence.] For this purpose, the term '*directly derivable*' will be defined, or—as it is more commonly expressed—*rules of inference* will be laid down. [$\mathfrak{S}_3$ is called 'directly derivable' from $\mathfrak{S}_1$ or from $\mathfrak{S}_1$ and $\mathfrak{S}_2$, when, with the help of one of the rules of inference, $\mathfrak{S}_3$ can be obtained from $\mathfrak{S}_1$, or from $\mathfrak{S}_1$ and $\mathfrak{S}_2$.]

By a *derivation* with the *premises* $\mathfrak{S}_1$, $\mathfrak{S}_2$, ... $\mathfrak{S}_m$ (of which the number is always finite, and may also be 0), we understand a series of sentences of any finite length, such that every sentence of the series is either one of the premises, or a definition-sentence, or directly derivable from one or more (in our object-languages I and II, at most two) of the sentences which precede it in the series. If $\mathfrak{S}_n$ is the final sentence of a derivation with the premisses $\mathfrak{S}_1$, ... $\mathfrak{S}_m$, then $\mathfrak{S}_n$ is called **derivable** from $\mathfrak{S}_1$, ... $\mathfrak{S}_m$.

If a sentence when materially interpreted is logically universally true (and therefore the consequence of any sentence whatsoever), then we call it an *analytic* (or tautological) sentence. [*Example:* 'Red (3) V $\sim$ Red (3)'; this sentence is true in every case, independently of the nature of the position 3.] But this is another concept that is not amenable to formal analysis by means of simple methods, and it will be discussed later. First, we propose to give the definition of the somewhat narrower term 'demonstrable'. [This is the usual procedure; Gödel was the first to show that not all analytic sentences are demonstrable.] $\mathfrak{S}_1$ is called **demonstrable** when $\mathfrak{S}_1$ is derivable from the null series of premises, and hence from any sentence whatsoever.

If a sentence when materially interpreted is logically invalid, we shall call it *contradictory*. [*Example:* 'Red (3) • $\sim$ Red (3)'; this sentence is false in every case, independently of the nature of the position 3.] We shall return later to the consideration of this concept. For the moment, we shall take, instead, the somewhat narrower term 'refutable'. $\mathfrak{S}_1$ is called **refutable** when at least one sentence $\sim \mathfrak{S}_2$ is demonstrable, $\mathfrak{S}_2$ being obtained from $\mathfrak{S}_1$ by the substitution of any accented expressions for all the 3 which occur as free variables. [*Example:* 'Prim (x)' is refutable because ' $\sim$ Prim (0^{11111})' is demonstrable.] A closed sentence $\mathfrak{S}_1$ is thus refutable when, and only when, $\sim \mathfrak{S}_1$ is demonstrable.

A sentence is called *synthetic* when it is neither analytic nor contradictory. A sentence is called **irresoluble** when it is neither demonstrable nor refutable. This last term is somewhat more comprehensive than the term 'synthetic'. We shall see later that every logical sentence is either analytic or contradictory; and that therefore synthetic sentences are only to be found amongst the descriptive sentences. On the other hand, in I—and likewise in every sufficiently rich language—there are logical sentences that are irresoluble. (Compare § 36.)

For reasons of technical simplicity, it is customary not to formulate the entire system of rules of inference, but only a few of these, and in place of the rest to set up certain sentences which are demonstrable (on the basis of the total system of rules), the so-called **primitive sentences**. The choice of rules and primitive sentences—even when a definite material interpretation of the calculus is assumed beforehand—is, to a large extent, arbitrary. Often a system can be changed (without changing the content) by omitting a primitive sentence, and, in its place, laying down a rule of inference—and conversely.

We also shall lay down rules of inference (that is to say, the definition of 'directly derivable') and set up primitive sentences for our object-languages. In this method, a **derivation** with certain premisses is to be defined as a series of sentences of which each one is either one of the premisses, or a primitive sentence, or a definition-sentence, or is directly derivable from sentences which precede it in the series. A derivation without premisses is called a **proof**. A proof is thus a series of sentences of which each is either a primitive sentence, or a definition-sentence, or is directly derivable from sentences which precede it in the series. The final sentence of a proof is called a **demonstrable** sentence.

§ 11. THE PRIMITIVE SENTENCES OF LANGUAGE I

We shall give here, not the individual primitive sentences, but a series of schemata of primitive sentences. Each schema will determine a kind of sentence to which an unlimited number of sentences belong. For instance, by means of the schema PSI 1 it is determined that every sentence of the form $\mathfrak{S}_1 \supset (\sim \mathfrak{S}_1 \supset \mathfrak{S}_2)$ is to be called a primitive sentence of the first kind, where $\mathfrak{S}_1$ and $\mathfrak{S}_2$ may be sentences which are constructed in any way whatsoever. [It is customary to lay down primitive sentences instead of schemata, and in Language II we also shall use that method. But for that purpose, variables for $\mathfrak{S}$, $\mathfrak{pr}$, and $\mathfrak{fu}$ are necessary. For example: the primitive sentence PSII 1 (p. 91) corresponds to the schema PSI 1. But, because in Language I we have not the necessary variables at our disposal, we cannot construct the primitive sentences themselves, but only schemata. The sentences which are here called primitive sentences of the first kind are, in II, indirectly demonstrable sentences. They follow from PSII 1 by substitution.]

Schemata of the Primitive Sentences of Language I

(*a*) Primitive sentences of the so-called *sentential calculus*.

PSI 1. $\mathfrak{S}_1 \supset (\sim \mathfrak{S}_1 \supset \mathfrak{S}_2)$

PSI 2. $(\sim \mathfrak{S}_1 \supset \mathfrak{S}_1) \supset \mathfrak{S}_1$

PSI 3. $(\mathfrak{S}_1 \supset \mathfrak{S}_2) \supset [(\mathfrak{S}_2 \supset \mathfrak{S}_3) \supset (\mathfrak{S}_1 \supset \mathfrak{S}_3)]$

(*b*) Primitive sentences of the *sentential operators* (limited).

PSI 4. $(\mathfrak{z}_1) \, \mathfrak{nu} \, (\mathfrak{S}_1) \equiv \mathfrak{S}_1 \begin{pmatrix} \mathfrak{z}_1 \\ \mathfrak{nu} \end{pmatrix}$

PSI 5. $(\mathfrak{z}_1) \mathfrak{z}_2{}' \, (\mathfrak{S}_1) \equiv \left[(\mathfrak{z}_3) \mathfrak{z}_2 \left(\mathfrak{S}_1 \begin{pmatrix} \mathfrak{z}_1 \\ \mathfrak{z}_3 \end{pmatrix} \right) \cdot \mathfrak{S}_1 \begin{pmatrix} \mathfrak{z}_1 \\ \mathfrak{z}_2{}' \end{pmatrix} \right]$

PSI 6. $(\exists \mathfrak{z}_1) \mathfrak{z}_2 \, (\mathfrak{S}_1) \equiv \sim (\mathfrak{z}_1) \mathfrak{z}_2 \, (\sim \mathfrak{S}_1)$

(*c*) Primitive sentences of *identity*.

PSI 7. $\mathfrak{z}_1 = \mathfrak{z}_1$

PSI 8. $(\mathfrak{z}_1 = \mathfrak{z}_2) \supset \left[\mathfrak{S}_1 \supset \mathfrak{S}_1 \begin{pmatrix} \mathfrak{z}_1 \\ \mathfrak{z}_2 \end{pmatrix} \right]$

(*d*) Primitive sentences of *arithmetic*.

PSI 9. $\sim (\mathfrak{nu} = \mathfrak{z}')$

PSI 10. $(\mathfrak{z}_1{}' = \mathfrak{z}_2{}') \supset (\mathfrak{z}_1 = \mathfrak{z}_2)$

(*e*) Primitive sentences of the *K-operator*.

PSI 11. $\mathfrak{S}_2 \begin{pmatrix} \mathfrak{z}_1 \\ (K_{\mathfrak{z}_1}) \mathfrak{z}_2 (\mathfrak{S}_1) \end{pmatrix} \equiv \left(\left[\sim (\exists \mathfrak{z}_1) \mathfrak{z}_2 (\mathfrak{S}_1) \cdot \mathfrak{S}_2 \begin{pmatrix} \mathfrak{z}_1 \\ \mathfrak{nu} \end{pmatrix} \right] \vee (\exists \mathfrak{z}_1) \mathfrak{z}_2 \right.$

$$\left. \left[(\mathfrak{z}_3) \mathfrak{z}_1 \left[\mathfrak{S}_1 \begin{pmatrix} \mathfrak{z}_1 \\ \mathfrak{z}_3 \end{pmatrix} \equiv (\mathfrak{z}_3 = \mathfrak{z}_1) \right] \cdot \mathfrak{S}_2 \right] \right)$$

We shall now see that all primitive sentences when materially interpreted are true, and (in the case of PSI 5–11) that by the substitution of any $\mathfrak{z}_3$ for the free $\mathfrak{z}$, true sentences follow from them.

For PSI 1–3: this is easy to show by means of the truth-value ables (on p. 20). For PSI 4: the two sides of the equivalence are equal in meaning according to the meaning already given for the limited universal operator—therefore both are true or both are false. For PSI 5: when something is true for every number up to $n+1$, then it is also true for every number up to n and for $n+1$, and conversely. For PSI 6: "There is a number in the series up to n having such and such a property", is equivalent in meaning to the sentence: "It is not true for every number up to n that it does not possess the property in question." PSI 4 and 5 represent, so to speak, the regressive definition of the limited universal operator. PSI 6 represents the explicit definition of the limited existential operator. While explicitly defined symbols can always be eliminated, it is not always possible to eliminate regressively defined symbols (compare p. 25). In like manner, a limited universal operator cannot be eliminated when the limiting expression contains a free variable (as, for example, in PSI 5). Limited universal operators and regressively defined fu are not mere abbreviations, and if we were to renounce them, the expressive capacity of the language would be very considerably diminished. On the other hand, to renounce the limited existential operator, the K-operator, and the symbols of conjunction and implication together with all explicitly defined ʒʒ, pr, and fu, would only succeed in rendering the language more clumsy without in the least diminishing the extent of the expressible.

The symbol of identity or equality ' = ' between ʒ is here intended (as in arithmetic) in the sense that $\mathfrak{Z}_1 = \mathfrak{Z}_2$ is true, if and only if $\mathfrak{Z}_1$ and $\mathfrak{Z}_2$ designate the same number, to use the common phrase. From this, it follows that PSI 7 and 8 are valid. PSI 9 means that zero is not the successor of any other number, and is therefore the initial term of the series. PSI 10 means that different numbers have not the same successor. PSI 9 and 10 correspond to the fourth and third axiom respectively in Peano's system of axioms for arithmetic. The material validity of PSI 11 follows from the meaning of the K-operator previously given (§ 7).

§ 12. The Rules of Inference of Language I

$\mathfrak{S}_3$ is called **directly derivable** in I from $\mathfrak{S}_1$ (RI 1, 2), or from $\mathfrak{S}_1$ and $\mathfrak{S}_2$ (RI 3, 4), when one of the following conditions RI 1–4 is fulfilled:

RI 1. (Substitution.) $\mathfrak{S}_3$ has the form $\mathfrak{S}_1\left(\dfrac{3}{3}\right)$.

RI 2. (Junctions.) (a) $\mathfrak{S}_3$ is obtained from $\mathfrak{S}_1$ by replacing a partial sentence (proper or improper) of the form $\mathfrak{S}_4 \vee \mathfrak{S}_5$ by $\sim \mathfrak{S}_4 \supset \mathfrak{S}_5$, or conversely;* (b) likewise with the forms $\mathfrak{S}_4 \cdot \mathfrak{S}_5$ and $\sim(\sim \mathfrak{S}_4 \vee \sim \mathfrak{S}_5)$; (c) likewise with the forms $\mathfrak{S}_4 \equiv \mathfrak{S}_5$ and $(\mathfrak{S}_4 \supset \mathfrak{S}_5) \cdot (\mathfrak{S}_5 \supset \mathfrak{S}_4)$.

RI 3. (Implication.) $\mathfrak{S}_2$ has the form $\mathfrak{S}_1 \supset \mathfrak{S}_3$.

RI 4. (Complete induction.) $\mathfrak{S}_1$ has the form $\mathfrak{S}_3\left(\dfrac{\mathfrak{z}_1}{\mathfrak{nu}}\right)$, and $\mathfrak{S}_2$ has the form $\mathfrak{S}_3 \supset \mathfrak{S}_3\left(\dfrac{\mathfrak{z}_1 \mathfrak{l}}{\mathfrak{z}_1}\right)$.

That which we here formulate in the form of a definition of 'directly derivable' is usually formulated in the form of rules of inference. Thus, the conditions just stated would correspond to the following four *rules of inference*:

1. Rule of *substitution*. Every substitution is allowed.

2. Rule of *junctions*. (a) A partial sentence $\mathfrak{S}_4 \vee \mathfrak{S}_5$ can always be replaced by $\sim \mathfrak{S}_4 \supset \mathfrak{S}_5$, and conversely. Correspondingly with (b) and (c).

3. Rule of *implication*. From $\mathfrak{S}_1$ and $\mathfrak{S}_1 \supset \mathfrak{S}_3$, $\mathfrak{S}_3$ may be deduced.

4. Rule of *complete induction*. *Example:* From $\mathfrak{pr}_1(\mathfrak{nu})$ and $\mathfrak{pr}_1(\mathfrak{z}_1) \supset \mathfrak{pr}_1(\mathfrak{z}_1\mathfrak{l})$, $\mathfrak{pr}_1(\mathfrak{z}_1)$ may be deduced.

These rules are formulated in such a way that, when the sentences are materially interpreted, they always lead from true sentences to further true sentences. In the case of RI 1, this follows

---

* (*Note*, 1935.) In the German original, RI 2 (a) relates to $\mathfrak{S}_4 \supset \mathfrak{S}_5$ and $\sim \mathfrak{S}_4 \vee \mathfrak{S}_5$, and replaces a definition of the implication symbol. Dr. Tarski has called my attention to the fact that, instead of this, the above form of RI 2 (a), which stands for a definition of the disjunction symbol, must be taken, because in PSI 1–3 the implication and not the disjunction symbol is employed. For the same reason PSII 4 has also been changed (see § 30).

from the interpretation of the free variables given earlier in the book, and in the case of both RI 2 and 3, from the truth-value tables (p. 20). RI 2 represents, so to speak, an explicit definition of the symbols of disjunction, conjunction, and equivalence, which merely serve as abbreviations. RI 4 corresponds to the ordinary arithmetical principle of complete induction: if a property belongs to the number 0, and if this property is an hereditary one (that is, one which, if it belongs to a number n, also belongs to $n + 1$) then it also belongs to every number (Peano's fifth axiom).

§ 13. Derivations and Proofs in Language I

That a certain sentence is demonstrable, or derivable from certain other sentences, will be shown by giving a proof or a derivation. We shall find the more fruitful method to be that of proving universal syntactical sentences which mean that all sentences of such and such a form are demonstrable, or derivable from other sentences of such and such a form. Sometimes the proof of a universal syntactical sentence of this kind can be effected by the construction of a *schema* for the proof or the derivation. The schema states how the proof or derivation can be carried out in individual cases. Another fruitful method, which in many cases obviates the construction of special schemata, is based on the fact that universal syntactical sentences about demonstrability or derivability can be inferred from other sentences of the same kind. That is, if S_3 is derivable from S_2, and S_2 from S_1, then S_3 is also derivable from S_1; for this derivation can be obtained by placing the first two derivations one after the other. If S_1 is demonstrable, and S_2 derivable from S_1, then S_2 is also demonstrable. Further, if $S_1 \supset S_2$ is demonstrable, then S_2 is derivable from S_1 (according to RI 3). The converse is not always true, but only the following: if S_1 is closed and S_2 derivable from S_1, $S_1 \supset S_2$ is demonstrable. [The counter-example for an open S_1 is as follows: let S_1 be '$x = 2$', and S_2 be '$(x) 3 (x = 2)$'; S_2 is derivable from S_1 (S_1 and S_2 are false); but $S_1 \supset S_2$ in this case is not demonstrable and is even false, for S_2 results from this sentence by the substitution of '2' for 'x', and by the application of RI 3.]

We will give simple examples of a proof-schema and a derivation-schema together with several universal syntactical sentences about demonstrability and derivability. [The references on the left-hand side of the page to primitive sentences and rules are only there to facilitate understanding—they do not belong to the schema. On the other hand, the special conditions stated in words, to which a particular expression is subjected (for instance, $\mathfrak{S}_3$ in the derivation schema below), are essential to the schema.]

EXAMPLE OF A PROOF-SCHEMA

PSI 1	$\mathfrak{S}_1 \supset (\sim \mathfrak{S}_1 \supset \mathfrak{S}_1)$	(1)
PSI 2	$(\sim \mathfrak{S}_1 \supset \mathfrak{S}_1) \supset \mathfrak{S}_1$	(2)

PSI 3, in which the sentence $\sim \mathfrak{S}_1 \supset \mathfrak{S}_1$ will be taken for $\mathfrak{S}_2$ and $\mathfrak{S}_1$ taken for $\mathfrak{S}_3$:

	$(\mathfrak{S}_1 \supset (\sim \mathfrak{S}_1 \supset \mathfrak{S}_1)) \supset ([(\sim \mathfrak{S}_1 \supset \mathfrak{S}_1) \supset \mathfrak{S}_1] \supset [\mathfrak{S}_1 \supset \mathfrak{S}_1])$	(3)
(1) (3) RI 3	$((\sim \mathfrak{S}_1 \supset \mathfrak{S}_1) \supset \mathfrak{S}_1) \supset (\mathfrak{S}_1 \supset \mathfrak{S}_1)$	(4)
(2) (4) RI 3	$\mathfrak{S}_1 \supset \mathfrak{S}_1$	(5)

Theorem 13.1. $\mathfrak{S}_1 \supset \mathfrak{S}_1$ is always (that is, for any sentential design $\mathfrak{S}_1$) demonstrable.

We shall designate the syntactical theorem No. n of § m by 'Theorem m•n'. The syntactical theorems 13.1–4 refer to that part of Language I which corresponds to the so-called *sentential calculus*. This part comprises PSI 1–3 and RI 1–3.

Theorem 13.2. $\mathfrak{S}_1 \vee \sim \mathfrak{S}_1$ is always demonstrable. This is the so-called *principle of excluded middle*.

Theorem 13.3. $\mathfrak{S}_1$ and $\sim\sim \mathfrak{S}_1$ are mutually derivable.

Theorem 13.4. If $\mathfrak{S}_1$ is refutable, then every sentence $\mathfrak{S}_2$ is derivable from $\mathfrak{S}_1$. — Since $\mathfrak{S}_1$ is refutable, a demonstrable sentence $\sim \mathfrak{S}_3$ exists such that $\mathfrak{S}_3$ is obtained from $\mathfrak{S}_1$ by means of substitution. Thus, in addition to $\mathfrak{S}_1$, we can use $\sim \mathfrak{S}_3$ as a premiss in the *derivation schema*:

	$\mathfrak{S}_1$	(1)
	$\sim \mathfrak{S}_3$	(2)
(1) RI 1	$\mathfrak{S}_3$	(3)
PSI 1	$\mathfrak{S}_3 \supset (\sim \mathfrak{S}_3 \supset \mathfrak{S}_2)$	(4)
(3) (4) RI 3	$\sim \mathfrak{S}_3 \supset \mathfrak{S}_2$	(5)
(2) (5) RI 3	$\mathfrak{S}_2$	(6)

The syntactical theorems which follow refer to that part of the language which goes beyond the calculus of sentences—namely, to the *calculus of predicates*. [This is usually known as the *functional calculus*. For the most part, up to the present, the term 'predicate' has been applied only to the one-termed pr.] In this domain Language I deviates further from the usual form of formal language (Russell and Hilbert). Since Language I is a language of co-ordinates, the method of complete induction (RI 4) will often be applied in the proofs and derivations.

A. Syntactical Theorems about Universal Sentences

Theorem 13.5. Every sentence of one of the following forms is demonstrable:

(a) $(\mathfrak{z}_1)\,\mathfrak{F}_1(\mathfrak{S}_1) \supset \mathfrak{S}_1\begin{pmatrix}\mathfrak{z}_1\\\mathfrak{n}\mathfrak{u}\end{pmatrix}$;

(b) $(\mathfrak{z}_1)\,\mathfrak{F}_1(\mathfrak{S}_1) \supset \mathfrak{S}_1\begin{pmatrix}\mathfrak{z}_1\\\mathfrak{z}_1\end{pmatrix}$;

(c) $(\mathfrak{z}_1)\,\mathfrak{F}_1(\mathfrak{S}_1) \equiv \mathfrak{S}_1$, provided $\mathfrak{z}_1$ does not occur as a free variable in $\mathfrak{S}_1$.

Theorem 13.6.

(a) $(\mathfrak{S}_1)\begin{pmatrix}\mathfrak{z}_1\\\mathfrak{z}_1\end{pmatrix}$ is always derivable from $(\mathfrak{z}_1)\,\mathfrak{F}_1(\mathfrak{S}_1)$;

(b) $(\mathfrak{z})\,\mathfrak{F}(\mathfrak{S}_1)$ is always derivable from $\mathfrak{S}_1$;

(c) $\mathfrak{S}_1$ is always derivable from $(\mathfrak{z}_1)\,\mathfrak{F}_1(\mathfrak{S}_1)$, provided $\mathfrak{z}_1$ does not occur as a free variable in $\mathfrak{S}_1$;

(d) $(\mathfrak{z}_1)\,\mathfrak{F}_1(\mathfrak{S}_1) \supset (\mathfrak{z}_1)\,\mathfrak{F}_1(\mathfrak{S}_2)$ is always derivable from

$$(\mathfrak{z}_1)\,\mathfrak{F}_1(\mathfrak{S}_1 \supset \mathfrak{S}_2);$$

(e) $(\mathfrak{z}_1)\,\mathfrak{F}_1(\mathfrak{S}_1) \equiv (\mathfrak{z}_1)\,\mathfrak{F}_1(\mathfrak{S}_2)$ is always derivable from $\mathfrak{S}_1 \equiv \mathfrak{S}_2$ (this follows from Theorem 6 *b*, *d*).

B. Syntactical Theorems about Existential Sentences

Theorem 13.7. The following sentences are always demonstrable:

(a) $(\exists\,\mathfrak{z}_1)\,\mathfrak{n}\mathfrak{u}(\mathfrak{S}_1) \equiv \mathfrak{S}_1\begin{pmatrix}\mathfrak{z}_1\\\mathfrak{n}\mathfrak{u}\end{pmatrix}$;

(b) $(\exists\,\mathfrak{z}_1)\,\mathfrak{F}_{1'}(\mathfrak{S}_1) \equiv \left[(\exists\,\mathfrak{z}_1)\,\mathfrak{F}_1(\mathfrak{S}_1) \vee \mathfrak{S}_1\begin{pmatrix}\mathfrak{z}_1\\\mathfrak{z}_{1'}\end{pmatrix}\right]$;

(c) $\mathfrak{S}_1 \left(\begin{matrix} \mathfrak{z}_1 \\ \mathfrak{z}_1 \end{matrix} \right) \supset (\exists \, \mathfrak{z}_1) \, \mathfrak{z}_1 \, (\mathfrak{S}_1).$

Theorem 13.8. $(\exists \, \mathfrak{z}_1) \, \mathfrak{z}_1 \, (\mathfrak{S}_1)$ is derivable from $\mathfrak{S}_1$; and if $\mathfrak{z}_1$ does not occur as a free variable in $\mathfrak{S}_1$, then the converse is also true. — Further relations of derivation analogous to Theorem 6 may be stated.

C. Syntactical Theorems about Equations

Theorem 13.9. The following sentences are always demonstrable:

(a) $(\mathfrak{z}_1 = \mathfrak{z}_2) \supset \left[\mathfrak{z}_3 \left(\begin{matrix} \mathfrak{z}_1 \\ \mathfrak{z}_1 \end{matrix} \right) = \mathfrak{z}_3 \left(\begin{matrix} \mathfrak{z}_1 \\ \mathfrak{z}_2 \end{matrix} \right) \right]$;

(b) $(\mathfrak{z}_1 = \mathfrak{z}_2) \supset (\mathfrak{z}_2 = \mathfrak{z}_1)$;

(c) $[(\mathfrak{z}_1 = \mathfrak{z}_2) \cdot (\mathfrak{z}_2 = \mathfrak{z}_3)] \supset (\mathfrak{z}_1 = \mathfrak{z}_3).$

Theorem 13.10. The following sentences are derivable from $\mathfrak{z}_1 = \mathfrak{z}_2$:

(a) $\mathfrak{S}_1 \left(\begin{matrix} \mathfrak{z}_1 \\ \mathfrak{z}_1 \end{matrix} \right) \equiv \mathfrak{S}_1 \left(\begin{matrix} \mathfrak{z}_1 \\ \mathfrak{z}_2 \end{matrix} \right)$;

(b) $\mathfrak{z}_3 \left(\begin{matrix} \mathfrak{z}_1 \\ \mathfrak{z}_1 \end{matrix} \right) = \mathfrak{z}_3 \left(\begin{matrix} \mathfrak{z}_1 \\ \mathfrak{z}_2 \end{matrix} \right).$

D. Syntactical Theorems about Replacement

Theorem 13.11. $\mathfrak{A}_1 \mathfrak{z}_2 \mathfrak{A}_2$ is derivable from $\mathfrak{z}_1 = \mathfrak{z}_2$ and $\mathfrak{A}_1 \mathfrak{z}_1 \mathfrak{A}_2$, provided the latter is a sentence. In other words: if an equation is assumed, then in any sentence, the left-hand term of the equation may be replaced by the right-hand term (and, similarly, the right-hand term by the left-hand term).

Theorem 13.12. $\mathfrak{A}_1 \mathfrak{S}_2 \mathfrak{A}_2$ is derivable from $\mathfrak{S}_1 \equiv \mathfrak{S}_2$ and $\mathfrak{A}_1 \mathfrak{S}_1 \mathfrak{A}_2$, provided the latter is a sentence. In other words: if an equivalence is assumed, then, in any sentence in which the second (or the first) equivalence-term occurs, it may be replaced by the first equivalence-term (or the second, respectively). The proof is obtained by means of the analysis of the different forms in which one sentence can occur in another one (compare, for instance, Theorem 6 e). [Compare also Hilbert [*Logik*] p. 61; the condition that the same free variables must occur in $\mathfrak{S}_1$ and $\mathfrak{S}_2$ is not necessary in our form of language.]

The difference between replacement and substitution: In the case of substitution, all expressions of the same kind (namely, the free variables) which occur in the sentence must be transformed simultaneously; on the other hand, in the case of a replacement, no attention need be paid to the remaining parts of the sentence.

The possibility of presenting the definitions in the form of equations depends upon Theorems 11 and 12 (compare § 8). On the basis of an explicit definition, the definiendum can in every case be replaced by the definiens, and conversely.

§ 14. RULES OF CONSEQUENCE FOR LANGUAGE I

The case may arise where, for a particular $\mathfrak{pr}_\mathfrak{l}$, say $\mathfrak{pr}_1$, every sentence of the form $\mathfrak{pr}_1(\mathfrak{St})$ is demonstrable, but not the universal sentence $\mathfrak{pr}_1(\mathfrak{z}_1)$. We shall encounter a $\mathfrak{pr}$ of this kind later on (§ 36). Although every individual case is inferable, there is no possibility of inferring the sentence $\mathfrak{pr}_1(\mathfrak{z}_1)$. In order to create that possibility, we will introduce the term 'consequence', which is wider than the term 'derivable', and, analogously, the term 'analytic', which is wider than 'demonstrable', and the term 'contradictory', which is wider than 'refutable'. The definition will be framed so that the universal sentence in question, $\mathfrak{pr}_1(\mathfrak{z}_1)$, although not demonstrable, will be analytic.

For this purpose it is necessary to deal also with *classes of sentences*. Hitherto we have spoken only of *finite* series of sentences or of other expressions. But a class may be of such a nature that it cannot be exhausted by means of a finite series. (It may then be called an *infinite* class; a more exact definition of this term is unnecessary for our purpose.) A class of expressions is given by means of a syntactical determination (either definite or indefinite) of the form of the expressions. For instance, by every schema of primitive sentences an infinite class of sentences is definitely determined. To speak of classes of expressions is only a more convenient way of speaking of syntactical forms of expressions. [Later on, we shall see that 'class' and 'property' are two words for the same thing.]

We shall apply the following designations (of the syntax-language) to classes of expressions (sentences for the most part). '$\mathfrak{K}$' (*Klasse*) will be the general term. '$\{\mathfrak{A}_1\}$' will be taken to represent the class of which the only element is $\mathfrak{A}_1$; '$\{\mathfrak{A}_1, \dots \mathfrak{A}_n\}$', the class consisting of the elements $\mathfrak{A}_1, \mathfrak{A}_2, \ldots \mathfrak{A}_n$; '$\mathfrak{R}_1 + \mathfrak{R}_2$', the sum of the classes $\mathfrak{R}_1$ and $\mathfrak{R}_2$. A class of expressions is called a *descriptive* class when at least one of the expressions in it is a descriptive expression; otherwise it is called a *logical* class. (In this Section, '$\mathfrak{R}_1$' and so on always designate classes of sentences.)

$\mathfrak{S}_1$ is called a *direct consequence* of $\mathfrak{R}_1$ (in I) when one of the following conditions, DC 1, 2, is fulfilled:

DC 1. $\mathfrak{R}_1$ is finite, and there exists a derivation in which RI 4 (complete induction) is not used and of which the premisses are the sentences of $\mathfrak{R}_1$ and the last sentence is $\mathfrak{S}_1$;

DC 2. There exists a $\mathfrak{z}_1$ such that $\mathfrak{R}_1$ is the class of all sentences of the form $\mathfrak{S}_1\left(\dfrac{\mathfrak{z}_1}{\mathfrak{S}t}\right)$; that is to say, the class

$$\left\{ \mathfrak{S}_1\left(\frac{\mathfrak{z}_1}{\mathfrak{n}\mathfrak{u}}\right),\ \mathfrak{S}_1\left(\frac{\mathfrak{z}_1}{\mathfrak{n}\mathfrak{u}^{\mathrm{I}}}\right),\ \mathfrak{S}_1\left(\frac{\mathfrak{z}_1}{\mathfrak{n}\mathfrak{u}^{\mathrm{II}}}\right), \ldots \right\}.$$

$\mathfrak{R}_2$ is called a *direct consequence-class* (in I) of $\mathfrak{R}_1$ when every sentence of $\mathfrak{R}_2$ is a direct consequence of a sub-class of $\mathfrak{R}_1$. A finite series of (not necessarily finite) classes of sentences, such that every class (except the first) is a direct consequence-class of the class which directly precedes it in the series, is called a *consequence-series* (in I). $\mathfrak{S}_1$ is called a **consequence** (in I) of $\mathfrak{R}_1$, when there exists a consequence-series of which $\mathfrak{R}_1$ is the first class, and $\{\mathfrak{S}_1\}$ the last. $\mathfrak{S}_n$ is called a consequence of $\mathfrak{S}_1$, or of $\mathfrak{S}_1, \mathfrak{S}_2, \ldots \mathfrak{S}_m$, when $\mathfrak{S}_n$ is a consequence of $\{\mathfrak{S}_1\}$, or of $\{\mathfrak{S}_1, \mathfrak{S}_2, \ldots \mathfrak{S}_m\}$, respectively.

In rule DC 1 we are not obliged to exclude rule RI 4 (complete induction). But its additional application would be superfluous since, on the basis of the definitions given, it can be shown that $\mathfrak{S}_3$ is always a consequence of $\left\{ \mathfrak{S}_3\left(\dfrac{\mathfrak{z}_1}{\mathfrak{n}\mathfrak{u}}\right),\ \mathfrak{S}_3 \supset \mathfrak{S}_3\left(\dfrac{\mathfrak{z}_1}{\mathfrak{z}_1^{\mathrm{I}}}\right) \right\}$. Let this class be $\mathfrak{R}_1$ Then, as is easily seen, every sentence of the form $\mathfrak{S}_3\left(\dfrac{\mathfrak{z}_1}{\mathfrak{S}t}\right)$ is derivable from $\mathfrak{R}_1$ and is therefore, according to DC 1, a direct consequence of $\mathfrak{R}_1$; thus, the class of these sentences, $\mathfrak{R}_2$, is a direct consequence-class of $\mathfrak{R}_1$; and according to DC 2, $\mathfrak{S}_3$ is a direct consequence of $\mathfrak{R}_2$, and therefore a consequence of $\mathfrak{R}_1$.

Theorem 14.1. If a sentence is derivable from other sentences, then it is also a consequence of them.

The consequence-relation has a wider extension than the derivability-relation. The rule DC 2 could, as the above exposition shows, be partially replaced by RI 4. A complete equivalent of DC 2 is impossible to obtain either by means of RI 4 or any other rules of inference of the former kind, that is to say, any rules concerned with the concept 'directly derivable'. For, since a derivation must consist of a finite number of sentences, these rules always refer to a finite number of premisses. But DC 2 in general refers to infinite classes of sentences. [Compare the example given at the beginning of the section. $\mathrm{pr}_1(3_1)$ is not a consequence of any proper sub-class of the class of sentences $\mathrm{pr}_1(\mathfrak{S}\mathfrak{t})$, still less a consequence of a finite sub-class.]

Thus we have now *two different methods of deduction*: the more restricted method of *derivation*, and the wider method of the *consequence-series*. A derivation is a finite series of sentences; a consequence-series is a finite series of not necessarily finite classes. In the case of derivation, every individual step (i.e. the relation 'directly derivable') is definite, but not the relation 'derivable', which is defined by the whole chain of derivations. In the case of the consequence-series, the single step (i.e. the relation 'direct consequence') is already indefinite, and therefore all the more the relation 'consequence'. The term 'derivable' is a narrower one than the term 'consequence'. The latter is the only one that exactly corresponds to what we mean when we say: "This sentence follows (logically) from that one", or: "If this sentence is true, then (on logical grounds) that one is also true." In the usual systems of symbolic logic, instead of the concept 'consequence', the narrower but much simpler concept 'derivable' is applied, by laying down certain rules of inference. And, in fact, the method of derivation always remains the fundamental method; every demonstration of the applicability of any term is ultimately based upon a derivation. Even the demonstration of the existence of a consequence-relation—that is to say, the construction of a consequence-series in the object-language—can only be achieved by means of a derivation (a proof) in the syntax-language.

A *sentence* $\mathfrak{S}_1$ is called **analytic** (in I) when it is a consequence of the null class of sentences (and thus a consequence of every sentence); it is called **contradictory** when every sentence is the consequence of $\mathfrak{S}_1$; it is called *L-determinate* when it is either analytic or contradictory; it is called **synthetic** when it is neither analytic nor contradictory.

A *sentential class* $\mathfrak{R}_1$ is called *analytic* when every sentence of $\mathfrak{R}_1$ is an analytic sentence; *contradictory* when every sentence is a consequence of $\mathfrak{R}_1$; and *synthetic* when it is neither analytic nor contradictory.

Two or more sentences are called **incompatible** (with one another) when the class consisting of them is a contradictory class; otherwise they are called **compatible**.

Theorem 14.2. Every demonstrable sentence is analytic; every refutable sentence is contradictory. The converse is, however, not universally true.

Theorem 14.3. Every $\mathfrak{S}_I$ (and $\mathfrak{R}_I$) is either analytic or contradictory. Only an $\mathfrak{S}_b$ (or a $\mathfrak{R}_b$) can be synthetic.

Proof: 1. Let $\mathfrak{S}_1$ be a closed $\mathfrak{S}_I$. The application of the rules of reduction which are to be given later (§ 34 a) leads, in a finite number of steps, either to '$\mathfrak{nu} = \mathfrak{nu}$', or to the negation thereof. Here, every reduction-step is in agreement with DC 1. Therefore $\mathfrak{S}_1$ is L-determinate.

2. Let us assume that every $\mathfrak{S}_I$ in which $\imath$ different free variables occur is L-determinate; we will show that, in that case, the same is true for every $\mathfrak{S}_I$ with $n+1$ free variables. Let $\mathfrak{S}_1$ be an $\mathfrak{S}_I$ with the $n+1$ free variables $\mathfrak{z}_1, \mathfrak{z}_2, \dots \mathfrak{z}_n, \mathfrak{z}_{n+1}$. Consider the class $\mathfrak{R}_1$ of the sentences of the form $\mathfrak{S}_1\begin{pmatrix}\mathfrak{z}_{n+1}\\\mathfrak{St}\end{pmatrix}$. Every one of these sentences contains n free variables, and therefore, according to our assumption, it is L-determinate. Then according to DC 2, $\mathfrak{S}_1$ is a direct consequence of $\mathfrak{R}_1$. Now, either all the sentences of $\mathfrak{R}_1$ are analytic or at least one of them is contradictory—say $\mathfrak{S}_2$. In the first case, $\mathfrak{S}_1$ is also analytic; in the second case, $\mathfrak{S}_1$ is contradictory because $\mathfrak{S}_2$ is a direct consequence of $\mathfrak{S}_1$. Therefore $\mathfrak{S}_1$ is L-determinate and consequently every $\mathfrak{S}_I$ with $n+1$ free variables is L-determinate.

3. By the Principle of Induction it follows from (1) and (2) that every $\mathfrak{S}_I$ is L-determinate.

Example: Fermat's Theorem:

$$`\big(\mathrm{Gr}(x,0)\bullet\mathrm{Gr}(y,0)\bullet\mathrm{Gr}(z,0)\bullet\mathrm{Gr}(u,0^{\mathrm{II}})\big)\supset$$
$$\sim\!\big(\mathrm{sum}\,[\mathrm{pot}(x,u),\mathrm{pot}(y,u)]=\mathrm{pot}(z,u)\big)'$$

(the definitions of 'Gr', 'sum', 'pot' will be given in § 20) is a logical sentence and therefore, according to Theorem 14.3, is certainly either analytic or contradictory. Up to the present it is not known which of these two is the case.

Theorem 14.4. A $\Re_I$ is contradictory if, and only if, at least one sentence belonging to it is contradictory. But a $\Re_b$ may be contradictory without any of the sentences belonging to it being contradictory. (For this reason it is important that not only the sentences, but also the classes of sentences, should be classified as analytic, contradictory, or synthetic.)

Example: Let pr_1 be an undefined pr_b; then the sentences $pr_1(nu)$ and $\sim pr_1(nu)$ are synthetic; but the class of these two sentences (like their conjunction) is contradictory.

By means of the concept 'analytic', an exact understanding of what is usually designated as 'logically valid' or 'true on logical grounds' is achieved. Hitherto it has for the most part been thought that logical validity was representable by the term 'demonstrable'—that is to say, by a process of derivation. But although, for the majority of practical cases, the term 'demonstrable' constitutes an adequate approximation, it does not exhaust the concept of logical validity. The same thing holds for the pairs 'demonstrable'—'analytic' and 'refutable'—'contradictory', as for the pair 'derivable'—'consequence'.

In material interpretation, an analytic sentence is absolutely true whatever the empirical facts may be. Hence, it does not state anything about facts. On the other hand, a contradictory sentence states too much to be capable of being true; for from a contradictory sentence both every fact and its opposite can be deduced. A synthetic sentence is sometimes true—namely, when certain facts exist—and sometimes false; hence it says something as to what facts exist. *Synthetic sentences* are the *genuine statements about reality.*

If we wish to determine what a sentence $\mathfrak{S}_1$ (in the material mode of speech) means, without leaving the domain of the formal to go over into that of the material interpretation of the sentence, we must find out what sentences are the consequences of that sentence. Among these sentences we may ignore those which are the consequences of every sentence—that is to say, the analytic sentences. The non-analytic consequences of $\mathfrak{S}_1$ constitute the whole domain of that which is "to be got out" of $\mathfrak{S}_1$. We therefore define as follows: by the logical **content** of $\mathfrak{S}_1$ or $\mathfrak{R}_1$ (in I) we understand the class of non-analytic sentences (of I) which are consequences of $\mathfrak{S}_1$ or $\mathfrak{R}_1$ respectively (in I). The "content" or "sense" of a sentence is often spoken of without determining exactly what is to be understood by the expression. The defined term 'content' seems to us to represent precisely what is meant by 'sense' or 'meaning'—so long as nothing psychological or extra-logical is intended by it.

We call sentences or classes of sentences having the same content **equipollent**. Two sentences are obviously equipollent when and only when each of them is a consequence of the other.

In discussions as to whether certain sentences have the same *sense* (or meaning), objections of the following nature are very often made to the logician: "But this sentence and that cannot have the same sense (or meaning) because they are connected with quite different thoughts, images, and so on." To this objection it may be replied that the question of *logical* congruence of meaning has no connection with that of the agreement of conceptions and the like. The latter is a question of a psychological nature and must therefore be decided by empirical and psychological investigation. It has nothing whatsoever to do with logic. (Furthermore, the question as to what ideas are connected with particular sentences is a vague and ambiguous one; the answer will differ according to the person who is the subject of experiment and to the particular circumstances.) The question whether two *sentences* have the same *logical* sense is concerned only with the agreement of the two sentences in all their consequence-relations. The concept of 'having logically the same sense' is thus adequately expressed by the above-defined syntactical term 'equipollent'. The concept of two *terms* having the same *meaning*, which will be comprehended by the syntactical term 'synonymous', is an analogous case.

Theorem 14.5. Mutually derivable sentences are equipollent. The converse is not universally true.

Two expressions, $\mathfrak{A}_1$ and $\mathfrak{A}_2$, are called **synonymous** when each sentence $\mathfrak{S}_1$ in which $\mathfrak{A}_1$ occurs is equipollent (not, for example, merely equal in truth-value) to that sentence $\mathfrak{S}_2$ which arises out of $\mathfrak{S}_1$ when $\mathfrak{A}_1$ is replaced by $\mathfrak{A}_2$. By means of this concept 'synonymous', the relation which is designated in the material mode of speech as that of 'having the same meaning', is formally comprehended.

Examples: '2', '0^{II}', '1^I', 'sum$(1, 1)$' are synonymous. Let 'te' be an undefined fu_b; then, even when 'te$(3) = 5$' is an empirically true sentence, 'te(3)' is not synonymous with '5', and, more generally, not with any 33_I or St. [But 'te(3)' is synonymous with '5' in relation to 'te$(3) = 5$'; on this point see § 65.] In the English language 'Odysseus' and 'the father of Telemachus' are not synonymous, even though they both designate the same person.

Theorem 14.6. If $3_1 = 3_2$ is analytic, then 3_1 and 3_2 are synonymous, and conversely.

Theorem 14.7. (*a*) If $S_1 \supset S_2$ is analytic, then S_2 is a consequence of S_1. (*b*) If S_2 is a consequence of S_1, and S_1 is closed, then $S_1 \supset S_2$ is analytic.

Proof of 7 b. (7 *a* follows naturally from DC 1 and RI 3.) Let S_1 be closed. We will state the proof for general cases; for the special case where S_1 is logical, the proof is a considerably simpler one. We will call S_2 an analytic implicate of S_1 if $S_1 \supset S_2$ is analytic.

(A) Every primitive sentence of I is an analytic implicate of S_1.

(B) If S_3 and S_4 are both analytic implicates of S_1, and if S_5 is directly derivable from S_3 and S_4, then S_5 is also an analytic implicate of S_1.

(C) It follows from A and B that: if S_3 is an analytic implicate of S_1, and S_4 is derivable from S_3 without the application of complete induction, then S_4 is also an analytic implicate of S_1. Therefore: if S_3 is an analytic implicate of S_1 and if, according to DC 1, S_4 is a direct consequence of S_3, then S_4 is also an analytic implicate of S_1.

(D) If, according to DC 2, S_4 is a direct consequence of $\Re_1$ and if every sentence of $\Re_1$ is an analytic implicate of S_1, then S_4 is also an analytic implicate of S_1.

(E) It follows from C and D that: if every sentence of $\Re_2$ is an analytic implicate of S_1, and if S_4 is a consequence of $\Re_2$, then S_4 is also an analytic implicate of S_1.

(F) Since S_1 is an analytic implicate of itself, therefore the following holds: if S_2 is a consequence of S_1, then S_2 is an analytic implicate of S_1.

Theorem 14.8. Two sentences are synonymous when and only when they are equipollent. [This is valid for Languages I and II and for certain other languages also. Compare Theorem 65.4 *b*.]

Theorem 14.9. If $S_1 \equiv S_2$ is analytic, then S_1 and S_2 are equipollent, and conversely.

From Theorems 6, 8, and 9, it follows that the definiendum and the definiens of a definition-sentence are synonymous.

Remarks on terminology. Instead of the expression 'analytic', Wittgenstein [*Tractatus*]—and, following him, the literature of the Vienna Circle up to the present time—uses the expression 'tautological' or 'tautology' (which, however, is only defined for the sentential calculus). On the other hand, it is customary to apply the term 'tautological' to transformations of sentences—namely, to those which do not enlarge the content. We say, for example: "The inferences of logic are tautological." It is a matter of experience, however, that the use of the word 'tautological' in these two different senses, especially as the first does not correspond to the usual mode of speech, easily leads to misunderstanding and confusion. It would seem, therefore, more practical to retain the expression in the second case only ('tautological conclusion') and to adopt the expression 'analytic' to apply to the first case ('analytic sentences'). This term, which was used in the first place by Kant, has been more sharply defined by Frege ([*Grundlagen*] p.4). He calls a sentence analytic when, for its proof, only "the universal logical laws" together with definitions are necessary. Dubislav [*Analytische*] has pointed out that the concept is a relative one; it must always be referred to a particular system of assumptions and methods of reasoning (primitive sentences and rules of inference), that is to say, in our terminology, to a particular language.

The expression 'contradictory' (or 'contradiction') was likewise introduced by Wittgenstein (within the calculus of propositions). In addition to the expressions 'analytic' and 'synthetic' Kant did not use a third expression for the negations of analytic sentences. It might be worth considering whether the expression 'analytic' should be taken as a generic term (according to the suggestion of Dubislav [*Analytische*], as opposed to ordinary usage) and then 'analytically true' and 'analytically false', or 'positively analytic' and 'negatively analytic', used in place of 'analytic' and 'contradictory'.

C. REMARKS ON THE DEFINITE FORM OF LANGUAGE

§ 15. DEFINITE AND INDEFINITE

The form of language most commonly used in modern logic is that which Whitehead and Russell [*Princ. Math.*] have built up on the foundations laid by the work of Frege, Peano, Schröder, and others. Hilbert [*Logik*] uses a different symbolism, but his form of language has remained the same in all essentials. In choosing the symbols for our object-languages I and II, we have adopted the symbolism of Russell, because it is the most widely known. In the form of the language we follow the main outlines of the system of Hilbert and Russell, but we deviate from it in some essential points, especially in our Language I. The most important deviations are the following: the use of symbols of position, instead of names of objects (language of co-ordinates); limited operators (definite language); and two different kinds of universality.

We have already spoken (§ 3) about the nature of our language considered as a *language of co-ordinates* (symbols of position as arguments). In this form of language there is an essential syntactical difference between the *situation-terms* for positions, and the other determinations by means of which any properties of positions are stated. The latter we shall call *qualitative terms*. A relation of situation in the simplest case will be expressed by means of an analytic (or contradictory) sentence (e.g. "Positions 7 and 6 are neighbouring positions"). On the other hand, a qualitative relation, in the simplest case, will be expressed by means of a synthetic descriptive sentence (e.g. "Position 7 and position 6 have the same colour"). The former sentence is determined by a logical operation, namely, a proof; the latter, on the other hand, can only be decided on the basis of empirical observations, that is to say, by derivation from observation-sentences. In this fact lies an essential difference which is obliterated when the language is so constructed—as by the methods hitherto accepted—that situation-determinations and qualitative relations are expressed in a syntactically identical manner.

We shall call a symbol of Languages I and II **definite** when it is either an undefined constant or a defined one in the definition-chain of which no unlimited operator occurs; otherwise **indefinite**.

An *expression* will be called *definite* when all the constants which occur in it are definite, and when all the variables in it are limitedly bound; otherwise *indefinite*.

All definite expressions are closed. In the case of the expressions in Language I, the concepts 'definite' and 'closed' are identical; similarly, 'indefinite' and 'open'. We call I a *definite language* because, in I, all constants and all closed expressions are definite. [In the strictest sense, only a language in which all the expressions are definite may be called a definite language.] [On the admissibility of indefinite concepts, compare §§ 43–45.]

To "calculate" a numerical expression, say $\mathfrak{Z}_1$, means: to transform $\mathfrak{Z}_1$ into an $\mathfrak{St}$; or, more exactly, to prove a sentence of the form $\mathfrak{Z}_1 = \mathfrak{St}$. To "resolve" a sentence, say $\mathfrak{S}_1$, means: either to prove or to refute it. Now it can be shown that *every definite $\mathfrak{Z}_1$ can be calculated; and that every definite $\mathfrak{S}_1$ can be resolved*. Moreover, there exists a definite method by means of which this calculation and resolution respectively can be achieved. This is the so-called reduction which will be explained later. If $\mathfrak{pr}_1$ is a definite $\mathfrak{pr}_1{}^n$ and $\mathfrak{fu}_1$ is a definite $\mathfrak{fu}_1{}^n$, then $\mathfrak{pr}_1 (\mathfrak{St}_1, \ldots \mathfrak{St}_n)$ is always resoluble, and $\mathfrak{fu}_1 (\mathfrak{St}_1, \ldots \mathfrak{St}_n)$ is always calculable.

§ 16. On Intuitionism

Some of the tendencies which are commonly designated as 'finitist' or 'constructivist' find, in a certain sense, their realization in our definite Language I. "In a certain sense", let it be noted; for inasmuch as these tendencies are, as a rule, only vaguely formulated, an exact statement is not possible. They are chiefly represented by *Intuitionism* (Poincaré; and in contemporary thought, above all Brouwer; also Weyl, Heyting, and Becker) and allied opinions (for example, F. Kaufmann and Wittgenstein). The points of contact will presently be stated precisely, but our own view differs from the tendencies in question in one essential respect. We hold that the problems dealt with by Intuitionism can be exactly formulated only by means of the construction of a calculus, and that all the non-formal discussions are to be regarded merely as more or less vague preliminaries to such a construction. The majority of the Intuitionists, however, are of the opinion that a calculus is something inessential, a mere supplementary appendix. Only Heyting has made an interesting attempt towards formalization from the standpoint of Intuitionism —we shall say something about his method later.

Once the fact is realized that all the pros and cons of the Intuitionist discussions are concerned with the forms of a calculus, questions will no longer be put in the form: "What *is* this or that like?" but instead we shall ask: "How *do we wish to arrange* this or that in the language to be constructed?" or, from the theoretical standpoint: "What consequences will ensue if we construct a language in this or that way?"

On this view the dogmatic attitude which renders so many discussions unfruitful disappears. When we here construct our Language I in such a way that it is a definite language, and thus fulfils certain conditions laid down by Intuitionism, we do not mean thereby to suggest that this is the only possible or justifiable form of language. We shall, on the contrary, include the definite Language I as a sub-language in the more comprehensive Language II, and the form of both languages will be looked upon as a matter of convention.

In Language I, all $\mathfrak{pr}_\mathfrak{l}$ and $\mathfrak{fu}_\mathfrak{l}$ are definite; the question whether a definite $\mathfrak{pr}_\mathfrak{l}$ can be attributed to a definite number or not, or whether a definite $\mathfrak{fu}_\mathfrak{l}$ has a definite value for a definite number or not, is always resoluble. This fact corresponds to the Intuitionist requirement that no concept be admitted for which a method of resolution is not stated. Further, the non-application of unlimited operators in I has the result that unlimited universality, although it can be positively expressed (namely, by means of free variables), cannot be negated. We can only say, either: '$P(x)$', which means: "All numbers have the property P"; or: '$\sim P(x)$', which means: "All numbers have the property not-P", "No number has the property P." On the other hand, "Not all numbers have the property P" is not expressible in I; in II it will be expressed by: '$\sim(x)\big(P(x)\big)$'. This sentence will be treated in II (as in the languages of Hilbert and Russell) as equivalent in meaning to '$(\exists x)\big(\sim P(x)\big)$', which means: "There is (at least) one number which has the property not-P." In I there are no such unlimited existential sentences, and this fact also corresponds to a condition laid down by Intuitionism, namely that an existential sentence may only be stated if either a concrete example can be produced, or, at least, a method given by the aid of which an example can be constructed in a finite, limited number of steps. For the Intuitionists, *existence without rules for construction* is considered to be "inadmissible" or "nonsensical" ("meaningless"). It is not quite clear, however, whether (and within exactly what limits), according to their point of view, existential sentences, and perhaps even negated universal sentences also, should be excluded by means of syntactical rules of formation, or whether only certain possibilities of transformation should be excluded. The issue involved is, above all, the question of indirect proof by means of the refutation of a universal sentence.

Let us take an example: (let 'P' be a $\mathfrak{pr}_l$):

$$(x)\big(P(x)\big)(\mathfrak{S}_1), \ \sim(x)\big(P(x)\big)(\mathfrak{S}_2), \ (\exists x)\big(\sim P(x)\big)(\mathfrak{S}_3).$$

In classical mathematics (and therefore also in the logic both of Russell and Hilbert, as well as in our II), when $\mathfrak{S}_1$ is reduced *ad absurdum*, first $\mathfrak{S}_2$ is inferred, and then from it the existential sentence $\mathfrak{S}_3$. It is in order to exclude this inference leading to an unlimited, non-constructive existential sentence that Brouwer renounces the so-called *Law of Excluded Middle*. The language-form of I, however, shows that the same result can be achieved by other methods—namely, by means of the exclusion of the unlimited operators. In I, $\mathfrak{S}_1$ can be translated into '$P(x)$', but $\mathfrak{S}_2$ and $\mathfrak{S}_3$ are not translatable into I. Here, the Law of Excluded Middle remains valid in I (Theorem 13.2). The exclusion of this law, as is well known, brings with it serious complications which do not occur in I. Thus Language I fulfils the fundamental conditions of Intuitionism in a simpler way than the form of language suggested by Brouwer (and partially carried out by Heyting).

In I universality is expressed in two different ways: by free variables, and by universal operators. Because the latter are always limited in I, the two methods of expression are not of equal value. We can make use of these two possibilities of expression in order to express *two different kinds of universality*.

Let us consider some examples: 1. "All the pieces of iron on this table are round." 2 *a*. "All pieces of iron are pieces of metal." 2 *b*. "All pieces of iron are magnetizable." In case 1, the sentence is dependent on an empirical test of a series of individual instances; a sentence of this kind is only determinable in a limited domain. Hence, the limited universal operator is best adapted to formulate it. In cases 2 *a* and 2 *b*, unlimited universality occurs. The validity of these sentences cannot be determined by the testing of individual instances. Sentence 2 *a* is analytic and follows from the definition of 'iron'. Sentence 2 *b* has (like all so-called laws of nature) the character of a hypothesis. Such a sentence is dependent upon the acceptance of a convention which in its turn is dependent upon a partial testing of individual instances. The use of free variables is adapted to the formulation of the unlimited universality of the examples 2 *a* and 2 *b*.

F. Kaufmann has rightly emphasized the difference between the two kinds of universality (he designates them, in common with Husserl, as individual (1) and specific (2 *a*) universality). [Whether his criticism, based on this differentiation, of the logic of the present time, especially that of Russell, and of the Theory of Aggregates, is entirely justified, is not here considered.] Perhaps the form of Language I represents the realization of a part of Kaufmann's ideas, but it is not possible to decide this point exactly, since Kaufmann, like Brouwer, has laid down no foundations for the construction of a formal system. A deviation from the language-form of Language I consists in the fact that Kaufmann, like Wittgenstein, considers sentences of the type 2 *b* to be inadmissible, since they are neither analytic nor limited, and in consequence cannot be completely verified in any way. In contrast with this view, the language-form of I also admits synthetic unlimitedly universal sentences.

§ 16*a*. IDENTITY

The following explanations are concerned with the symbol ' = ' considered as the symbol of identity in the narrower sense (that is to say, as used between ꝫ or between object-designations) and not as the symbol of equivalence (that is to say, as used between ⲋ). The symbol of identity occurs in Languages I and II (as also in the languages of Frege, Behmann, Hilbert) as an undefined symbol. Following Leibniz, Russell defines '$x=y$' in the following way: "x and y agree in all their (elementary) properties." Wittgenstein rejects the symbol altogether and suggests a new method for the use of variables by which it may be avoided.

Philosophical discussions concerning the justification of these various methods seem to us to be wrong. The whole thing is only a question of the establishment of a convention whose technical efficiency can be discussed. No fundamental reasons exist why the second or third of these methods should not be used instead of the first in Languages I and II. As it happens, the Leibniz-Russell method is only applicable in Language II; there the definition would take the form $(\mathfrak{z}_1 = \mathfrak{z}_2) \equiv (\mathfrak{p}_1) \big(\mathfrak{p}_1 (\mathfrak{z}_1) \supset \mathfrak{p}_1 (\mathfrak{z}_2) \big)$. Against this definition the objection is sometimes raised (for instance on the part of Wittgenstein, Ramsey, Behmann) that it is at least conceivable for two different objects to coincide in all their properties. But this objection is dismissed as soon as "all properties" are understood as including those of position. That is already true even for name-languages, and most certainly true for co-ordinate languages: $\mathfrak{z}_1$ and $\mathfrak{z}_2$ designate the same place when every property of position which holds for $\mathfrak{z}_1$ holds also for $\mathfrak{z}_2$. It would in any case be sufficient in the definition instead of 'all properties' to say 'all properties of position' (for which, for instance, instead of $\mathfrak{p}$ a sort of variable limited to $\mathfrak{pr}_1$, say $\mathfrak{p}_1$, could be used).

Wittgenstein's criticism goes still further: he does not merely reject Russell's definition, but refuses to make use of the symbol of identity at all. But it seems to us that all that emerges from his remarks about this symbol is that sentences of the form $\mathfrak{A} = \mathfrak{B}$ are —at least in the simplest cases—not synthetic, but analytic: it does not seem to us to follow that such sentences are altogether inadmissible. In order to avoid the use of the symbol of identity, Wittgenstein proposes to use a rule of substitution which differs from the one usually employed both in mathematics and in logic. His rule is that, for different variables, different constants must be substituted. The shorter form, '$P(x,y)$', of Wittgenstein's language corresponds to the usual form of sentence '$\sim (x=y) \supset P(x,y)$'. On the other hand, '$P(x,y) \vee P(x,x)$' corresponds to the sentence '$P(x,y)$'. Since Wittgenstein does not formulate any new rule of substitution but only states a number of examples, it is not clear how he intends to carry out his method. A closer examination shows that his method of variables leads to certain complications. Hence it seems to us to be better to retain the ordinary use of the symbol of identity and with it at the same time the ordinary rule of substitution.

According to Wittgenstein's idea, '$P(0,0)$', for instance, cannot be derivable from '$P(x,y)$'. But if, by a derivation step, '$P(0,y)$' is obtained from '$P(x,y)$', then it is not possible to see why in the derived sentence '0' may not be substituted for 'y'. Hence in order to prevent this substitution at some later stage in the derivation, a special expedient must be introduced by writing something of this sort: '$^{0,y}P(0,y)$'; and for this purpose suitable new rules must be laid down.

Russell's use of the symbol of identity for the definition of finite classes by the enumeration of their elements is equally reected by Wittgenstein. In our opinion, however, there is no need to reject these classes, but only to observe the difference (certainly an important one) subsisting between them and those classes which are defined by means of properties in the narrower sense. This is effected by means of suitable syntactical differentiations; the essential point is the difference between the pr_I (and in particular the finite definite pr_I) and the pr_b.

§ 17. The Principle of Tolerance in Syntax

In the foregoing we have discussed several examples of negative requirements (especially those of Brouwer, Kaufmann, and Wittgenstein) by which certain common forms of language —methods of expression and of inference—would be excluded. Our attitude to requirements of this kind is given a general formulation in the *Principle of Tolerance: It is not our business to set up prohibitions, but to arrive at conventions.*

Some of the prohibitions which have hitherto been suggested have been historically useful in that they have served to emphasize important differences and bring them to general notice. But such prohibitions can be replaced by a definitional differentiation. In many cases, this is brought about by the simultaneous investigation (analogous to that of Euclidean and non-Euclidean geometries) of language-forms of different kinds—for instance, a definite and an indefinite language, or a language admitting and one not admitting the Law of Excluded Middle. Occasionally it is possible to replace a prohibition by taking into account the intended distinctions within one particular form of language, by means of a suitable classification of the expressions and an investigation of the different kinds. Thus, for example, while Wittgenstein and Kaufmann reject both logical and arithmetical properties, in I descriptive and logical predicates have been distinguished. In II definite and indefinite predicates will be distinguished and their different properties determined. And further, in II, we shall differentiate between limitedly universal sentences, analytic unlimitedly universal sentences, and synthetic unlimitedly universal sentences, whereas Wittgenstein, Kaufmann, and Schlick all exclude sentences of the third kind (laws of nature) from language altogether, as not being amenable to complete verification.

In logic, there are no morals. Everyone is at liberty to build up his own logic, i.e. his own form of language, as he wishes. All that is required of him is that, if he wishes to discuss it, he must state his methods clearly, and give syntactical rules instead of philosophical arguments.

The tolerant attitude here suggested is, as far as special mathematical calculi are concerned, the attitude which is tacitly shared by the majority of mathematicians. In the conflict over the logical foundations of mathematics, this attitude was represented with especial emphasis (and apparently before anyone else) by Menger (*[Intuitionismus]* pp. 324 f.). Menger points out that the concept of constructivity, which Intuitionism absolutizes, can be interpreted both in a much narrower and in a much wider sense. The importance for the clarification of the pseudo-problems of philosophy of applying the attitude of tolerance to the form of language as a whole will become clear later (see § 78).

PART II

THE FORMAL CONSTRUCTION OF THE SYNTAX OF LANGUAGE I

§ 18. THE SYNTAX OF I CAN BE FORMULATED IN I

Up to the present, we have differentiated between the object-language and the syntax-language in which the syntax of the object-language is formulated. Are these necessarily two separate languages? If this question is answered in the affirmative (as it is by Herbrand in connection with metamathematics), then a third language will be necessary for the formulation of the syntax of the syntax-language, and so on to infinity. According to another opinion (that of Wittgenstein), there exists only one language, and what we call syntax cannot be expressed at all—it can only "be shown". As opposed to these views, we intend to show that, actually, it is possible to manage with one language only; not, however, by renouncing syntax, but by demonstrating that without the emergence of any contradictions the syntax of this language can be formulated within this language itself. In every language S, the syntax of any language whatsoever—whether of an entirely different kind of language, or of a sub-language, or even of S itself—can be formulated to an extent which is limited only by the richness in means of expression of the language S. Thus, with the means of expression of our definite Language I, the definite part of the syntax of any language whatsoever—for instance, of Russell's language or of Language II, or even of Language I itself—can be formulated. In the following pages, the latter undertaking will be carried out—that is to say, we shall *formulate the syntax of I*—as far as it is definite—*in I itself*. In this process it may happen that a sentence $\mathfrak{S}_1$ of I, when materially interpreted as a syntactical sentence, will say something about $\mathfrak{S}_1$ itself, and without any contradiction arising.

We differentiate between descriptive and pure syntax (see pp. 6f.). A sentence in the *descriptive syntax* of any language may state, for instance, that an expression of such and such a kind occurs in a certain series of positions. [A symbol occupies a position, an expression occupies a series of positions.] *Example:* "On page 33 line 32 of this book, an expression of the form '$3 = 33_1$' occurs (namely, '$x = 2$')." Since Language I has sufficient means of expression at its command for the purpose of describing the property of a domain of discrete positions, a descriptive-syntactical sentence of this kind may be formulated in I no matter whether it describes an expression of another language or an expression of I itself. It would, for instance, be possible to proceed by introducing in I undefined pr_b for the different kinds of symbols of the expressions to be described (later, we shall instead set up a single undefined fu_b, namely 'zei' [*Zeichen*]); for example, the pr_b 'Var' for the variables, the pr_b 'LogZz' for the logical numerals, the pr_b 'Id' for the symbol of identity, and so on. Let us now designate the position on page 33 at which '$x = 2$' begins, by 'a'. Then the aforementioned descriptive-syntactical sentence can be formulated in I in the following manner:

$$\text{'Var}(a) \bullet \text{Id}(a^I) \bullet \text{LogZz}(a^{II})\text{'}.$$

This is a synthetic descriptive sentence. We can then, further, define the pr_b 'LogSatz' so that 'LogSatz (x, u)' means: "In the series of positions extending from x to $x + u$, an $\mathfrak{S}_I$ occurs." Then the sentence: "Every expression of the form $3 = 33_1$ is an $\mathfrak{S}_I$" will be rendered in I by

$$\text{'}\big(\text{Var}(x) \bullet \text{Id}(x^I) \bullet \text{LogZz}(x^{II})\big) \supset \text{LogSatz}(x, 2)\text{'};$$

this is an analytic sentence which follows from the definition of 'LogSatz'.

§ 19. The Arithmetization of Syntax

As we have already mentioned, it is always possible to replace any pr_b by an fu_b. Several different pr_b may be called homogeneous if at most one of them can appertain to any position. Then it is always possible to replace a class of homogeneous pr_b by one fu_b, by correlating one value of the fu_b, either systematically or arbitrarily, to each one of the individual pr_b. [*Example:* Let the class of colours which are to be expressed be finite. We can express every colour by a pr_b, 'Blue', 'Red', and so on. These pr_b are then homogeneous and therefore we can replace them by a single fu_b, say 'col', by numbering the colours in some way, and stipulating that 'col(a) = b' shall mean: 'The position a has the colour No. b.'] Similarly, in the formulation of the syntax of I in I, we shall not designate the different kinds of symbols by different $\mathfrak{pr}_b$ (as, for instance, in the example given in § 18 by 'Id', etc.) but by one $\mathfrak{fu}_b$, namely 'zei'. We shall correlate the values of 'zei' to the different symbols (symbol-designs), partly arbitrarily and partly in accordance with certain rules. These values are called the *term-numbers* of the symbols. For instance, we shall co-ordinate the term-number 15 to the symbol of identity. This means that (instead of 'Id(a)') we shall write 'zei(a) = 15' when we wish to express the fact that the symbol of identity occurs at the position a. Not only the economy in primitive syntactical concepts, but other reasons which will be discussed later, justify the choice of this method of the *arithmetization* of syntax. (In this arithmetization, we make use of the method which Gödel [*Unentscheidbare*] has applied with such success in meta-mathematics or the syntax of mathematics.)

In general, the establishment of term-numbers for the different symbols can be effected arbitrarily. All that must be provided for is the fact that, for the variables, of which the number is un-limited, an unlimited number of term-numbers must be available —likewise for the $\mathfrak{z}\mathfrak{z}$, $\mathfrak{pr}$, and $\mathfrak{fu}$. We will now specify infinite classes of numbers for the term-numbers of these kinds of symbols in the following way. Let p run through all the prime numbers greater than 2. *Stipulations:* the **term-number** of a $\mathfrak{z}$ shall be a p (that is, a prime number greater than 2); the term-number of a defined $\mathfrak{z}\mathfrak{z}$ shall be a p^2 (that is, the second power of some prime number greater than 2); the term-number of an undefined $\mathfrak{pr}$ shall be a p^3; that of a defined $\mathfrak{pr}$, a p^4; that of an undefined $\mathfrak{fu}$, a p^5 (and specifically, the term-number of 'zei' shall be 3^5, which is 243); and that of a defined $\mathfrak{fu}$, a p^6. But not all the numbers of the classes determined in this way will be used as term-numbers: the choice of them will be determined later. To the remaining symbols—namely, the *undefined logical constants*—we assign (arbitrarily) other numbers, namely:

to the symbol: 0   (   )   ,   '   =   ∃   K   ∼   ∨   •   ⊃   ζ   π   φ
the term-number: 4   6   10   12   14   15   18   20   21   22   24   26   30   33   34.

[The last three symbols are auxiliary symbols which do not occur in the expressions of the language itself; see p. 68 concerning them.]

When any empirical theory is formulated in I, then the descriptive primitive symbols of this theory are added to the logical primitive symbols of Language I. Likewise in the formulation of the descriptive syntax; here 'zei' is the only additional primitive symbol. In the following construction of the system of syntactical definitions, however, 'zei' will not at first be used. For, at this stage, we are not concerned with descriptive but with pure syntax, and in this there are *no additional primitive symbols*, since pure syntax is nothing more than arithmetic. Just as term-numbers correspond to symbols, so series of term-numbers correspond to expressions. For example the series, 3, 15, 4, corresponds to the expression '$x = 0$'. The concepts and sentences of pure syntax refer now not to the series of symbols but to the corresponding series of term-numbers. Thus they are arithmetical concepts or sentences.

The formulation of the syntax becomes technically simpler if we go one step further with the method of the correlation of numbers. We will lay down a rule by which, to every series of term-numbers, one number—we call it the **series-number** of the series—will be uniquely correlated. In this way we shall no longer have to deal with series of numbers but only with single numbers. The rule is expressed as follows: $p_1^{k_1} \bullet p_2^{k_2} \bullet \ldots \bullet p_n^{k_n}$ is to be taken as the series-number for a series which consists of n term-numbers, $k_1, k_2, \ldots k_n$, where $p_i (i = 1$ to $n)$ is the ith prime number in the order of magnitude. [*Example:* The series 3, 15, 4, and with it the expression '$x = 0$', has the series-number $2^3 \bullet 3^{15} \bullet 5^4$.] Since the factorization of a number into its prime factors is unique, the series of term-numbers in its original order may be regained from a series-number, and thereby also the language-expression to which the series-number is correlated. [The rules stated earlier concerning term-numbers are in addition —but not necessarily—so arranged that no term-number is at the same time the series-number of any series.]

The method of the construction of series-numbers may be repeatedly applied. For instance, to a proof as a series of sentences, there corresponds, to begin with, a series of series-numbers. In accordance with the method described we can then correlate a *series-series-number* to this series of series-numbers.

By means of these stipulations about term- and series-numbers, all the definitions of pure syntax become arithmetical definitions, namely, definitions of properties of, or relations between, numbers. For instance, the verbal definition of 'sentence' will no longer have the form: "An expression is called a sentence when it consists of symbols combined in such and such a way"; but instead: "An expression is called a sentence when its series-number fulfils such and such conditions"; or, more exactly: "A number is called the series-number of a sentence when it fulfils such and such conditions." These conditions are only concerned with the kinds and order of the symbols of the expression, that is to say, with the kinds and order of the exponents of the prime factors of the series-number. We shall thus be able to express them purely arithmetically. All the sentences of pure syntax follow from these arithmetical definitions and are thus analytic sentences of elementary arithmetic. The definitions and sentences of syntax arithmetized in this way do not differ fundamentally from the other definitions and sentences of arithmetic, but only in so far as we give them a particular interpretation (namely the syntactical interpretation) within a particular system.

If this method of arithmetization is not applied, certain difficulties arise in the exact formulation of the syntax. For instance, let us consider the syntactical sentence: " $\mathfrak{S}_1$ is not demonstrable", which means: "No sentential series having $\mathfrak{S}_1$ as its final sentence is a proof." If the syntax is not arithmetized but, instead, as was suggested earlier, is constructed by the help of $\mathrm{pr_b}$ ('Var', etc.), we may interpret it as a theory concerning certain series of physical objects, namely, the series of written symbols. In a syntax of that kind, it is certainly possible to express: "There exists no actual written proof for $\mathfrak{S}_1$", but the sentence concerning the non-demonstrability of $\mathfrak{S}_1$ means much more, namely: "No proof for $\mathfrak{S}_1$ is *possible*." In order to be able to express such a sentence about possibility in the non-arithmetized syntax (no matter whether it is physically interpreted or not), the syntax would have to be supplemented by a theory (not empirical but analytic) concerning the possible arrangements of any elements—that is to say, by pure combinatorial analysis. It proves, however, to be much simpler, instead of constructing a new combinatorial analysis of this kind in a non-arithmetical form, to use

the arithmetic of the natural numbers which already contains
within itself the whole of combinatorial analysis (whether of a
finite or a denumerable number of elements). This is *the most
important reason for the arithmetization of syntax.* In the
arithmetized syntax, the sentence under discussion would run as
follows: "There exists no number which is the series-series-
number of a proof of which $\mathfrak{S}_1$ is the final sentence." We shall see
that it is possible to frame an arithmetical definition for that
property of a number which consists in its being the series-series-
number of a proof which has a given series-number as the final
number. Our sentence will then have the form: "There is no
number having such and such an arithmetical property." This is a
purely arithmetical sentence. By the arithmetization we are en-
abled, without using new and complicated auxiliary methods, to
express even those syntactical concepts (such as derivability and
demonstrability) which are concerned with a determinate *possibility.*

§ 20. GENERAL TERMS *

We shall now formulate the construction of the syntax of I
presented in I as a system of arithmetical definitions. Explanations, which indicate the interpretation of the terms involved
as syntactical terms, are appended to the definitions (in small
print). For the sake of brevity, the explanations are often inexactly and incorrectly formulated. *The exact presentation of the
syntax consists solely of the symbolically formulated definitions.* All
the symbols which are used in these definitions are either among
the logical primitive symbols of I (compare p. 24) or are defined
in the following pages. The defined symbols are, specifically,
certain $\mathfrak{z}_{\mathfrak{z}1}$, $\mathfrak{pr}_1$, and $\mathfrak{fu}_1$. In the following definitions, we shall use
the letters 'k', 'l',...'z' as $\mathfrak{z}$. (Later on, in Language II,
'p',...,'t' will be used as sentential variables, which do not occur
in I.)

The first definitions (D 1–23) are of a general nature and are
applicable to the syntax of any language whatsoever.

---

* Key to the symbols defined in this section:

nf: successor (*Nachfolger*)   prod: product (*Produkt*)
sum: sum (*Summe*)   po, pot: power (*Potenz*)

D 1. $\mathrm{nf}(x) = x^!$

D 2. 1. $\mathrm{sum}(0, y) = y$
   2. $\mathrm{sum}(x^!, y) = \mathrm{nf}\big(\mathrm{sum}(x, y)\big)$

D 3. 1. $\mathrm{prod}(0, y) = 0$
   2. $\mathrm{prod}(x^!, y) = \mathrm{sum}\big(\mathrm{prod}(x, y), y\big)$

D 4. 1. $\mathrm{po}(0, y) = 0^!$
   2. $\mathrm{po}(k^!, y) = \mathrm{prod}\big(\mathrm{po}(k, y), y\big)$

D 5. $\mathrm{pot}(x, k) = \mathrm{po}(k, x)$

D 6. 1. $\mathrm{fak}(0) = 0^!$
   2. $\mathrm{fak}(x^!) = \mathrm{prod}\big(\mathrm{fak}(x), x^!\big).$

Explanation, D 1–6: Explicit (D 1, 5) or regressive (D 2, 3, 4, 6) definitions are here given for six fuɪ having the meanings: Successor (to x); sum (of x and y); product; power ('$\mathrm{pot}(x, y)$': 'x^y' in ordinary symbols); factorial (compare p. 14). 'po' is only an auxiliary concept for 'pot'; it is necessary because we have stipulated that the first argument-place is to be taken as that to which the regression refers.

By means of the regressive definitions stated for 'sum' and 'prod', the ordinary fundamental laws of arithmetic (the commutative, associative, and distributive laws) and, further, all the known theorems of elementary arithmetic can be proved with the help of RI 4 (complete induction).

D 7. 1. $1 = 0^!$; 2. $2 = 1^!$; ... 10. $10 = 9^!$; ... 34. $34 = 33^!$.

Explanation: There are as many defined ʒʒ as we shall require. Here, a decimal to several places is taken as one indivisible ʒʒ.

D 8. $\mathrm{Grgl}(x, y) \equiv (\exists u)\, x\, \big(x = \mathrm{sum}(y, u)\big)$

D 9. $\mathrm{Gr}(x, y) \equiv \big(\mathrm{Grgl}(x, y) \,\bullet\, {\sim}(x = y)\big)$

D 10. $\mathrm{Tlb}(x, y) \equiv (\exists u)\, x\, \big(x = \mathrm{prod}(y, u)\big)$

Key to the symbols defined in this section (*continued*):

fak: factorial (*Fakultät*)
Grgl: greater or equal (*grösser oder gleich*)
Gr: greater (*grösser*)
Tlb: divisible (*teilbar*)
Prim, pr, prim: prime number (*Primzahl*)
gl: term-number (*Gliedzahl*)
lng: length (*Länge*)
letzt: last (*letzte*)
reihe: series (*Reihe*)

zus: composed (*zusammengesetzt*)
ers: replaced (*ersetzt*)
InA: in the expression (*im Ausdruck*)
InAR: in the expressional series (*in der Ausdrucksreihe*)
AInA: expression in the expression (*Ausdruck im Ausdruck*)
AInAR: expression in expressional series (*Ausdruck in der Ausdrucksreihe*)

D 11. $\mathrm{Prim}\,(x) \equiv \big({\sim}(x=0)\bullet{\sim}(x=1)\bullet(u)\,x\,((u=1)\vee$
$(u=x)\vee{\sim}\mathrm{Tlb}\,(x,u))\big)$

Explanation, D 8–11: These are four $\mathrm{pr_I}$ having the meanings: $x\geqq y$; $x>y$; x is divisible by y; x is a prime number (compare p. 13).

D 12. 1. $\mathrm{pr}\,(0,x)=0$
    2. $\mathrm{pr}\,(n^{\mathrm{l}},x)=(\mathrm{K}y)\,x\,\big(\mathrm{Prim}\,(y)\bullet\mathrm{Tlb}\,(x,y)\bullet$
       $\mathrm{Gr}\,\big(y,\mathrm{pr}\,(n,x)\big)\big)$

Explanation: $\mathrm{pr}\,(n,x)$ is the nth (in magnitude) prime number contained as a factor in x.

D 13. 1. $\mathrm{prim}\,(0)=0$
    2. $\mathrm{prim}\,(n^{\mathrm{l}})=(\mathrm{K}m)\,\mathrm{nf}\,[\mathrm{fak}\,(\mathrm{prim}\,(n))]\,\big[\mathrm{Prim}\,(m)\bullet$
       $\mathrm{Gr}\,\big(m,\mathrm{prim}\,(n)\big)\big]$

Explanation: $\mathrm{prim}\,(n)$ is the nth prime number (according to magnitude).

D 14. $\mathrm{gl}\,(n,x)=(\mathrm{K}y)\,x\,\big[{\sim}\mathrm{Tlb}\,\big(x,\mathrm{pot}\,[\mathrm{pr}\,(n,x),y^{\mathrm{l}}]\big)\big]$

Explanation: $\mathrm{gl}\,(n,x)$ is the nth term-number of the series with the series-number x.

D 15. $\mathrm{lng}\,(x)=(\mathrm{K}n)\,x\,\big(\mathrm{pr}\,(n^{\mathrm{l}},x)=0\big)$

Explanation: $\mathrm{lng}\,(x)$ is the length (that is to say the number of terms) of the series with the series-number x.

D 16. $\mathrm{letzt}\,(x)=\mathrm{gl}\,\big(\mathrm{lng}\,(x),x\big)$

Explanation: $\mathrm{letzt}\,(x)$ is the last term-number of the series with the series-number x.

D 17. 1. $\mathrm{reihe}\,(s)=\mathrm{pot}\,(2,s)$
    2. $\mathrm{reihe2}\,(s,t)=\mathrm{prod}\,\big(\mathrm{reihe}\,(s),\mathrm{pot}\,(3,t)\big)$
    3. $\mathrm{reihe3}\,(s,t,u)=\mathrm{prod}\,\big(\mathrm{reihe2}\,(s,t),\mathrm{pot}\,(5,u)\big)$

Explanation: $\mathrm{reihe}\,(s)$ is the series-number (2^s) of a series of which s is the only term-number; $\mathrm{reihe2}\,(s,t)$ is the series-number ($2^s\cdot3^t$) of a series of which the term-numbers are s and t; and so on. (In 'reihe2' '2' is not a $\mathrm{33}$ but a component part of the indivisible symbol 'reihe2'.)

We will now introduce the following abbreviations for the *explanations.* Instead of writing 'term-number of…' we will write '^{TN}…' (for instance '^{TN}negation symbol', which is 21). Instead of 'series-number of…' we will write '^{SN}…' (for instance '$^{\mathrm{SN}}\mathfrak{A}_1$', '^{SN}Operator' and so forth). Instead of 'series-series-number of…' we will write '^{SSN}…' (for instance

'SSN proof'). If we read the verbal transcription of a definition neglecting the indices, we shall get the syntactical interpretation of the definition. (For instance in the explanation of D 18: "zus (x,y) is the series which is composed of two partial series x and y".) On the other hand, if we read the transcription including the indices, we shall get (usually in a form not literally accurate) the arithmetical interpretation of the definition. (For instance, in the case of D 18: "zus (x,y) is the series-number of the series which is composed of two partial series having the series-numbers x and y".) In what follows we shall at first always work with the indices but later on we shall use them only when it seems necessary to do so for the sake of clarity.

D 18. 1. zus $(x, y) = (Kz)$ pot $\big[$prim $\big($sum $[\lng (x),\ \lng (y)]\big)$, sum $(x,y)\big]$ $\big[(n) \lng (x) \big($gl $(n, z) = $gl $(n, x)\big) \bullet (n) \lng (y)$ $\big(\sim(n=0)\supset \big[$gl $\big($sum $[\lng (x), n], z\big) = $gl $(n, y)\big]\big)\big]$

2. zus3 $(x, y, z) = $ zus $\big($zus $(x, y), z\big)$

3. zus4 $(x, y, z, u) = $ zus $\big($zus3 $(x, y, z), u\big)$

and so on.

Explanation: zus (x, y) is the SN series which is *composed* of two SN sub-series x and y (not: of TN terms; as different from 'reihe2 (s, t)'). Correspondingly 'zus3', etc., in the case of composition from three or more SN sub-series.

D 19. ers $(x, n, y) = (Kz)$ pot $\big[$prim $\big($sum $[\lng (x),\ \lng (y)]\big)$, sum $(x,y)\big]$ $\big((\exists u) x (\exists v) x \big[(x = $zus3 $(u,$ reihe $[$gl $(n, x)],$ $v)\big) \bullet \big(z = $zus3 $(u, y, v)\big) \bullet \big(n = $nf $[\lng (u)]\big)\big]\big)$

Explanation: ers (x, n, y) is the SN expression, which results from the SN expression x when the nth SN term in x is *replaced* by the SN expression y.

D 20. InA $(t, x) \equiv (\exists n) \lng (x) \big(\sim(n=0) \bullet [$gl $(n, x) = t]\big)$

D 21. InAR $(t, r) \equiv (\exists k) \lng (r) \big(\sim(k=0) \bullet$ InA $[t,$ gl $(k, r)]\big)$

D 22. AInA $(x, y) \equiv (\exists u) y (\exists v) y \big(y = $zus3 $(u, x, v)\big)$

D 23. AInAR $(x, r) \equiv (\exists k) \lng (r) \big(\sim(k=0) \bullet$ AInA $[x,$ gl $(k, r)]\big)$

Explanation, D 20: The TN symbol t occurs in the SN expression x. D 21: t occurs in an SN expression of the SSN expression-series r. D 22: The expression x occurs (either as a proper or improper part) in the expression y. D 23: The expression x occurs in an expression of the expression-series r.

§ 21. RULES OF FORMATION: (1) NUMERICAL EXPRESSIONS AND SENTENCES *

D 24. einkl (x) = zus3 $\big($reihe $(6), x,$ reihe $(10)\big)$

Explanation: If x is an ^{SN} $\mathfrak{A}_1$, then einkl (x) is the ^{SN} bracketing of x, that is, the expression $(\mathfrak{A}_1)$.

D 25. Var $(s) \equiv \big($Prim $(s) \cdot$ Gr $(s, 2)\big)$

Explanation: 'Var (s)' means that s is a prime number greater than 2 (thus, as a term-number it is a ^{TN} variable).

D 26. DeftZz1 $(s) \equiv (\exists\, m)\, s\, \big($Var $(m) \cdot [s = \mathrm{pot}\, (m, 2)]\big)$
D 27. DeftPräd1 (s), and **D 28.** DeftFu1 (s), may be analogously formulated.

Explanation, D 26–28: s is a defined ^{TN} 331 (or pr1, fu1 respectively) when s is the second (or fourth or sixth respectively) power of a prime number greater than 2. (Concerning the additional '1' see later.)

Remark concerning the term-number of defined symbols

We have assigned as term-numbers to the defined symbols of the different kinds numbers of three classes—namely the second, fourth, and sixth powers of prime numbers greater than 2. We

---

* Key to the symbols:

einkl: bracketing (*Einklamme-rung*)
Var: variable (*Variable*)
DeftZz, DeftPräd, DeftFu: defined numeral, predicate, functor (*definiertes Zahlzeichen, Prädikat, Funktor*)
UndPräd, UndFu: undefined... (*undefiniertes ...*)
Zz: numeral (*Zahlzeichen*)
Präd: predicate (*Prädikat*)
AOp, EOp, KOp, SOp: universal, existential, descriptional, sentential operator (*All-, Existenz-, K-, Satz-Operator*)
Op: operator (*Operator*)
ZA: numerical expression (*Zahlausdruck*)
neg: negation (*Negation*)

dis: disjunction (*Disjunktion*)
kon: conjunction (*Konjunktion*)
imp: implication (*Implikation*)
äq: equivalence (*Äquivalenz*)
Verkn: function (*Verknüpfung*)
glg: equation (*Gleichung*)
Satz: sentence
VR: variable-series (*Variablen-reihe*)
UKstr: directly constructed (*unmittelbar konstruiert*)
Konstr: construction (*Konstruktion*)
KonstrA: constructed expression (*konstruierter Ausdruck*)
Geb: bound (*gebunden*)
Frei, Fr: free
Offen: open
Geschl: closed (*geschlossen*)

shall, however, later establish the method of defining symbols in such a way that not all numbers of the three classes mentioned will be used as term-numbers for defined symbols, but, instead, only those numbers which fulfil certain conditions. We call a ^{TN} symbol *based*, when it either fulfils these conditions or is a primitive symbol. These conditions will be formulated in such a way that any symbol which fulfils them will refer back by means of its chain of definitions to the primitive symbols. We call an ^{SN} expression based when everyone of its ^{TN} terms is a based term.

Those terms which will next be defined and of which the designations (namely, the word-designation, the Gothic symbol, and the predicate in the formal system) contain the additional '1' or '2' (from "defined $_{331}$", D 26, to "constructed2", D 78) also include symbols and expressions which are not based. These are only auxiliary terms for the definitions which will follow later.

D 29. $\mathrm{UndPräd}(s,n) \equiv (\exists k)s \big[\mathrm{Var}(k) \bullet$
$$\big(s = \mathrm{pot}(\mathrm{prim}[\mathrm{pot}(k,n)],3)\big)\big]$$
Analogously **D 30:** $\mathrm{UndFu}\,(s,n)$.

Explanation: s is an undefined $\mathfrak{pr}^n$ (or $\mathfrak{fu}^n$) when a prime number k greater than 2 exists, such that s is the third (or fifth) power of the k^nth prime number. (This rule is laid down so that the number n, which is essential for the syntactical rules, may follow univocally from the term-number of a $\mathfrak{pr}^n$ or an $\mathfrak{fu}^n$.)

D 31. $\mathrm{Zz1}\,(s) \equiv \big(\mathrm{DeftZz1}\,(s) \vee \mathrm{Var}\,(s) \vee (s=4)\big)$

Explanation: s is a ^{TN} $_{331}$, when s is either a defined ^{TN} $_{331}$ or else a $_3$ or a $\mathfrak{nu}$ (see p. 26).

D 32. $\mathrm{Präd1}\,(s) \equiv \big[\mathrm{DeftPräd1}\,(s) \vee (\exists n)s\,\big(\mathrm{UndPräd}\,(s,n)\big)\big]$

Explanation: s is a ^{TN} $\mathfrak{pr}1$ when s is either a defined $\mathfrak{pr}1$ or an undefined $\mathfrak{pr}$.

Analogously **D 33:** $\mathrm{Fu1}\,(s)$.

(That is, $\mathfrak{fu}1$.)

D 34. $\mathrm{AOp1}\,(z, s, v) \equiv \big[\mathrm{Var}\,(s) \bullet \big(z = \mathrm{zus}\,(\mathrm{einkl}\,[\mathrm{reihe}\,(s)], v)\big)$
$\bullet \sim \mathrm{InA}\,(s,v)\big]$
Analogously **D 35:** $\mathrm{EOp1}\,(z,s,v)$; **D 36:** $\mathrm{KOp1}\,(z,s,v)$.

D 37. $\mathrm{SOp1}\,(z,s,v) \equiv \big(\mathrm{AOp1}\,(z,s,v) \vee \mathrm{EOp1}\,(z,s,v)\big)$

D 38. $\mathrm{Op1}\,(z,s,v) \equiv \big(\mathrm{SOp1}\,(z,s,v) \vee \mathrm{KOp1}\,(z,s,v)\big)$

Explanation, D 34: z is an ^{SN}*universal operator*1 with the ^{TN}operator-variable s and the ^{SN}limit v; that is to say, z has the form $(\mathfrak{z}_1)\,\mathfrak{A}_1$, where $\mathfrak{z}_1$ does not occur in $\mathfrak{A}_1$. — D 35–D 38: *existential operator*1, *K-operator*1, *sentential operator*1 (that is to say, universal or existential operator1), *operator*1 (that is to say, sentential or K-operator1).

D 39.   ZA1 $(z) \equiv (\exists\, s)\, z\, (\exists\, v)\, z\, (\exists\, w)\, z\, (\exists\, y)\, z\, ($[Zz1 (s) . [$z =$ reihe (s)]] ∨ [$z =$ zus [v, reihe (14)]] ∨ [Fu1 (s) . $(z =$ zus [reihe (s), einkl (w)]] ∨ [KOp1 (y, s, v) . $(z =$ zus [y, einkl (w)])])

Explanation: z is an ^{SN}31, when z has one of the following forms: $\mathfrak{z}$31, $\mathfrak{A}_1{}^1$, fu1 $(\mathfrak{A}_2)$, (K$\mathfrak{z}$) $\mathfrak{A}_1(\mathfrak{A}_3)$ (see p. 26). Here, $\mathfrak{A}_1$, $\mathfrak{A}_2$, and $\mathfrak{A}_3$ are any expressions whatsoever; on the other hand, in the case of a $\mathfrak{z}$2(D 53) $\mathfrak{A}_1$ is a $\mathfrak{z}$2, $\mathfrak{A}_2$ is a series composed of several $\mathfrak{z}$2 and commas, and $\mathfrak{A}_3$ is an $\mathfrak{S}$2. In contradistinction to a $\mathfrak{z}$2, a $\mathfrak{z}$3 ('ZA', D 87) is based. Analogously in the case of $\mathfrak{S}$1 (D 47), $\mathfrak{S}$2 (D 54), and $\mathfrak{S}$ ('Satz', D 88).

D 40.   neg $(x) =$ zus (reihe (21), einkl (x))

D 41.   dis $(x, y) =$ zus3 (einkl (x), reihe (22), einkl (y))

D 42: kon (x, y); **D 43:** imp (x, y), and **D 44:** äq (x, y), are analogous.

Explanation: If x and y are ^{SN}expressions $\mathfrak{A}_1$, $\mathfrak{A}_2$, then neg (x) is the ^{SN}*negation* $\sim(\mathfrak{A}_1)$, dis (x, y) the *disjunction* $(\mathfrak{A}_1)$ ∨ $(\mathfrak{A}_2)$; the cases of *conjunction* (kon), *implication* (imp), and *equivalence* (äq) are analogous.

D 45.   Verkn $(x, y, z) \equiv [(x =$ dis $(y, z))$∨$(x =$ kon $(y, z))$∨$(x =$ imp $(y, z))$ ∨ $(x =$ äq$(y, z))]$.

Explanation: x is an ^{SN}*junction* of y and z: that is to say, x has the form $(\mathfrak{A}_1)$ ver!n$(\mathfrak{A}_2)$ where y is $\mathfrak{A}_1$ and z is $\mathfrak{A}_2$.

D 46.   glg $(x, y) =$ zus3 $(x,$ reihe $(15), y)$

Explanation: If x and y are expressions $\mathfrak{A}_1$, $\mathfrak{A}_2$, then glg(x, y) is the ^{SN}*equation* $\mathfrak{A}_1 = \mathfrak{A}_2$.

D 47.   Satz1 $(z) \equiv (\exists\, s)\, z\, (\exists\, v)\, z\, (\exists\, w)\, z\, (\exists\, y)\, z\, ($[$z =$ glg (v, w)] ∨ [Präd1 (s) . $(z =$ zus [reihe (s), einkl (v)])] ∨ [$z =$ neg (v)] ∨ Verkn (z, v, w) ∨ [SOp1 (y, s, w) . $(z =$ zus [y, einkl (w)])])

Explanation: z is an $\mathfrak{S}$1, when z has one of the following forms: $\mathfrak{A}_1 = \mathfrak{A}_2$, pr1 $(\mathfrak{A}_3)$, $\sim(\mathfrak{A}_4)$, $(\mathfrak{A}_4)$ ver!n$(\mathfrak{A}_5)$, $(\mathfrak{z})\,\mathfrak{A}_1(\mathfrak{A}_4)$ or $(\exists\,\mathfrak{z})\,\mathfrak{A}_1(\mathfrak{A}_4)$ (see p. 26). The difference between $\mathfrak{S}$1, $\mathfrak{S}$2, and $\mathfrak{S}$ is analogous to that between $\mathfrak{z}$1, $\mathfrak{z}$2, and $\mathfrak{z}$3.

D 48.   VR $(x, n) \equiv ($[lng $(x)^I =$ prod $(2, n)$] . (k) lng (x) $(\exists\, m)$ k [$(k = 0)$ ∨ ([$k =$ prod $(2, m)^I$] . Var [gl (k, x)]] ∨ ([$k =$ prod $(2, m)$] . [gl $(k, x) = 12$])])

Explanation: An expression x is called an n-termed *variable-series* when it consists of n variables and intervening commas.

D 49. UKstr1 $(z, w) \equiv \big([\text{ZA1}\,(w) \bullet (z = \text{zus}\,[w, \text{reihe}\,(14)])] \lor [\text{Satz1}\,(w) \bullet (z = \text{neg}\,(w))] \lor (\exists\,n)\,\text{lng}\,(w)\,(\exists\,s)\,z\,[(\text{VR}\,(w,n) \bullet (\text{Fu1}\,(s) \lor \text{Präd1}\,(s)) \bullet (z = \text{zus}\,[\text{reihe}\,(s), \text{einkl}\,(w)])) \lor (\text{VR}\,(w,n) \bullet \text{Var}\,(s) \bullet (z = \text{zus}\,[w, \text{reihe2}\,(12,s)]))]\big)$

Explanation: An expression z is called *directly constructed* from *one* expression w, say $\mathfrak{A}_1$, when it has one of the following forms: 1. $\mathfrak{A}_1{}^1$, where $\mathfrak{A}_1$ is a $\mathfrak{Z}1$; 2. $\sim(\mathfrak{A}_1)$, where $\mathfrak{A}_1$ is an $\mathfrak{S}1$; 3. $\mathfrak{fu1}\,(\mathfrak{A}_1)$ or $\mathfrak{pr1}\,(\mathfrak{A}_1)$, where $\mathfrak{A}_1$ is a variable-series; 4. $\mathfrak{A}_{1,3}$, where $\mathfrak{A}_1$ is a variable-series.

D 50. UKstr2 $(z, v, w) \equiv \big[(\exists\,s)\,z\,(\exists\,y)\,z\,(\text{ZA1}\,(v) \bullet \text{Satz1}\,(w) \bullet \text{Op1}\,(y,s,v) \bullet (z = \text{zus}\,[y, \text{einkl}\,(w)])) \lor (\text{ZA1}\,(v) \bullet \text{ZA1}\,(w) \bullet [z = \text{glg}\,(v,w)]) \lor (\text{Satz1}\,(v) \bullet \text{Satz1}\,(w) \bullet \text{Verkn}\,(z,v,w)) \lor (\exists\,n)\,\text{lng}\,(v)\,(\text{Var}\,[\text{gl}\,(n,v)] \bullet \text{ZA1}\,(w) \bullet [z = \text{ers}\,(v,n,w)])\big]$

Explanation: An expression z is called *directly constructed* from *two* other expressions v, w, say $\mathfrak{A}_1$, $\mathfrak{A}_2$, when it has one of the following forms: 1. $(\mathfrak{z})\,\mathfrak{A}_1\,(\mathfrak{A}_2)$ or $(\exists\,\mathfrak{z})\,\mathfrak{A}_1\,(\mathfrak{A}_2)$ or $(\text{K}\mathfrak{z})\,\mathfrak{A}_1\,(\mathfrak{A}_2)$, where $\mathfrak{A}_1$ is a $\mathfrak{Z}1$ and $\mathfrak{A}_2$ an $\mathfrak{S}1$; 2. $\mathfrak{A}_1 = \mathfrak{A}_2$, where $\mathfrak{A}_1$ and $\mathfrak{A}_2$ are $\mathfrak{Z}1$; 3. $(\mathfrak{A}_1)\,\mathfrak{verfn}\,(\mathfrak{A}_2)$, where $\mathfrak{A}_1$ and $\mathfrak{A}_2$ are $\mathfrak{S}1$; or when, 4., z results from $\mathfrak{A}_1$ if a $\mathfrak{z}$ is replaced by $\mathfrak{A}_2$, where $\mathfrak{A}_2$ is a $\mathfrak{Z}1$.

D 51. Konstr1 $(r) \equiv (n)\,\text{lng}\,(r)\,\big[\sim(n=0) \supset \big((\exists\,s)\,r\,[\text{Zz1}\,(s) \bullet (\text{gl}\,(n,r) = \text{reihe}\,(s))] \lor (\exists\,k)\,n\,(\exists\,l)\,n\,[\sim(k=0) \bullet \sim(l=0) \bullet (\text{UKstr1}\,[\text{gl}\,(n,r), \text{gl}\,(k,r)] \lor \text{Ukstr2}\,[\text{gl}\,(n,r), \text{gl}\,(k,r), \text{gl}\,(l,r)])]\big)\big]$

Explanation: r is an SSNconstruction1, when r is an SSNseries of SNexpressions of which each either is a $\mathfrak{z}\mathfrak{z}1$ or is directly constructed from one or two of the previous expressions occurring in the series. (A series of this kind consists of $\mathfrak{Z}1$ and $\mathfrak{S}1$, or, more precisely, in accordance with the following definitions, of $\mathfrak{Z}2$ and $\mathfrak{S}2$.)

D 52. KonstrA1 $(x) \equiv (\exists\,r)\,\text{pot}\,\big(\text{prim}\,[\text{lng}\,(x)], \text{prod}\,[x, \text{lng}\,(x)]\big)\,\big[\text{Konstr1}\,(r) \bullet (\text{letzt}\,(r) = x)\big]$

Explanation: An SNexpression x is called *constructed1* when it is the last expression in an SSNconstruction1. [The limit for r results from the following consideration. Let r be the shortest SSNconstruction1 of which the final SNexpression is x. Then $\text{lng}(r) \leq \text{lng}(x)$, every prime factor of r is $\leq \text{prim}\,(\text{lng}(x))$, the number of these factors is $\leq \text{lng}(x)$, their exponents are $\leq x$; therefore

$$r \leq \text{prim}\,(\text{lng}(x))^{x \bullet \text{lng}(x)}.]$$

D 53. ZA2 $(x) \equiv \big(\text{KonstrA1}\,(x) \bullet \text{ZA1}\,(x)\big)$

5

D 54. $\text{Satz2}(x) \equiv \big(\text{KonstrA1}(x) \bullet \text{Satz1}(x)\big)$

Explanation: An expression x is a 32 (or an $\mathfrak{S}2$), when it is both constructed1 and a 31 (or an $\mathfrak{S}1$, respectively); see explanation of D 39.

D 55. $\text{Geb}(s, x, n) \equiv (\exists\, t)\, x\, (\exists\, z)\, x\, (\exists\, u)\, x\, (\exists\, y)\, z\, (\exists\, v)\, y\, (\exists\, w)\, z$
$\big[(x = \text{zus3}\, (t, z, u)\big) \bullet \big(z = \text{zus}\, [y, \text{einkl}\, (w)]\big) \bullet \text{Op1}\, (y, s, v) \bullet$
$\text{ZA2}\, (v) \bullet \text{Satz2}\, (w) \bullet \text{Gr}\, \big(n, \text{lng}\, (t)\big) \bullet \text{Grgl}\, \big(\text{sum}\, [\text{lng}\, (t),$
$\text{lng}\, (z)], n\big)\big]$

Explanation: The ^{TN}variable s is called *bound* in the ^{SN}expression x at the nth place (where the variable need not occur at this place) if the following conditions are fulfilled: In x an expression z of the form $\mathfrak{A}_1(\mathfrak{A}_2)$ occurs, where $\mathfrak{A}_1$ is an Operator1 having a 32 as limit and s as operator-variable; $\mathfrak{A}_2$ is an $\mathfrak{S}2$; the nth place of x belongs to z (see p. 21).

D 56. $\text{Frei}(s, x, n) \equiv \big[\text{Var}(s) \bullet \big(\text{gl}\, (n, x) = s\big) \bullet \sim \text{Geb}\, (s, x, n)\big]$

Explanation: The *free variable* s occurs at the nth place in x.

D 57. $\text{Fr}(s, x) \equiv (\exists\, n)\, \text{lng}\, (x)\, \big(\text{Frei}\, (s, x, n)\big)$

Explanation: s occurs as a *free variable* in x.

D 58. $\text{Offen}(x) \equiv (\exists\, s)\, x\, \big(\text{Fr}\, (s, x)\big)$
D 59. $\text{Geschl}(x) \equiv \sim \text{Offen}\, (x)$

Explanation: x is *open*; x is *closed* (see p. 21).

§ 22. Rules of Formation: (2) Definitions*

If a calculus is to contain definitions, then, under certain circumstances, there arises in its formulation a difficulty which is very seldom taken into account. If all that is demanded of the defini-

---

* Key to the symbols:

VRDef: variable-series for the definiens
DefZz, DefPräd: definition of a numeral, predicate
DefexpFu, DeftexpFu: explicit definition of a functor
DefrekFu, DeftrekFu: regressive (*rekursiv*) definition of a functor
Def, Df: definition sentence (*Definitionssatz*)

Deft: defined (*definiert*)
Z: symbol (*Zeichen*)
UndDeskr: undefined descriptive (*deskriptiv*) symbol
Undeft: undefined symbol
DefKette, DeftKette: definition-chain (*Definitionenkette*)
Bas: based (*basiert*)
Deskr: descriptive
Log: logical (*logisch*)

tions admitted in the calculus is that they satisfy certain rules of formation, the calculus will generally be a contradictory one.

Example: For instance, D 1 (p. 59) satisfies the formation rules for definitions in I (§ 8). With the help of D 1, the sentence 'nf(0) = 0¹' is demonstrable. But the sentence 'nf$(x) = x$¹¹¹' is likewise a definition of the admitted form and with its help the sentence '$\sim$(nf(0) = 0¹)' is demonstrable. Thus, in I, sentences which are mutually contradictory are demonstrable.

In order to avoid the contradiction, we usually make the additional requirement "that the symbol to be defined must not have occurred in a definition which has already been framed". But a requirement of this kind is a departure from the domain of the calculus and of the formal method. In strictly formal procedure, the decision as to whether a given sentence is an admissible definition in a particular calculus or not is dependent solely upon the form of the sentence and upon the formation-rules of the calculus. But by virtue of the above non-formal requirement this decision would become dependent upon the historical statement as to whether certain sentences had been previously formulated or not. And the same is true for the decision concerning the demonstrability of a given sentence (as our example shows). Now, how can this difficulty be overcome?

1. To begin with, it is obvious that the difficulty disappears if in the formation of the language S in question, one of the following procedures is adopted:

(*a*) No definitions at all are admitted in S.

(*b*) Only a finite number of particular definitions are admitted in S, and these are ranged amongst the primitive sentences of S.

(*c*) Any number of definitions, for which rules of formation are given, may be formulated in S. But the definitions are not admitted in proofs; they are only admitted as premisses of derivations. [Thus in the above example 'nf(0) = 0¹' is not demonstrable, but only derivable from 'nf$(x) = x$¹'.] If a sentence $\mathfrak{S}_1$ contains defined symbols (i.e. symbols based on certain definitions) then, although it is not itself demonstrable, that sentence which follows from $\mathfrak{S}_1$ as a result of the elimination of the defined symbols is demonstrable.

Regressively defined symbols are not always eliminable. In a definite language, in which the sentences of elementary arithmetic (for instance: 'prod$(2,3)=6$') are to be demonstrable, an unlimited number of regressive definitions, which must be employable in the proofs, is necessary. Thus, for a language of this kind—for instance, Language I—the above-mentioned ways out of the difficulty are of no use. We shall have to discover some other solution:

2. In Language I we shall allow an unlimited number of definitions, including regressive ones; but by means of suitable rules we shall take care that from each defined symbol it is recognizable how it is defined. This is possible in an arithmetized syntax. We have previously established a class of numbers for the term-numbers of the defined symbols of each of the three kinds, $\mathfrak{z}\mathfrak{z}$, $\mathfrak{pr}$, and $\mathfrak{fu}$; but, inside this class, so far, we have left the choice open. Now, however, the rules to be laid down will determine this choice in such a way that from the term-number of a defined symbol not only its definition but also, indirectly, its whole chain of definitions will follow univocally. In this way every so-called logical property of any sentence—for instance, its demonstrability—becomes a syntactical or formal property; it depends solely upon the formal structure of the sentence, that is, upon the arithmetical properties of the term-numbers which constitute the sentence.

Rule for the choice of the term-number of a defined symbol $\mathfrak{a}_1$ *in Language I:* In the definition of $\mathfrak{a}_1$, let $\mathfrak{a}_1$ be replaced by a permanent *auxiliary* symbol as follows: a $\mathfrak{z}\mathfrak{z}$ by 'ζ' with the term-number 30, a $\mathfrak{pr}$ by 'π' with the term-number 33, an $\mathfrak{fu}$ by 'ϕ' with the term-number 34. The *definition schema* which arises as a result of this process then contains only old symbols; thus its series-number r—or in the case of the schema of a regressive definition, since it consists of two sentences, its series-series-number r—can be determined. Let us take as the term-number for $\mathfrak{a}_1$, when $\mathfrak{a}_1$ is a $\mathfrak{z}\mathfrak{z}$ (or a $\mathfrak{pr}$, or an $\mathfrak{fu}$), the second (or fourth, or sixth, respectively) power of the rth prime number. By applying this rule the term-number for $\mathfrak{a}_1$ is determined univocally; and conversely, from this term-number, r, and hence the definition schema, and finally the definition, of $\mathfrak{a}_1$, are univocally determinable.

By means of this rule, we can now establish the difference between *based* and non-based ^{TN}symbols. For instance, the fourth power of a prime number p (greater than 2) is based (see p. 63) when p is obtained in the manner described from a definition schema with the auxiliary symbol 'π'—assuming that the analogous condition holds for every defined ^{TN}symbol occurring in the definition schema. In order to formulate this condition, we shall later define the concept of a chain of definitions (D 81). Before that, however, it is necessary to define a list of auxiliary terms.

D 60. $\text{VRDef}\ (x,\ y,\ n) \equiv \big[\text{VR}\ (x,\ n) \centerdot (k)\ \lng\ (x)\ (l)\ \lng\ (x)\ \big(\big[\text{Var}$
$\big(\gl\ (k,\ x)\big) \centerdot \big(\gl\ (k,\ x) = \gl\ (l,\ x)\big)\big] \supset (k = l)\big) \centerdot (s)\ y\ \big(\text{Fr}\ (s,\ y) \supset$
$\text{InA}\ (s,\ x)\big)\big]$

Explanation: x is an n-termed ^{SN}variable-series which is suitable (as argument-expression of the definiendum) for the ^{SN}definiens y when the following is true: x is an n-termed variable-series; no two equal variables occur in x; every variable which occurs as a free variable in y occurs in x also. ('VRDef' is an auxiliary term for the purpose of abbreviation.)

D 61. $\text{DefZz1}\ (x) \equiv (\exists\ z)\,x\ \big[\big(x = \glg\ [\text{reihe}\ (30),\ z]\big) \centerdot \text{Geschl}\ (z)\big]$

Explanation: x is called an ^{SN}definition1 of a ^{TN}33 (that is to say, an expression similar to the definition schema of a 33), when x has the form $\zeta = \mathfrak{A}_1$ where $\mathfrak{A}_1$ is closed.

D 62. $\text{DefPräd1}\ (x, n) \equiv (\exists\ w)\,x\ (\exists\ v)\,w\ (\exists\ z)\,x\ \big[(w = \zus\ [\text{reihe}\ (33),$
$\text{einkl}\ (v)]\big) \centerdot \big(x = \text{äq}\ (w,\ z)\big) \centerdot \text{VRDef}\ (v,\ z,\ n)\big]$
Analogously **D 63:** $\text{DefexpFu1}\ (x, n)$.

Explanation: x is called a definition1 of a $\pr^n$ (or an explicit definition1 of an $\fu^n$, respectively) when x has the form $(\mathfrak{A}_1) \equiv \mathfrak{A}_2$ (or $(\mathfrak{A}_1) = \mathfrak{A}_2$, respectively), where $\mathfrak{A}_1$ is an n-termed variable-series which is suitable to $\mathfrak{A}_2$.

D 64. $\text{DefrekFu1}\ (r, n) \equiv (\exists\ x_1)\,r\ (\exists\ x_2)\,r\ (\exists\ u_1)\,x_1\ (\exists\ v_1)\,x_1\ (\exists\ u_2)\,x_2$
$(\exists\ v_2)\,x_2\ (\exists\ s)\,u_2\ (\exists\ z)\,u_2\ (\exists\ m)\,n\ \big[\big(r = \text{reihe2}\ (x_1,\ x_2)\big) \centerdot \big(x_1 =$
$\glg\ (u_1,\ v_1)\big) \centerdot \big(x_2 = \glg\ (u_2,\ v_2)\big) \centerdot \text{Var}\ (s) \centerdot (t)\ v_2\ \big(\text{Fr}\ (t,\ v_2) \supset$
$\text{InA}\ (t, u_2)\big) \centerdot (k)\ \lng\ (v_2)\ \big([\gl\ (k,\ v_2) = 34] \supset (l)\ \lng\ (z)\big(\sim(l = 0)$
$\supset \big[[\gl\ [\sum\ (k,\ l),\ v_2] = \gl\ (l,\ z)] \centerdot \sim \text{Geb}\ [\gl\ [\sum\ (k,\ l),\ v_2],$
$v_2,\ \sum\ (k,\ l)]\big]\big)\big) \centerdot (n = m^1) \centerdot \big([(m = 0) \centerdot (u_1 = \text{reihe4}\ (34,\ 6,\ 4,$
$10)) \centerdot (u_2 = \text{reihe5}\ (34,\ 6,\ s,\ 14,\ 10)) \centerdot (z = \text{reihe3}\ (6,\ s,\ 10))]\lor$
$(\exists\ w)\,u_1\ [\sim(m = 0) \centerdot (u_1 = \zus\ [\text{reihe}\ (34),\ \text{einkl}\ (\zus\ [\text{reihe2}$
$(4,\ 12),\ w])]\big) \centerdot (u_2 = \zus\ [\text{reihe}\ (34),\ \text{einkl}\ (\zus\ [\text{reihe3}\ (s,\ 14,$
$12),\ w])]\big) \centerdot (z = \text{einkl}\ (\zus\ [\text{reihe2}\ (s,\ 12),\ w])) \centerdot \text{VRDef}\ (w,$
$v_1, m) \centerdot \sim \text{InA}\ (s, w)]\big)\big]$

Explanation: r is called an ^{SSN}regressive definition1 of an $\fu^n$ when r is a series of two expressions x_1, x_2 of the following kind. x_1 has the form $\mathfrak{A}_1 = \mathfrak{A}_2$, x_2 has the form $\mathfrak{A}_4 = \mathfrak{A}_5$; every variable which occurs as a free variable in $\mathfrak{A}_5$ occurs in $\mathfrak{A}_4$ also; $\mathfrak{A}_6$, where the variables of $\mathfrak{A}_6$ are not bound in $\mathfrak{A}_5$, occurs directly after every term ϕ' which occurs in $\mathfrak{A}_5$.. n is greater than 0; we put $n = m + 1$. Now there are two cases to be distinguished from one another. First case: $m = 0$; then $\mathfrak{A}_1$ has the form $\phi(\mathfrak{nu})$, $\mathfrak{A}_4$ the form $\phi(\mathfrak{z}_1{}^1)$, and $\mathfrak{A}_6$ the form $(\mathfrak{z}_1)$. Second case: $m > 0$; then $\mathfrak{A}_1$ has the form $\phi(\mathfrak{nu}, \mathfrak{A}_3)$, $\mathfrak{A}_4$ the form $(\mathfrak{z}_1{}^1, \mathfrak{A}_3)$, and $\mathfrak{A}_6$ the form $(\mathfrak{z}_1, \mathfrak{A}_3)$; here $\mathfrak{A}_3$ is an m-termed variable-series adapted to $\mathfrak{A}_2$ and $\mathfrak{z}_1$ does not occur in $\mathfrak{A}_3$. [It is u_1: $^{\text{SN}}\mathfrak{A}_1$; v_1: $\mathfrak{A}_2$; u_2: $\mathfrak{A}_4$; v_2: $\mathfrak{A}_5$; s: $^{\text{TN}}\mathfrak{z}_1$; z: $\mathfrak{A}_6$; w: $\mathfrak{A}_3$.]*

D 65. $\mathrm{DeftZz2}\,(t, y) \equiv \left[\mathrm{DefZz1}\,(y) \bullet (t = \mathrm{pot}\,[\mathrm{prim}\,(y), 2])\right]$

Similarly **D 66:** $\mathrm{DeftPräd2}\,(t, n, y)$; **D 67:** $\mathrm{DeftexpFu2}(t, n, y)$; **D 68:** $\mathrm{DeftrekFu2}\,(t, n, r)$.

Explanation: t is a $\mathfrak{z}\mathfrak{z}$ (or $\mathfrak{pr}^n$, or $\mathfrak{fu}^n$, respectively), which is "defined2" by means of the definition1 y (or the explicit definition1 y, or the regressive definition1 r, respectively).

D 69. $\mathrm{DefZz2}\,(x, t) \equiv (\exists\, y)\, x\, \left[\mathrm{DeftZz2}\,(t, y) \bullet (x = \mathrm{ers}\,[y, 1, \mathrm{reihe}\,(t)])\right]$

Similarly **D 70:** $\mathrm{DefPräd2}\,(x, n, t)$; **D 71:** $\mathrm{DefexpFu2}\,(x, n, t)$.

Explanation, D 69–71: x is called a definition2 of a $\mathfrak{z}\mathfrak{z}$ t (or of a $\mathfrak{pr}^n$ t, or an explicit definition2 of an $\mathfrak{fu}^n$ t, respectively) when t is defined2 by means of y, and x results from y when the first (or second or first, respectively) ^{TN}term, namely 'ζ' (or 'π' or 'ϕ', respectively) is replaced by the ^{TN}symbol t.

D 72. $1\,\mathrm{DefrekFu2}\,(x, n, t) \equiv (\exists\, r)\, x\, (\exists\, y)\, r\, \left[\mathrm{DeftrekFu2}\,(t, n, r) \bullet (\mathrm{gl}\,(1, r) = y) \bullet (x = \mathrm{ers}\,[y, 1, \mathrm{reihe}\,(t)])\right]$

Similarly **D 73:** $2\,\mathrm{DefrekFu2}\,(x, n, t)$.

Explanation: x is called the first (or second) ^{SN}part of an ^{SSN}regressive definition2 of an $\mathfrak{fu}^n t$ when the following conditions are satisfied: t is regressively defined2 by means of the (regressive definition1) r; y is the first (or second) part of r, and x results from y when in y 'ϕ' is replaced at the first place (or in all places at which it occurs) by the ^{TN}symbol t.

D 74. $\mathrm{Def2}\,(x, t) \equiv \big[\mathrm{DefZz2}\,(x, t) \vee (\exists\, n)\, \mathrm{lng}\,(x)\, \big(\mathrm{DefPräd2}\,(x, n, t) \vee \mathrm{DefexpFu2}\,(x, n, t) \vee 1\mathrm{DefrekFu2}\,(x, n, t) \vee 2\mathrm{DefrekFu2}\,(x, n, t)\big)\big]$

---

* (*Note*, 1935.) The stipulation that the variables of $\mathfrak{A}_6$ are free, and the corresponding term of D 64 " $\sim\mathrm{Geb}[\mathrm{gl}\,[\mathrm{sum}\,(k, l), v_2],\, v_2,\, \mathrm{sum}\,(k, l)]$ ", are obviously necessary, but they are omitted in the German original (also in § 8). My attention was called to this oversight by Dr. Tarski.

Explanation: x is called a *definition-sentence2* of t when x is either a definition2 of a ꝛꝛ t or a ꝓꞃ t, or an explicit definition2 of an ꝼu t, or the first or second part of a regressive definition2 of an ꝼu t.

D 75. Deft2 $(t, n) \equiv (\exists\, y)\; t \;\big(\mathrm{DeftPräd2}\, (t, n, y) \vee \mathrm{DeftexpFu2}$
$(t, n, y) \vee \mathrm{DeftrekFu2}\,(t, n, y)\big)$

Explanation: t is an n-termed symbol (ꝓꞃ^n or ꝼu^n) which is defined2.

D 76. Z2 $(t, n) \equiv \big[\mathrm{UndPräd}\,(t, n) \vee \mathrm{UndFu}\,(t, n) \vee \mathrm{Deft2}\,(t, n)\big]$

Explanation: t is called an n-termed symbol2 when t is either a ꝓꞃ^n or an ꝼu^n and is either undefined or defined2.

D 77. Konstr2 $(r) \equiv \big(\mathrm{Konstr1}\,(r)\, .\, (x)\, r\, (t)\, x\, (y)\, x\, (m)\, t\, (n)\, \mathrm{lng}\, (y)$
$\big[\big(\mathrm{AInAR}\,(x, r)\, .\, (x = \mathrm{zus}\, [\mathrm{reihe}\,(t), \mathrm{einkl}\,(y)]\big)\, .\, \mathrm{Z2}\,(t, m)\, .$
$\mathrm{VR}(y, n)\big) \supset (m = n)\big]\big)$

D 78: KonstrA2 (x), is analogous to D 52.

Explanation, D 77: An SSN*construction2* r is a construction1 which fulfils the following condition. In each expression $\mathfrak{a}_1(\mathfrak{A}_1)$ occurring in r, where $\mathfrak{a}_1$ is an m-termed symbol2 and $\mathfrak{A}_1$ an n-termed variable-series, m is equal to n. Thus, in a construction2, every ꝓꞃ and every ꝼu has the correct number of arguments. — D 78: The last expression of a construction2 is called constructed2.

D 79. UndDeskr $(t) \equiv (\exists\, n)\, t\, \big(\mathrm{UndPräd}\,(t, n) \vee \mathrm{UndFu}\,(t, n)\big)$

Explanation: t is an *undefined descriptive symbol* (namely ꝓꞃ or ꝼu).

D 80. Undeft $(t) \equiv \big[(t = 4) \vee (t = 6) \vee (t = 10) \vee (t = 12) \vee (t = 14) \vee$
$(t = 15) \vee (t = 18) \vee (t = 20) \vee (t = 21) \vee (t = 22) \vee (t = 24) \vee$
$(t = 26) \vee \mathrm{Var}\,(t) \vee \mathrm{UndDeskr}\,(t)\big]$

Explanation: t is an *undefined* TN*symbol* when t is either one of the twelve undefined logical constants (see p. 55), or a variable, or an undefined descriptive symbol.

D 81. DefKette $(r) \equiv (n)\, \mathrm{lng}\,(r)\, (x)\, \mathrm{gl}\,(n, r)\, (t)\, x\, \big[\big(\sim (n = 0)\, .$
$[\mathrm{gl}\,(n, r) = x]\, .\, \mathrm{InA}\,(t, x)\big) \supset \big(\mathrm{KonstrA2}\,(x)\, .\, (\exists\, s)\, x\, \big(\mathrm{Def2}$
$(x, s)\big)\, .\, \big[\mathrm{Undeft}\,(t) \vee (\exists\, m)\, n\, \big(\mathrm{Def2}\,[\mathrm{gl}\,(m, r), t]\big)\big]\, .\, (l)\, \mathrm{lng}\,(x)$
$\big[\big(\mathrm{1DefrekFu2}\,(x, l, t) \supset \mathrm{2DefrekFu2}\,[\mathrm{gl}\,(n^l, r), l, t]\big)\, .$
$\big(\mathrm{2DefrekFu2}\,(x, l, t) \supset (\exists\, m)\, n\, ([n = m^l]\, .\, \mathrm{1DefrekFu2}$
$[\mathrm{gl}\,(m, r), l, t])\big)\big]\big)\big]\big)$

Explanation: r is called an SSN*definition-chain* when the following is true. Every SN expression occurring as a member of the chain r is constructed2 and is a definition-sentence2. If t is a TN symbol in an expression $\mathfrak{A}_1$ which is a member of r, then either t is undefined, or $\mathfrak{A}_1$ or some previous expression of r is a definition-sentence2 of t.

If an expression of r is the first part of a regressive definition2, then the expression which immediately follows is the second part of this definition; if an expression is the second part of a regressive definition2, then the immediately preceding expression is the first part of this definition.

D 82. DeftKette $(t,\ r) \equiv (\exists\ x)\ r$ [DefKette (r) . [letzt $(r)=x]$. Def2 (x,t)]

D 83. Deft $(t) \equiv (\exists\ r)$ pot $(2,$ pot $[2,$ pot $(2,$ pot $[2$ pot $(2,\ t)])])$ [DeftKette (t,r)]

Explanation, D 82: t is defined by means of the definition-chain r. — D 83: A symbol t is called *defined* when there is a definition-chain r by means of which t is defined.

D 84. Bas $(t) \equiv ($Undeft $(t) \lor$ Deft $(t))$

Explanation: A symbol t is called *based* either when it is undefined or when it is defined (by means of a definition-chain).

D 85. Konstr $(r) \equiv [$Konstr2 $(r).(t)r ($InAR $(t,r) \supset$ Bas $(t))]$

D 86: KonstrA (x), is analogous to D 52.

Explanation, D 85: A *construction* of expressions is a construction2 of which all the symbols are based symbols. — D 86: An expression is called *constructed* when it is the last expression of a construction.

D 87. ZA $(x) \equiv ($ZA1 $(x).$KonstrA $(x))$

D 88. Satz $(x) \equiv ($Satz1 $(x).$KonstrA $(x))$

Explanation: x is called a $\mathfrak{Z}$ (or an $\mathfrak{S}$, respectively) when x is both a $\mathfrak{Z}1$ (or an $\mathfrak{S}1$) and constructed. Thus *the most important concepts of the rules of formation are attained*; in contradistinction to the previously defined auxiliary terms ($\mathfrak{Z}1$, $\mathfrak{Z}2$, $\mathfrak{S}1$, $\mathfrak{S}2$), 'ZA' and 'Satz' refer to *based* expressions only, and hence to the $\mathfrak{Z}$ (or to the $\mathfrak{S}$, respectively) in the proper sense.

D 89. Def $(x,t) \equiv ($Def2 $(x,t).$KonstrA $(x))$

D 90. Df $(x) \equiv (\exists\ t)x ($Def $(x,t))$

Explanation, D 89: x is a *definition-sentence* of t. (This definition is analogous to D 87 and D 88.) — D 90: x is a *definition-sentence.*

D 91. DeskrZ $(t) \equiv ($UndDeskr $(t) \lor$ [Deft (t) . (r) — (DeftKette $(t,r) \supset (\exists\ s)r$ [InAR $(s,r).$UndDeskr $(s)]$)])

D 92. DeskrA $(x) \equiv (\exists\ t)x ($InA $(t,x).$DeskrZ $(t))$

Explanation, D 91: t is a *descriptive symbol* $\mathfrak{a_b}$, either when t is an undefined $\mathfrak{a_b}$ or when t is defined and every definition-chain of t contains an undefined $\mathfrak{a_b}$ ('—' stands for the same limiting expression as in D 83).—D 92: x is a descriptive expression $\mathfrak{A_b}$ when x contains an $\mathfrak{a_b}$.

D 93. $\text{LogZ}(t) \equiv \big(\text{Bas}(t) \cdot \sim \text{DeskrZ}(t)\big)$

D 94. $\text{LogA}(x) \equiv (t)\,x\,\big(\text{InA}(t,x) \supset \text{LogZ}(t)\big)$

Explanation, D 93: A *logical symbol* α_1 is based and not descriptive.—D 94: x is a logical expression $\mathfrak{A}_1$ when all symbols of x are logical symbols.

D 95. $\text{DeftZz}(s) \equiv \big(\text{DeftZz1}(s) \cdot \text{Bas}(s)\big)$

D 96. $\text{Zz}(s)$, **D 97.** $\text{Präd}(s)$, and **D 98.** $\text{Fu}(s)$, are analogous.

Explanation, D 95–98: Defined 33; 33; $\mathfrak{pr}$; $\mathfrak{fu}$. In contradistinction to the auxiliary terms which were defined at an earlier stage, the terms defined here refer to based ᵀᴺsymbols only.

§ 23. RULES OF TRANSFORMATION *

The following definitions constitute the formalization of the previously stated transformation-rules of Language I (§ 11 and § 12). For this purpose substitution must first be defined (D 102); D 99–101 introduce auxiliary terms for the definition of substitution.

D 99. 1. $\text{stfrei}(0,s,x) = (\text{K}n)\,\text{lng}(x)\,\big[\text{Frei}(s,x,n) \cdot \sim (\exists m)\,\text{lng}(x)$
$\big(\text{Gr}(m,n) \cdot \text{Frei}(s,x,m)\big)\big]$

  2. $\text{stfrei}(k^1,s,x) = (\text{K}n)\,\text{stfrei}(k,s,x)\,\big[\sim \big(n = \text{stfrei}(k,s,x)\big) \cdot$
$\text{Frei}(s,\ x,\ n) \cdot \sim (\exists\ m)\,\text{stfrei}(k,\ s,\ x)\,\big(\sim [m = \text{stfrei}$
$(k,s,x)] \cdot \text{Gr}(m,n) \cdot \text{Frei}(s,x,m)\big)\big]$

D 100. $\text{anzfrei}(s,x) = (\text{K}n)\,\text{lng}(x)\,\big(\text{stfrei}(n,s,x) = 0\big)$

D 101. 1. $\text{sb}(0,x,s,y) = x$

  2. $\text{sb}(k^1,x,s,y) = \text{ers}\,\big(\text{sb}(k,x,s,y),\text{stfrei}(k,s,x),y\big)$

Explanation, D 99–101: Let s be ᵀᴺ$\mathfrak{z}_1$. $\text{stfrei}(k,s,x)$ is the position-number of the $(k+1)$th $\mathfrak{z}_1$ (counted from the end of the expression x) which occurs freely in x (0 in the case where there are not $k+1$ free $\mathfrak{z}_1$ in x). $\text{anzfrei}(s,x)$ is the number of the $\mathfrak{z}_1$ which occur freely

---

* Key to the symbols:

stfrei: position-number of free $\mathfrak{z}$ (*Stellennummer des freien* $\mathfrak{z}$)

anzfrei: number of free $\mathfrak{z}$ (*Anzahl freier* $\mathfrak{z}$)

sb, subst: substitution (*Substitution*)

GrS: primitive sentence (*Grundsatz*)

AErs: expression-replacement (*Ausdrucksersetzung*)

KV: no free variable (*keine freie Variable*)

UAblb: directly derivable (*unmittelbar ableitbar*)

Abl: derivation (*Ableitung*)

Ablb: derivable (*ableitbar*)

Bew: proof (*Beweis*)

Bewb: demonstrable (*beweisbar*)

in x. sb(k,x,s,y) is that expression which results from the expression x when, starting with the last free $\mathfrak{z}_1$, the k last free $\mathfrak{z}_1$ of x are successively replaced by the expression y.

D 102. subst $(x,s,y) = $ sb $\left(\text{anzfrei}\,(s,x),x,s,y\right)$

Explanation: If x is the ^{SN}expression $\mathfrak{A}_1$; $y,\mathfrak{A}_2$; $s,\mathfrak{z}_1$; then subst(x,s,y) is the ^{SN}expression $\mathfrak{A}_1\!\left(\dfrac{\mathfrak{z}_1}{\mathfrak{A}_2}\right)$. (On substitution, see p. 22.)

D 103. GrS1 $(x) \equiv (\exists\, y)\, x\, (\exists\, z)\, x\, \big[\text{Satz}\,(x) \bullet (x \overset{.}{=} \text{imp}\,(y,\,\text{imp}\,[\text{neg}(y),z]))\big]$

Correspondingly **D 104–113**: GrS2 (x) to GrS11 (x); to give one further example:

D 106. GrS4 $(x) \equiv (\exists\, s)\, x\, (\exists\, y)\, x\, \big[\text{Satz}\,(x) \bullet \big(x = \text{äq}\,(\text{zus}\,[\text{reihe4}\,(6,s,10,4),\text{einkl}\,(y)],\,\text{subst}\,[y,s,\text{reihe}\,(4)]\big)\big)\big]$

D 114. GrS $(x) \equiv \big(\text{GrS1}\,(x) \vee \text{GrS2}\,(x) \vee \dots \vee \text{GrS11}\,(x)\big)$

Explanation, D 103–113: x is a primitive sentence of the first kind; second kind; …eleventh kind (PSI 1–11).—D 114: x is a primitive sentence.

D 115. AErs $(x_1, x_2, w_1, w_2) \equiv (\exists\, u)\, x_1\, (\exists\, v)\, x_1\, \big[(x_1 = \text{zus3}\,(u, w_1, v)) \bullet (x_2 = \text{zus3}\,(u, w_2, v))\big]$

Explanation: Expression-replacement: x_2 results from x_1 when the partial expression w_1 is replaced by w_2. (In the case of the term 'ers' a symbol, whereas here an expression, is replaced.)

D 116. KV $(y, x, s) \equiv\, \sim (\exists\, n)\, \text{lng}\,(x)\, (\exists\, t)\, y\, \big(\text{Fr}\,(t, y) \bullet \text{Geb}\,(t, x, n) \bullet \text{Frei}\,(s, x, n)\big)$

Explanation: 'KV(y,x,s)' means that no variable which is bound in x at a place of substitution for s occurs as a free variable in y. (See p. 22.)

D 117. UAblb1 $(z, x) \equiv (\exists\, y)\, z\, (\exists\, s)\, x\, \big[\text{ZA}\,(y) \bullet (z = \text{subst}\,(x, s, y)) \bullet \text{KV}(y, x, s)\big]$

D 118. UAblb2 $(z, x) \equiv (\exists\, w_1)\, \text{sum}\,(x, z)\, (\exists\, w_2)\, \text{sum}\,(x, z)\, (\exists\, u)\, w_1\, (\exists\, v)\, w_1\, \big([\,[w_1 = \text{imp}\,(u, v)] \bullet (w_2 = \text{dis}\,[\text{neg}\,(u), v])) \vee ([w_1 = \text{kon}\,(u, v)] \bullet [w_2 = \text{neg}\,(\text{dis}\,[\text{neg}\,(u), \text{neg}\,(v)])]) \vee ([w_1 = \text{äq}\,(u, v)] \bullet (w_2 = \text{kon}\,[\text{imp}\,(u, v), \text{imp}\,(v, u)]))\big) \bullet [\text{AErs}\,(x, z, w_1, w_2) \vee \text{AErs}\,(x, z, w_2, w_1)]\big)$

D 119. UAblb3 $(z, x, y) \equiv (x = \text{imp}\,(y, z))$

D 120. UAblb4 $(z, x, y) \equiv (\exists\, s)\, z\, \big[(x = \text{subst}\,[z, s, \text{reihe}\,(4)]) \bullet \big(y = \text{imp}\,(z, \text{subst}\,[z, s, \text{reihe2}\,(s, 14)])\big)\big]$

D 121. UAblb $(z, x, y) \equiv \big(\text{UAblb1}\,(z, x) \vee \text{UAblb2}\,(z, x) \vee \text{UAblb3}\,(z, x, y) \vee \text{UAblb4}\,(z, x, y)\big)$

Explanation, D 117: z is called directly-derivable1 from x when x is $\mathfrak{A}_1$ and z has the form $\mathfrak{A}_1\left(\begin{smallmatrix} 3 \\ 3 \end{smallmatrix}\right)$ (according to RI 1; see § 12).— D 118–120: 'directly-derivable2 (or 3, 4, respectively)' in accordance with RI 2, 3, 4.—D 121: z is directly derivable from x or from x and y.

D 122. $\mathrm{Abl}\,(r,p) \equiv (\exists\,q)\,r\,(n)\,\mathrm{lng}\,(r)\,(x)\,r\,\big([r = \mathrm{zus}\,(p,q)] \bullet \sim [\mathrm{lng}\,(r) = 0] \bullet \big[(\sim(n=0) \bullet [\mathrm{gl}\,(n,r) = x]\big) \supset \big(\mathrm{Satz}\,(x) \bullet \big[\mathrm{Gr}\,[n, \mathrm{lng}\,(p)] \supset (\mathrm{GrS}\,(x) \vee \mathrm{Df}\,(x) \vee (\exists\,k)\,n\,(\exists\,l)\,n\,[\sim(k=n) \bullet \sim(l=n) \bullet \mathrm{UAblb}\,[x, \mathrm{gl}\,(k,r), \mathrm{gl}\,(l,r)]])\big]\big)\big]\big)$

Explanation: r is an ^{SSN}derivation having the ^{SSN}series of premisses p, if the following conditions hold: r is composed of p and q; every expression which is a member of r is a sentence; every expression which is a member of q is either a primitive sentence or a definition-sentence, or is directly derivable from one or two previous sentences in r (see p. 29).

D 123. $\mathrm{AblSatz}\,(r,x,p) \equiv \big(\mathrm{Abl}\,(r,p) \bullet [\mathrm{letzt}\,(r) = x]\big)$

Explanation: r is a *derivation of the sentence* x from the series of premisses p.

D 124. $\mathrm{Bew}\,(r) \equiv \mathrm{Abl}\,(r,0)$
D 125. $\mathrm{BewSatz}\,(r,x) \equiv \big(\mathrm{Bew}\,(r) \bullet [\mathrm{letzt}\,(r) = x]\big)$

Explanation, D 124: r is a *proof* when r is a derivation without premisses.—D 125: r is a proof of the sentence x.

Let '$\mathrm{Ablb}\,(x,p)$' mean: x is *derivable* from the series of premisses p; and '$\mathrm{Bewb}\,(x)$': x is *demonstrable*. These syntactical concepts which refer to Language I cannot be defined in I. The definitions are as follows:

$$\mathrm{Ablb}\,(x,p) \equiv (\exists\,r)\,\big(\mathrm{AblSatz}\,(r,x,p)\big)$$
$$\mathrm{Bewb}\,(x) \equiv (\exists\,r)\,\big(\mathrm{BewSatz}\,(r,x)\big)$$

For the formulation of these definitions, the unlimited operators, which do not occur in Language I, are required. The concepts 'derivable' and 'demonstrable' are *indefinite*. In I only definite concepts of derivability and demonstrability can be defined; for instance, such as refer to the derivation itself, or to the proof itself, respectively (see D 123, D 125), or concepts like 'derivable from p by means of a derivation consisting of at most n symbols', or 'demonstrable by means of a proof consisting of at most n symbols'. If indefinite syntactical concepts are to be defined as well, then an indefinite language must be taken as the syntax-language—such as, for instance, our Language II.

For certain indefinite concepts, although they cannot be defined in I, the universal sentence which states that they are predicable for every single case can, however, be formulated in I. In the definition of concepts like 'not demonstrable' and 'not derivable' in the indefinite language, a negated unlimited existential operator, which can be replaced by a universal operator, occurs; and unlimited universality can be expressed in I by means of a free variable. '∼BewSatz(r, a)' means: "Every r is not a proof of a", in other words: "a is not demonstrable"; '∼AblSatz$[r, b,$reihe (a)]' means: "Every r is not a derivation of b from a", in other words: "b is not derivable from a".

§ 24. DESCRIPTIVE SYNTAX

We have now completed our exposition of the *pure syntax* of Language I; this example makes it clear that pure syntax is nothing other than a part of arithmetic. *Descriptive syntax*, on the other hand, uses descriptive symbols as well, and by so doing goes beyond the boundaries of arithmetic. For instance, a sentence of descriptive syntax may state that at a particular place a linguistic expression of such and such a form occurs. It has been pointed out earlier (p. 54) that a possible method is to introduce a series of undefined $\mathfrak{pr}_b$ as additional primitive symbols (for instance: 'Var', 'Id', 'Präd', and so on). But, as we have already announced (p. 54), we shall proceed differently. We shall take the undefined $\mathfrak{fu}_b$ 'zei' as the only additional primitive symbol. (If the sentences in which this symbol occurs are, in their turn, syntactically treated, we shall co-ordinate to it the term-number 243 ($= 3^5$).) The construction of descriptive syntax takes exactly the same form as the construction of any other descriptive *axiomatic system* A. First the syntax of the language S in which A is to be formulated must be established. In this way the method of formulating sentences and of deriving them from A is determined. For some A (for instance, geometry and syntax) it is necessary that S should contain an arithmetic.

The following *basis* of A will now be established in S: 1. the *descriptive primitive symbols* of A which are added to the primitive symbols of S; from these, according to the syntactical rules of S, further symbols can be defined; 2. the *axioms* as additional primitive sentences of S; from these, with the help of the transformation-rules of S, consequences can be derived (the so-called theorems of A); 3. additional *rules of inference*; in most cases, however, these are not introduced. If we use undefined $\mathfrak{pr}_b$ as primitive symbols of descriptive syntax, then a large number of axioms is necessary; by means of these it is stated, for instance, that unlike symbols may not occur at the same place, and so on. Further, a number of axioms in the form of unrestricted existential sentences is required, in order to make it possible to derive even simple sentences about derivability and demonstrability. If, on the other hand, we take the $\mathfrak{fu}_b$ 'zei' as a primitive symbol, then no axioms of any kind are necessary. That which in the other case is excluded by the negative axioms is here already excluded by means of the syntactical rules concerning functors (a particular $\mathfrak{fu}$ can only have one value for a particular place); the necessary existential sentences follow from the arithmetic.

With the help of the *primitive symbol* 'zei', we shall here give the definition—a regressive one—of only one further symbol belonging to descriptive syntax. This is the $\mathfrak{fu}^2_b$ 'ausdr' (*Ausdruck*)—the most important term of descriptive syntax.

D 126. 1. ausdr $(0, x) = $ pot $[2, \text{zei} (x)]$

2. ausdr $(k^!, x) = $ prod $\big[$ausdr (k, x), pot $\big($prim $(k^{!!})$, zei $[\text{sum} (x, k^!)]\big)\big]$

Explanation: ausdr(k,x) is the $^{SN}expression$ (with $k+1$ symbols) which occurs at the positions x to $x+k$. Since the ^{TN}symbol at the position y is zei(y), therefore ausdr $(k,x) = 2^{\text{zei}(x)} \cdot 3^{\text{zei}(x^!)} \cdot 5^{\text{zei}(x^{!!})} \ldots \cdot \text{prim}(k^!)^{\text{zei}(x+k)}$ (see p. 56).

With the help of the functors 'zei' and 'ausdr', together with that of the previously defined symbols of pure syntax (D 1–125), we are now in a position to formulate *sentences of the descriptive syntax of* I *in* I *itself*.

A. *Examples of sentences about individual symbols* (with the help of 'zei'):

1. " A symbol of negation occurs at the position a ":'zei$(a) = 21$ '.

2. "Equal symbols occur at the positions a and b ": 'zei$(a) = $ zei(b)'.

B. *Examples of sentences about expressions* (with the help of
'ausdr'):

1. "In the series of positions a to a+b occurs a $\mathcal{3}$":
'ZA(ausdr(b, a))'.

2. "..., a demonstrable sentence does not occur": '∼BewSatz
(r, ausdr(b, a))' (with the free variable 'r', see p. 76).

§ 25. ARITHMETICAL, AXIOMATIC AND
PHYSICAL SYNTAX

Within the domain of descriptive syntax we can distinguish two
different theories: the axiomatic syntax which we have just been
discussing (with or without axioms) and physical syntax. The
latter is to the former as physical geometry is to axiomatic geometry. Physical geometry results from axiomatic geometry by
means of the establishment of the so-called *correlative definitions*
(cf. Reichenbach [*Axiomatik*], [*Philosophie*]). These definitions determine to which of the physical concepts (either of physics or of
everyday language) the axiomatic primitive symbols are to be
equivalent in meaning. It is only by means of these definitions
that the axiomatic system is applicable to empirical sentences.

The following schematic survey is intended to exhibit more
clearly the character of the three kinds of syntax, by means of the
analogy with the three kinds of geometry. In addition, it is meant
to show the relation which subsists generally between arithmetic,
an axiomatic system, and the empirical application of the latter.

The three kinds of geometry.	The three kinds of syntax.
I. *Arithmetical geometry.*	I. *Arithmetical (or pure) syntax.*
A *partial domain of arithmetic* which (in the usual method of arithmetiza-tion, namely by means of co-ordinates) is concerned with ordered triads of real numbers, the linear equations occur-ring between them, and the like.	A *partial domain of arithmetic* which (in the method of arithmetization pre-viously explained) is concerned with certain products of certain powers of prime numbers, the relations between such products, and so on.

This partial domain is selected by means of certain purely arithmetical
definitions. The practical reason for framing precisely *these* definitions is given
by a certain model, namely, a system of physical structures for the theoretical
treatment of which these definitions are appropriate. This is the system

of physico-spatial relations which is the subject of physical geometry, IIB.	of physical linguistic structures—e.g. the sentences occurring on a sheet of paper—which is the subject of physical syntax, II B.

II. *Descriptive geometry.*	II. *Descriptive syntax.*
(This designation is here not intended in the usual sense, but in the sense of the syntactical term 'descriptive'.)	

II A. *Axiomatic geometry.*	II A. *Axiomatic syntax.*
	Two different representational forms:
	(a) *Proper axiomatization* (compare § 18) ('Axiomatized descriptive syntax').
	(b) *Arithmetization* (compare §§ 19, 24) ('Arithmetized descriptive syntax').

A language with established logical primitive symbols, primitive sentences, and rules of inference is presupposed for the axiomatic system.

Basis of the axiomatic system:

1. *Axiomatic primitive symbols* (descriptive primitive symbols which are added to the primitive symbols of the language):

"Point", "straight line", "between", and so on.	'Var', 'Nu', 'Präd', 'Gl' (positions with equal symbols), and so on.	'zei' as the only primitive symbol.

2. *Axioms* (descriptive primitive sentences which are added to the primitive sentences of the language):

For example, Hilbert's axioms.	Numerous axioms, for instance: "a ჳ is not a pr", "Gl$(x, y) \supset$ Gl(y, x)", and so on.	*No* axioms.

Valid descriptive sentences of the axiomatic system:

1. *Analytic sentences.* For proofs of these the *definitions* belonging to the axiomatic system may be used, but not the *axioms* themselves.

Examples. "Every point is a point"; "If each of three straight lines intersects the other two at different points, then the segments between the points of intersection form a triangle" (this follows from the definition of "triangle").	Examples. 'Var$(x) \supset$ Var(x)'; 'Nu$(x) \supset$ Zz(x)' (that is to say, "nu is a ჳჳ"; this follows from the definition of 'Zz'); '[Nu$(x) \cdot$ Str$(x')] \supset$ ZA$(x, 1)$' (that is to say, "nu' is a ჳ"; this follows from the definition of 'ZA'; here 'ZA' is a prᵦ).	Examples. 'zei$(x) =$ zei(x)'; '[zei$(x) = 4] \supset$ Zz[zei(x)]' '([zei$(x) = 4] \cdot$ [zei(x') $= 14]) \supset$ ZA[ausdr$(1, x)$]' (a prᵢ).

2. *Synthetic sentences.* These are the axioms themselves together with the synthetic sentences which are proved with their assistance.

Example. "The sum of the angles of a triangle is equal to 2R."	Example. 'Nu$(x) \supset \sim$ Ex(x)' (that is to say, "an nu is not a 'Ǝ'").	None. Since there are no axioms here, all valid sentences are analytic.

II B. *Physical geometry.*	II B. *Physical syntax.*

By means of correlative definitions it is determined which symbols of the physical language are to correspond to the primitive symbols (or to certain defined symbols) of the axiomatic system.

Examples.

1. "A physical segment (for instance, the edge of a body) is said to have the length 1 when it is such and such a number of times longer than the wave-length of such and such a spectral line of cadmium."

2. "A physical segment is said to have the length 1 when it is congruent with the segment between the two marks on the standard metre measure in Paris."

3. "Physical objects of such and such a kind (for instance, light-rays in a vacuum or stretched strings) are to be considered as straight segments."

Examples.

1. "'Nu (x)' is to be taken as true

when and only when a written character having the figure of an upright ellipse ('0') is to be found at the position x."

2. "'Nu (x)' is to be taken as true

when and only when a character which has a sufficient resemblance in design to the character occurring at such and such a place (for instance of this book) is to be found at the position x."

Examples.

1. "'zei $(x) = 4$' is to be taken as true

2. "'zei $(x) = 4$' is to be taken as true

[Examples (1) are *qualitative definitions*; here the term is defined by the statement of the properties which an object must have in order to be comprehended by the term. Examples (2) are *ostensive definitions*; here the term is defined by the stipulation that the objects comprehended by the term must have a certain relation (for instance, congruence or likeness) to a certain indicated object; in linguistic formulation the ostension takes the form of a statement of the spatio-temporal position. It is to be noted that, according to this, an ostensive definition likewise defines a symbol by means of other symbols (and not by means of extra-linguistic things).]

Valid descriptive sentences

1. *Analytic sentences.* These are either analytic sentences of the axiomatic system, of which the axiomatic terms have acquired a physical sense by means of the correlative definitions (Examples (*a*); compare the examples of analytic sentences under IIA), or on the other hand (Examples (*b*)) sentences which are translated from such sentences, by means of the correlative definitions, into the non-axiomatic terminology (that is to say, into a terminology which does not belong to the axiomatic system, but to the general language).

Examples.

(*a*) "If each of three (physical) straight lines intersects the other two at different points, then the (physical) segments between the points of intersection form a (physical) triangle."

(*b*) "If each of three light-rays in a vacuum intersects the other two

Examples.

(*a*) "A zero symbol (physical character in ink) is a numeral."

(*b*) "A (physical) character having the design of an upright ellipse is a numeral."

Examples.

(*a*) "A (physical) object which possesses the term-number 4 (that is, a certain physical property) is a numeral."

at different points, then the segments of rays between the points of intersection form a triangle."

2. *Valid laws*. These are either indefinite synthetic sentences of the axiomatic system, which in this case have a physical meaning (Examples 1 (*a*), 2 (*a*)), or translations of such into non-axiomatic terminology (Examples 1 (*b*), 2 (*b*)).

Examples.	Examples.	None, because there are no axioms.
1 (*a*). "Two (physical) straight lines intersect one another at one point at most."	1 (*a*). "If a (physical) zero symbol occurs at a place, then no existential symbol occurs there."	
1 (*b*). "Two light-rays in a vacuum intersect one another at one point at most."	1 (*b*). "If a character in ink having the figure of an upright ellipse occurs at a place, then no character consisting of one vertical and three horizontal strokes occurs at that place."	
2 (*a*). "The sum of the angles of a (physical) triangle is 2 R."		
2 (*b*). "The sum of the angles between three light-rays in a vacuum which intersect one another is 2 R."		

The question of the validity of a particular axiomatic system having certain correlative definitions is the question of the validity of the laws which result from the translation of the axioms into the language of science (of physics) (Example 1 (*b*)).

Here arises, for instance, the important question of validity in relation to Euclidean or to one particular non-Euclidean geometry.	Here the question of validity is a critical one in relation to the existential axioms, and particularly to the axioms of infinity (for instance, "there are infinitely many variables").	Here there is no question of validity at all. (On the dispensability of an axiom of infinity for arithmetic, see p. 97.)

3. *Empirical sentences*. Hereby are to be understood definite synthetic sentences which state the empirical (namely, the geometrical or graphical) properties of certain physical objects, whether demonstrable by means of the axioms or not. The sentences may either employ the non-axiomatic terminology (Examples 1 (*a*), 2 (*a*)) or be translated into the axiomatic (geometrical or syntactical) terminology (Examples 1 (*b*), 2 (*b*)).

Examples.	Examples.	Examples.
1 (*a*). "This object A is a light-ray in a vacuum."	1 (*a*). "A symbol consisting of two horizontal strokes occurs at the place c in this book."	
1 (*b*). "A forms a straight segment."	1 (*b*). "A symbol of identity occurs at the place c in this book"; in the symbols of our system:	
2 (*a*). "These three objects A, B, C are light-rays in a vacuum each one of which intersects	'Id (c)'.	'zei (c) = 15'.
	2 (*a*). "A series of figures of such and such a form occurs in the places ranging from a to b in this book."	

6

the other two at different points."

2 (b). "The physical objects A, B, C together form a triangle."

2 (b). "A primitive sentence of Language I occurs...."

The following sentences are of a like kind:

3. "The sentence 'docendo discimus' occurs in that book."

4. "It is maintained in that book that one learns by teaching."

5. "In such and such a treatise, the sentences occurring at places so and so contradict one another."

6. "The word-series at such and such a place is meaningless (that is to say, is not a sentence of such and such a language)."

7. "An empirically false sentence occurs at such and such a place." (Cf. 'P-contravalid', p. 185.)

The sentences of the whole history of language and literature belong here, especially those of the history of science, including mathematics and metaphysics. Among them are both sentences which merely cite something (Examples 2 (a), 3) and sentences (Examples 2 (b), 4 to 7) which presuppose the syntax of the language in question and sometimes also certain synthetic premisses, particularly such as criticize formulations and theses on the basis of logical analysis (Examples 5, 6) or of experience (Example 7).

PART III

THE INDEFINITE LANGUAGE II

A. RULES OF FORMATION FOR LANGUAGE II

§ 26. The Symbolic Apparatus of Language II

Language I, with which we have been concerned up to the present, contains only definite concepts; in the domain of mathematics it contains only the arithmetic of the natural numbers, and that only to an extent which corresponds approximately to a finitist or intuitionist standpoint. Language II includes Language I as a sub-language; all the symbols of I are likewise symbols of II, and all the sentences of I are likewise sentences of II. But Language II is far richer in modes of expression than Language I. It also contains indefinite concepts; it includes the whole of classical mathematics (functions with real and complex arguments; limiting values; the infinitesimal calculus; the theory of aggregates); and in it, in addition, the sentences of physics may be formulated.

We shall first state the symbols and the most important expressions which occur in Language II. The exact rules of formation for $\mathfrak{Z}$ and $\mathfrak{S}$ will be given later (§ 28). The Gothic symbols used in the syntax of Language I will also be used here, together with some additional ones.

In Language II, in addition to the limited operators of Language I, we have also *unlimited operators* of the forms $(\mathfrak{z})$, $(\exists\,\mathfrak{z})$, and $(K\mathfrak{z})$. [*Example:* '$(\exists\,x)\,(\mathrm{Prim}\,(x))$'; see § 6.]

In Language II, $\mathfrak{fu}$ and $\mathfrak{pr}$ of new syntactical kinds occur, and these are divided into levels and types (§ 27). In the sentence $\mathfrak{fu}\,(\mathfrak{A}_1) = \mathfrak{A}_2$, we shall, as hitherto, call $\mathfrak{A}_1$ the *argument-expression*; and, further, we shall call $\mathfrak{A}_2$ the *value-expression*. In II there are $\mathfrak{fu}$ for which not only $\mathfrak{A}_1$ consists of several terms—the so-called arguments—but $\mathfrak{A}_2$ also consists of several terms—the so-called value-terms [$\mathfrak{Z}_3$, $\mathfrak{Z}_4$, and $\mathfrak{Z}_5$ in $\mathfrak{fu}\,(\mathfrak{Z}_1, \mathfrak{Z}_2) = \mathfrak{Z}_3, \mathfrak{Z}_4, \mathfrak{Z}_5$, for instance]. There are not only the predicates $\mathfrak{pr}$ but also *predicate-expressions* $\mathfrak{Pr}$ (of the different types) which may consist of several symbols, but are used syntactically just like the pr. Further, there are *functor-expressions* $\mathfrak{Fu}$ (of the different types) which are used syntactically like the fu (examples will be given later). Just as a one-symbol expression $\mathfrak{z}\mathfrak{z}$ is a $\mathfrak{z}$, so a pr is a $\mathfrak{Pr}$ and an fu an $\mathfrak{Fu}$. There are pr (and other $\mathfrak{Pr}$) of which the arguments are not $\mathfrak{z}$ but either $\mathfrak{Pr}$ or $\mathfrak{Fu}$ (of one type or another); further, there are fu (and other $\mathfrak{Fu}$) of which the arguments and value-terms are not $\mathfrak{z}$ but are either $\mathfrak{Pr}$ or $\mathfrak{Fu}$ (of one type or another). Thus, an argument-expression or a value-expression (syntactical designation, '$\mathfrak{Arg}$') consists of one or more expressions of the forms $\mathfrak{z}$, $\mathfrak{Pr}$, or $\mathfrak{Fu}$, separated from one another by commas.

In Language II, there are *variables* of different kinds: not only numerical variables $\mathfrak{z}$ ('u', 'v', ... 'z'), but also predicate-variables p ('F', 'G', 'H'; 'M', 'N') and functor-variables f ('f', 'g', 'h'). [Just as we assign the $\mathfrak{z}$ to the $\mathfrak{z}\mathfrak{z}$, so we assign the p to the pr and the f to the fu.] The variables p and f (of all types) also occur in unlimited operators: (p); ($\exists$ p); (f); ($\exists$ f).

In Language II, the symbol of identity ' = ' is not only used between $\mathfrak{z}$ and between $\mathfrak{S}$ (here also when used between $\mathfrak{S}$ it is usually written ' $\equiv$ ') but also between $\mathfrak{Pr}$ and between $\mathfrak{Fu}$. [*Examples* (for the simplest type): '$P_1 = P_2$' is equivalent in meaning to '$(x)\left(P_1(x) \equiv P_2(x)\right)$'; '$fu_1 = fu_2$' is equivalent in meaning to '$(x)\left(fu_1(x) = fu_2(x)\right)$'.] We shall designate the *zero-equation* '$0 = 0$' by '$\mathfrak{N}$'.

In Language II, *sentential symbols* [*Satzzeichen*] fa also occur; these are in part *sentential constants*, that is to say symbols which are used as abbreviations for certain sentences, and in part *sentential variables* f ('p', 'q', ... 't'). The f also occur in operators of the form (f) and ($\exists$f). We use '$\mathfrak{v}$' as the common designation for the *variables* of the four kinds which we have mentioned, namely, $\mathfrak{z}$, p, f, f; all the remaining symbols are called *constants* ($\mathfrak{k}$).

§ 27. The Classification of Types

Every $\mathfrak{Pr}$, and hence every pr and every p, belong to a certain type. Further, we assign a type to all the $\mathfrak{z}$—namely, the type 0. A particular $\mathfrak{Pr}$ can only have arguments of certain types, and an $\mathfrak{Fu}$ can only have arguments and value-terms of certain types. In order that $\mathfrak{Pr}_1(\mathfrak{A}_1, \mathfrak{A}_2, ... \mathfrak{A}_n)$ and $\mathfrak{Pr}_1(\mathfrak{A}'_1, \mathfrak{A}'_2, ... \mathfrak{A}'_n)$ may be sentences, it is necessary that $\mathfrak{A}_1$ and $\mathfrak{A}'_1$ should belong to the same type, and furthermore that $\mathfrak{A}_2$ and $\mathfrak{A}'_2$ should belong to the same type (which may, however, be of another kind than that to which $\mathfrak{A}_1$ belongs), and so on. In order that $\mathfrak{Fu}_1(\mathfrak{A}_1, \ldots \mathfrak{A}_m) = \mathfrak{A}_{m+1}, \ldots$ $\mathfrak{A}_{m+n}$ and $\mathfrak{Fu}_1(\mathfrak{A}'_1, \ldots \mathfrak{A}'_m) = \mathfrak{A}'_{m+1}, \ldots \mathfrak{A}'_{m+n}$ may be sentences, $\mathfrak{A}_i$ and $\mathfrak{A}'_i (i = 1$ to $m+n)$ must be of the same type. The type of a $\mathfrak{Pr}$ is determined by the types of the arguments (in which number and order must be taken into account); the type of an $\mathfrak{Fu}$ is determined by the types both of the arguments and of the value-terms.

The **type** of an expression is determined in accordance with the following rules. Every $\mathfrak{Z}$ (and hence also every $\mathfrak{ZZ}$) belongs to the type 0. If the n terms of an $\mathfrak{Arg}$ have the types $t_1, t_2, \ldots t_n$ (in this order), we assign the type $t_1, t_2, \ldots t_n$ to the $\mathfrak{Arg}$. [The symbols 't' with suffix are not themselves syntactical type-designations, but are syntactical variables of such.] If $\mathfrak{Arg}_1$ belongs to the type t_1 in the sentence $\mathfrak{Pr}_1(\mathfrak{Arg}_1)$, then we assign the type (t_1) to $\mathfrak{Pr}_1$. If $\mathfrak{Arg}_1$ belongs to the type t_1 and $\mathfrak{Arg}_2$ to the type t_2 in the sentence $\mathfrak{Fu}_1(\mathfrak{Arg}_1) = \mathfrak{Arg}_2$, then we assign the type $(t_1 : t_2)$ to $\mathfrak{Fu}_1$ and the type t_2 to the expression $\mathfrak{Fu}_1(\mathfrak{Arg}_1)$.

Examples. 1. '$\mathrm{Gr}(5, 3)$' is a sentence; '5' belongs to the type 0, '5, 3' to the type 0, 0; hence the pr 'Gr' belongs to the type $(0, 0)$. —2. '$\mathrm{sum}(2, 3) = x$' is a sentence; therefore the fu 'sum' belongs to the type $(0, 0 : 0)$.—3. Let 'M' be a pr of which the arguments are not $\mathfrak{Z}$ but a pr and an fu of the types just mentioned, so that, for instance, '$\mathrm{M}(\mathrm{Gr}, \mathrm{sum})$' is a sentence. Then '$\mathrm{M}$' belongs to the type $((0, 0), (0, 0 : 0))$.

The **level-number** of an expression is also determined by its type, in accordance with the following rules. We assign the level-number 0 to the $\mathfrak{Z}$. The level-number of an $\mathfrak{Arg}$ is equal to the greatest level-number of its terms. The level-number of a $\mathfrak{Pr}$ is greater by 1 than that of the argument-expression belonging to it. The level-number of an $\mathfrak{Fu}$ is greater by 1 than the greatest of the two $\mathfrak{Arg}$ belonging to it. In accordance with our previous rules, every type-designation, apart from commas and colons, consists of zeros and brackets. The level-number is easily obtainable from a designation of this kind; it is the largest number of pairs of brackets in which a zero of the type-designation is included. To the Gothic symbols, '$\mathfrak{Pr}$' and so on, we append (as before), where

necessary, *indices* in the right-hand upper corner to designate the
number of argument-terms, and further, where necessary, indices
in the left-hand upper corner to designate the level-number.

The *classification of types* outlined above is, in its essential points,
the so-called *simple* classification of types proposed by Ramsey. But
it is here completed by being extended not only to $\mathfrak{pr}$ but to $\mathfrak{fu}$,
$\mathfrak{Pr}$ and $\mathfrak{Fu}$ as well; and further, by the introduction of type-designations. In Russell's so-called "branched" classification of types, the
$\mathfrak{pr}$ are further subdivided so that not only the type of the arguments
of a $\mathfrak{pr}$ is taken into consideration but also the form of its definition.
Further, in his system the sentences also are subdivided into types,
whereas in our Language II any sentence can be substituted for an
$\mathfrak{f}$. In order to avoid certain difficulties which arise in the application
of his branched subdivision, Russell formulated the *Axiom of Reducibility*. But this axiom is rendered unnecessary by restricting
ourselves to the simple classification of types.

Examples. 1. 'Gr' belongs to the type $(0, 0)$ (see above), and thus
has the level-number 1; 'Gr' is thus a $^1\mathfrak{pr}^2$, or, in words, a two-
termed predicate of the first level.—2. Since every $\mathfrak{Z}$ belongs to the
type 0 and has the level-number 0, all the $\mathfrak{pr}$ in Language I are $^1\mathfrak{pr}$;
the types which occur are as follows: (0); $(0, 0)$; $(0, 0, 0)$, and so on.
All the $\mathfrak{fu}$ of Language I are $^1\mathfrak{fu}$ and of the types: $(0:0)$; $(0, 0:0)$;
$(0, 0, 0:0)$, etc.—3. In the example (3) above, 'M' is a $^2\mathfrak{pr}^2$.—4. If,
in any connection, sentences of the form $(\mathfrak{Z}_1)\left(\mathfrak{pr}_1(\mathfrak{Z}_1) \supset \mathfrak{pr}_2(\mathfrak{Z}_1)\right)$
occur frequently, then, for the purpose of abbreviation, it is ex-
pedient to introduce the $\mathfrak{pr}$ 'Sub' ("...is a partial property or a
sub-class of..."); the definition is as follows: 'Sub$(F, G) \equiv (x)$
$[F(x) \supset G(x)]$'. Since 'F' and 'G' in this case are $^1\mathfrak{pr}^1$ of the type
(0), 'Sub' is a $^2\mathfrak{pr}^2$ of the type $((0), (0))$.—5. Let '$(x)[(P_1(x) \vee
P_2(x)) \equiv P_3(x)]$' be demonstrable. In accordance with the termino-
logy of the theory of aggregates or classes, we may here designate
P_3 (the property or class) as the sum of P_1 and P_2. For the purpose
of abbreviation, we propose to introduce the symbol 'sm' in such
a way that the expression 'sm(P_1, P_2)' means the sum of P_1 and P_2,
and hence, in the case given, is equivalent in meaning to 'P_3'.
'sm(P_1, P_2)' is accordingly a $\mathfrak{Pr}$ belonging to the same type as
'P_3', i.e. to (0). The above-mentioned demonstrable sentence may
now be formulated more shortly, as follows: 'sm$(P_1, P_2) = P_3$'.
'sm' is an $\mathfrak{fu}$; each of the two arguments as well as the value-term
belongs to the type (0); hence 'sm' is a $^2\mathfrak{fu}^2$ of the type $((0), (0):(0))$.
The definition of 'sm' is as follows: 'sm$(F, G)(x) \equiv (F(x) \vee G(x))$'.
Here the $\mathfrak{Pr}$ 'sm(F, G)' is used syntactically in the same way as a
$\mathfrak{pr}$ of the same type (0).—6. Let 'F' be a $^1\mathfrak{p}$ of the type (0) and 'Cl'
a $^2\mathfrak{pr}$ of the type $((0))$ (in another mode of speech: a class of classes;
see § 37), so that 'Cl(F)' is a sentence. 'clsm(Cl)' represents the
class-sum of Cl; by this is meant that property (or class) which is
applicable to all those numbers, and only to those, which have at

least one property having the second-level property Cl. Let us take 'M' as a $^2\mathfrak{p}$ of the type $((0))$; the definition will then be as follows: 'clsm $(M)(x) = (\exists F)(M(F) \cdot F(x))$'. 'clsm (M)' is a $^1\mathfrak{Pr}$ of the type (0); hence 'clsm' is a $^3\mathfrak{fu}$ of the type $(((0)):(0))$.—7. Let '$\mathrm{scn}(F,G)$' mean: the smallest number which has the two properties F and G; and let it mean 0 for the case in which no such number exists. The definition is as follows: '$\mathrm{scn}(F,G) = (Kx)$ $(F(x) \cdot G(x))$'. Each of the two arguments of 'scn' belongs to the type (0). The value-expression of 'scn' (the right-hand side of the equation) is a $\mathfrak{Z}$ and therefore belongs to the type 0. Thus 'scn' is a $^2\mathfrak{fu}$ of the type $((0),(0):0)$, and '$\mathrm{scn}(F,G)$' is likewise a $\mathfrak{Z}$.— Further examples will be given in § 37.

§ 28. Formation Rules for Numerical Expressions and Sentences

On the basis of the foregoing explanations, which were bound up with material interpretations, the rules of formation for Language II may now be laid down formally in the following manner. (Compare the analogous rules for Language I, § 9.)

We assume the previously given definitions of the following concepts: 'bound' and 'free variables' (now with reference to all $\mathfrak{v}$, namely $\mathfrak{Z}$, $\mathfrak{p}$, $\mathfrak{f}$, and $\mathfrak{f}$); 'open' and 'closed' (p. 21); 'definite' and 'indefinite' (p. 45); 'descriptive' and 'logical' (p. 25); '$\mathfrak{Z}\mathfrak{Z}$' and '$\mathfrak{St}$' (p. 26).

An expression belongs to the type 0—in which case it is called a **numerical expression** $(\mathfrak{Z})$—when and only when it has one of the following forms: 1. $\mathfrak{Z}\mathfrak{Z}$; 2. $\mathfrak{Z}'$; 3. $(K\mathfrak{Z}_1)\mathfrak{Z}_1(\mathfrak{S})$, or $(K\mathfrak{Z}_1)(\mathfrak{S})$, where $\mathfrak{Z}_1$ does not occur freely in $\mathfrak{Z}_1$; 4. $\mathfrak{A}_2(\mathfrak{A}_1)$, where $\mathfrak{A}_1$ belongs to any type t_1 and $\mathfrak{A}_2$ belongs to the type $(t_1:0)$, and is therefore an $\mathfrak{Fu}$.

In general, the following is true: if $\mathfrak{A}_1$ belongs to the type t_1 and $\mathfrak{A}_2$ to the type $(t_1:t_2)$—in which case $\mathfrak{A}_2$ is called a **functor-expression** $(\mathfrak{Fu})$—then $\mathfrak{A}_2(\mathfrak{A}_1)$ belongs to the type t_2 (but not only in this case). The formation rule (4) which has already been given for $\mathfrak{Z}$ is a special case of this. An expression of a type of the form (t_1), where t_1 is any type whatsoever, is called a **predicate-expression** $(\mathfrak{Pr})$.

Regressive rules for 'n-termed *argument-expression*' (or 'value-expression') $(\mathfrak{Arg}^n)$ are as follows: an $\mathfrak{Arg}^1$ has one of the forms $\mathfrak{Z}$, $\mathfrak{Pr}$, or $\mathfrak{Fu}$. An $\mathfrak{Arg}^{n+1}$ has the form $\mathfrak{Arg}^n, \mathfrak{Arg}^1$; if $\mathfrak{Arg}_1$ and

$\mathfrak{Arg}_2$ here belong to the types t_1 and t_2, respectively, then $\mathfrak{Arg}_1$, $\mathfrak{Arg}_2$ belongs to the type t_1, t_2.

An expression is called a **sentence** ($\mathfrak{S}$) when and only when it has one of the following forms: 1. $\lceil\mathfrak{a}$; 2. $\mathfrak{A}_1 = \mathfrak{A}_2$, where $\mathfrak{A}_1$ and $\mathfrak{A}_2$ are either $\mathfrak{Z}$, $\mathfrak{Pr}$, or $\mathfrak{Fu}$ of the same type; 3. $\sim(\mathfrak{S})$ or $(\mathfrak{S})\,\mathfrak{verit}\,(\mathfrak{S})$; 4. $(\mathfrak{z}_1)\,\mathfrak{Z}_1\,(\mathfrak{S})$ or $(\exists\,\mathfrak{z}_1)\,\mathfrak{Z}_1\,(\mathfrak{S})$, where $\mathfrak{z}_1$ does not occur freely in $\mathfrak{Z}_1$; 5. $(\mathfrak{v})\,(\mathfrak{S})$ or $(\exists\,\mathfrak{v})\,(\mathfrak{S})$; 6. $\mathfrak{A}_2(\mathfrak{A}_1)$, where $\mathfrak{A}_1$ belongs to any type t_1 whatsoever and $\mathfrak{A}_2$ belongs to the type (t_1) (and is accordingly a $\mathfrak{Pr}$).

$\mathfrak{S}_1$ is called an *atomic sentence* when $\mathfrak{S}_1$ has any one of the forms $\mathfrak{N}$, $\mathfrak{pr}_1(\mathfrak{A}_1)$, or $\mathfrak{fu}_1(\mathfrak{A}_2) = \mathfrak{A}_3$, where $\mathfrak{pr}_1$ is an undefined $^1\mathfrak{pr}_\mathfrak{b}$ and $\mathfrak{fu}_1$ is an undefined $^1\mathfrak{fu}_\mathfrak{b}$, and $\mathfrak{A}_1$, $\mathfrak{A}_2$, and $\mathfrak{A}_3$ are argument-expressions of which all the terms are $\mathfrak{St}$. $\mathfrak{S}_1$ is called a *molecular sentence* when $\mathfrak{S}_1$ is either an atomic sentence itself, or is formed from one or more such by means of symbols of negation and junction (and brackets).

Some of the syntactical definitions become simpler if we do not consider the whole of Language II, but instead only certain concentric language-regions II_1, II_2, ..., which form an infinite series. As regards the apparatus of symbols, sentences, and derivations, every region is contained in all the successive regions, and I is contained in II_1. In a certain sense, Language II represents the sum of all these regions. The subdivision into regions takes place in the following way. Not counting $\mathfrak{pr}$ and $\mathfrak{fu}$, all the symbols already occur in II_1, and thus in every region. Operators with $\lceil$ occur for the first time in II_2. In II_1, $^1\mathfrak{pr}$ and $^1\mathfrak{fu}$ occur both as constants and as free variables, but not as bound variables. Further, in a region II_n ($n = 2, 3, ...$) $\mathfrak{pr}$ and $\mathfrak{fu}$ occur as constants and as free variables up to the level n, but as bound variables only up to the level $n - 1$. [The line of demarcation between II_1 and the further regions corresponds approximately to that between Hilbert's elementary and higher calculus of functions.]

§29. FORMATION RULES FOR DEFINITIONS

In Language II we shall admit only *explicit definitions.** This involves no restriction, since, by the use of unlimited operators,

---

* (*Note*, 1935.) I would now prefer to admit *regressive definitions* of $^1\mathfrak{fu}$ in II as in I. By that means the term 'definite' (§ 43) would

every regressive definition can be replaced by an explicit definition. Let $\mathfrak{fu}_1^m$ be defined by means of a regressive definition which is composed of $\mathfrak{S}_1$ and $\mathfrak{S}_2$. From these sentences we construct $\mathfrak{S}_3$ and $\mathfrak{S}_4$, by replacing $\mathfrak{fu}_1$ by $\mathfrak{f}_1$ throughout, and then we define $\mathfrak{fu}_2^m$ by means of the following explicit definition (on '( )' see p. 94; here it is used only in relation to the $\mathfrak{z}$):

$$\mathfrak{fu}_2(\mathfrak{z}_1, \ldots \mathfrak{z}_m) = (K\mathfrak{z}_n)(\exists \mathfrak{f}_1)[( )\,(\mathfrak{S}_3 \bullet \mathfrak{S}_4) \bullet (\mathfrak{z}_n = \mathfrak{f}_1(\mathfrak{z}_1, \ldots \mathfrak{z}_m))].$$

Then $\mathfrak{fu}_1 = \mathfrak{fu}_2$ is demonstrable, and $\mathfrak{fu}_2$ is thus equivalent in meaning to $\mathfrak{fu}_1$. Hence, the regressive definition can be replaced by this explicit definition.

Primitive symbols in Language II: 1. Twelve logical constants, namely nu and the eleven individual symbols (as in Language I, see pp. 16 and 23); 2. all ʋ; 3. pr$_b$ and fu$_b$, when and as required, of any type. ['∨' and '•' could also be introduced as defined symbols, but we place them amongst the primitive symbols and state their definitions as primitive sentences so as to be able to formulate the remaining primitive sentences more simply.]

Formation rules for definitions. Every definition is a sentence of the form $\mathfrak{A}_1 = \mathfrak{A}_2$; $\mathfrak{A}_1$ is called the definiendum and $\mathfrak{A}_2$ the definiens. The symbol which is to be defined (a $\mathfrak{z}\mathfrak{z}$, pr, fu, ʋerȋn, or $\mathfrak{f}$a) only occurs in $\mathfrak{A}_1$; beyond this, the only symbols which may occur in $\mathfrak{A}_1$ are unequal variables as arguments, commas, and brackets. No ʋ which does not occur in $\mathfrak{A}_1$ occurs freely in $\mathfrak{A}_2$. Thus, a defined $\mathfrak{f}$a is always an abbreviation for a closed sentence. [For examples of definitions, see §§ 27 and 37.]

Since all definitions are explicit, it is in general possible to *eliminate* a defined symbol $\mathfrak{a}_1$ occurring in a sentence $\mathfrak{S}_1$; with the following qualification: when $\mathfrak{a}_1$ is a pr or an fu, the elimination cannot be carried out from $\mathfrak{S}_1$, as it stands, if $\mathfrak{a}_1$ occurs at least once in $\mathfrak{S}_1$ without an $\mathfrak{Arg}$ following it (that is, either as an argument or as a value-term, or together with ' = '). In order to dispose of this difficulty, we can transform $\mathfrak{S}_1$ into $\mathfrak{S}_3$ in the following manner. We construct $\mathfrak{S}_2$ from $\mathfrak{S}_1$ by replacing $\mathfrak{a}_1$ at all places at

---

have the intended wide extent. Dr. Tarski has pointed out to me that the exclusion of regressive definitions would make even 'sum', 'prod', and almost all arithmetical terms indefinite.—In the case of the elimination required in RR 1 (§ 34 b) a regressive definition would then, where necessary, have to be transformed, in the way indicated in this section, into an explicit definition.

which it occurs in $\mathfrak{S}_1$ without argument by a variable $\mathfrak{v}_n$ of the same type (a $\mathfrak{p}$ or an $\mathfrak{f}$), which does not otherwise occur in $\mathfrak{S}_1$. $\mathfrak{S}_3$ is then constructed in the form:

$$(\mathfrak{v}_1)(\mathfrak{v}_2)\ldots(\mathfrak{v}_m)(\mathfrak{v}_n(\mathfrak{v}_1,\ldots\mathfrak{v}_m)=\mathfrak{a}_1(\mathfrak{v}_1,\ldots\mathfrak{v}_m))\supset\mathfrak{S}_2.$$

Example. Let 'P$_3$' be defined by means of 'P$_3(x)\equiv(\mathrm{P}_1(x)\bullet$ P$_2(x))$'. 'P$_3$' cannot be immediately eliminated in 'M(P$_3$)' ($\mathfrak{S}_1$). We transform $\mathfrak{S}_1$ into $\mathfrak{S}_3$ thus: '$(x)(F(x)\equiv\mathrm{P}_3(x))\supset\mathrm{M}(F)$'; the elimination is then possible: '$(x)(F(x)\equiv[\mathrm{P}_1(x)\bullet\mathrm{P}_2(x)])\supset\mathrm{M}(F)$'.

B. RULES OF TRANSFORMATION
FOR LANGUAGE II

§ 30. THE PRIMITIVE SENTENCES OF LANGUAGE II

To the *range of values* of a variable $\mathfrak{z}$, $\mathfrak{p}$, or $\mathfrak{f}$ belong those expressions which are of the same type as the variable (thus to the range of values of a $\mathfrak{z}$ belong the $\mathfrak{Z}$). The $\mathfrak{S}$ belong to the range of values of an $\mathfrak{f}$.

Simple substitution. '$\mathfrak{A}_2\begin{pmatrix}\mathfrak{v}_1\\\mathfrak{A}_1\end{pmatrix}$' is a syntactical description of the expression which results from $\mathfrak{A}_2$ when $\mathfrak{v}_1$ is replaced by $\mathfrak{A}_1$ at all places at which it occurs freely in $\mathfrak{A}_2$. Here $\mathfrak{A}_1$ must be an expression from the range of values of $\mathfrak{v}_1$ which contains no free variable that is bound at one of the places of substitution in $\mathfrak{A}_2$.

Substitution with arguments. '$\mathfrak{A}_m\begin{pmatrix}\mathfrak{p}_1(\mathfrak{Arg}_1)\\\mathfrak{S}_1\end{pmatrix}$' is a syntactical description of the expression $\mathfrak{A}_n$ constructed in the following manner. $\mathfrak{p}_1(\mathfrak{Arg}_1)$ is a sentence; the terms of $\mathfrak{Arg}_1$ are unequal variables, e.g. $\mathfrak{v}_1,\mathfrak{v}_2,\ldots\mathfrak{v}_k$. It is not necessary that these should occur in $\mathfrak{S}_1$; on the other hand, free variables which do not occur in $\mathfrak{Arg}_1$ may occur in $\mathfrak{S}_1$, but these may only be such as are not bound at the substitution-places in $\mathfrak{A}_m$ (that is to say, at those places at which $\mathfrak{p}_1$ occurs freely in $\mathfrak{A}_m$). $\mathfrak{p}_1$ may not occur at any substitution-place in $\mathfrak{A}_m$ without being followed by an argument-expression. [An occurrence of this kind can, under certain circumstances, be obviated in the way described in § 29.] Unequal $\mathfrak{Arg}$ may come after $\mathfrak{p}_1$ at the various substitution-places. Let the argument-expression $\mathfrak{A}_1,\mathfrak{A}_2,\ldots\mathfrak{A}_k$ follow $\mathfrak{p}_1$ at a certain substitution-place. Then at this place $\mathfrak{p}_1(\mathfrak{A}_1,\ldots\mathfrak{A}_k)$ is to be replaced by

$\mathfrak{S}_1 \begin{pmatrix} \mathfrak{v}_1 \\ \mathfrak{A}_1 \end{pmatrix} \begin{pmatrix} \mathfrak{v}_2 \\ \mathfrak{A}_2 \end{pmatrix} \dots \begin{pmatrix} \mathfrak{v}_k \\ \mathfrak{A}_k \end{pmatrix}$. $\mathfrak{A}_n$ is obtained when a replacement of this kind in $\mathfrak{A}_m$ is carried out at all substitution-places.

Example. Let $\mathfrak{A}_m$ be ‘$(x)(F(x,3)) \vee F(0,z) \vee (\exists F)(\mathrm{M}(F))$’. The substitution $\begin{pmatrix} F(x,y) \\ u = \mathrm{fu}(x) \end{pmatrix}$, where ‘fu’ is an fu, is to be carried out. ‘F’ is only free in $\mathfrak{A}_m$ at the first and second occurrence; therefore only these are substitution-places. Thus the fact that ‘F’ is without $\mathfrak{Arg}$ at its third and fourth occurrence does not matter. $\mathfrak{S}_1$ is ‘$u = \mathrm{fu}(x)$’. At the first substitution-place we must replace ‘$F(x,3)$’ by $\mathfrak{S}_1 \begin{pmatrix} x \\ x \end{pmatrix} \begin{pmatrix} y \\ 3 \end{pmatrix}$, that is by $\mathfrak{S}_1$ itself. Then, at the second substitution-place, we must replace ‘$F(0,z)$’ by $\mathfrak{S}_1 \begin{pmatrix} x \\ 0 \end{pmatrix} \begin{pmatrix} y \\ z \end{pmatrix}$, which is ‘$u = \mathrm{fu}(0)$’. The result of the substitution is the following: ‘$(x)(u = \mathrm{fu}(x)) \vee (u = \mathrm{fu}(0)) \vee (\exists F)(\mathrm{M}(F))$’. The fact that the variable ‘x’, which is bound at the first substitution-place, occurs freely in the substitute expression here given, does not matter; only the “surplus” variable ‘u’ must not be bound at any of the substitution-places in $\mathfrak{A}_m$.

Primitive sentences of Language II. Since in Language II we have the variables ⨍ and p at our disposal, we are able in many cases to state a primitive sentence itself instead of a schema of primitive sentences. PSII 1–3 and 7–14 correspond to the schemata PSI 1–11 of Language I (§ 11), PSII 10 and 11 being extended to the new kinds of variables.

(*a*) Primitive sentences of the *sentential calculus.*

PSII 1. $p \supset (\sim p \supset q)$
PSII 2. $(\sim p \supset p) \supset p$
PSII 3. $(p \supset q) \supset ((q \supset r) \supset (p \supset r))$
PSII 4.* $(p \vee q) \equiv (\sim p \supset q)$
PSII 5. $(p \cdot q) \equiv \sim (\sim p \vee \sim q)$
PSII 6. $((p \supset q) \cdot (q \supset p)) \supset (p \equiv q)$

(*b*) Primitive sentences of the *limited sentential operators.*

PSII 7. $(x) 0 (F(x)) \equiv F(0)$
PSII 8. $(x)y^{\mathsf{l}} (F(x)) \equiv [(x)y (F(x)) \cdot F(y^{\mathsf{l}})]$
PSII 9. $(\exists x)y (F(x)) \equiv \sim (x)y (\sim F(x))$

---

* (*Note*, 1935.) In the German original, GII 4 (our PSII 4) runs: $(p \supset q) \equiv (\sim p \vee q)$. For the reason for the change see the footnote on p. 32.

(c) Primitive sentences of *identity*.

PSII 10. Every sentence of the form $\mathfrak{v}_1 = \mathfrak{v}_1$

PSII 11. Every sentence of the form $(\mathfrak{v}_1 = \mathfrak{v}_2) \supset \left[\mathfrak{S}_1 \supset \mathfrak{S}_1 \begin{pmatrix} \mathfrak{v}_1 \\ \mathfrak{v}_2 \end{pmatrix} \right]$

(d) Primitive sentences of *arithmetic*.

PSII 12. $\sim (0 = x^{\mathfrak{l}})$

PSII 13. $(x^{\mathfrak{l}} = y^{\mathfrak{l}}) \supset (x = y)$

(e) Primitive sentences of the *K-operators*.

PSII 14. $G\left((Kx)\,y\,[F(x)]\right) \equiv \left[(\sim (\exists\,x)\,y\,[F(x)] \cdot G(0)) \vee (\exists\,x)\,y\right.$
$\left.((z)x[F(z) \equiv (z = x)] \cdot G(x))\right]$

PSII 15. $G\left((Kx)\,[F(x)]\right) \equiv \left[(\sim (\exists\,x)\,[F(x)] \cdot G(0)) \vee (\exists\,x)\right.$
$\left.((z)x[F(z) \equiv (z = x)] \cdot G(x))\right]$

(f) Primitive sentences of the *unlimited sentential operators*.

PSII 16. Every sentence of the form $(\mathfrak{v}_1)\,(\mathfrak{S}_1) \supset \mathfrak{S}_1 \begin{pmatrix} \mathfrak{v}_1 \\ \mathfrak{A} \end{pmatrix}$

PSII 17. Every sentence of the form $(\mathfrak{p}_1)\,(\mathfrak{S}_1) \supset \mathfrak{S}_1 \begin{pmatrix} \mathfrak{p}_1\,(\mathfrak{Arg}_1) \\ \mathfrak{S}_2 \end{pmatrix}$

PSII 18. Every sentence of the form $(\exists\,\mathfrak{v}_1)\,(\mathfrak{S}_1) \equiv \sim (\mathfrak{v}_1)\,(\sim \mathfrak{S}_1)$

PSII 19. Every sentence of the form $(\mathfrak{v}_1)(\mathfrak{f}_1 \vee \mathfrak{S}_1) \supset [\mathfrak{f}_1 \vee (\mathfrak{v}_1)(\mathfrak{S}_1)]$,
where $\mathfrak{v}_1$ is not $\mathfrak{f}_1$.

(g) Primitive sentence of *complete induction*.

PSII 20. $\left[F(0) \cdot (x)\,(F(x) \supset F(x^{\mathfrak{l}}))\right] \supset (x)\,(F(x))$

(h) Primitive sentences of *selection*.

PSII 21. Every sentence of the form $\left((\mathfrak{p}_2)\,[\mathfrak{p}_1\,(\mathfrak{p}_2) \supset (\exists\,\mathfrak{v}_1)\,[\mathfrak{p}_2\,(\mathfrak{v}_1)]\right] \cdot$
$(\mathfrak{p}_2)\,(\mathfrak{p}_3)\,[(\mathfrak{p}_1\,(\mathfrak{p}_2) \cdot \mathfrak{p}_1\,(\mathfrak{p}_3) \cdot (\exists\,\mathfrak{v}_1)\,[\mathfrak{p}_2\,(\mathfrak{v}_1) \cdot \mathfrak{p}_3\,(\mathfrak{v}_1)]) \supset$
$(\mathfrak{p}_2 = \mathfrak{p}_3)]) \supset (\exists\,\mathfrak{p}_4)\,(\mathfrak{p}_2)\,(\mathfrak{p}_1\,(\mathfrak{p}_2) \supset [(\exists\,\mathfrak{v}_1)\,[\mathfrak{p}_2\,(\mathfrak{v}_1) \cdot \mathfrak{p}_4\,(\mathfrak{v}_1)] \cdot$
$(\mathfrak{v}_1)\,(\mathfrak{v}_2)\,([\mathfrak{p}_2\,(\mathfrak{v}_1) \cdot \mathfrak{p}_4\,(\mathfrak{v}_1) \cdot \mathfrak{p}_2\,(\mathfrak{v}_2) \cdot \mathfrak{p}_4\,(\mathfrak{v}_2)] \supset (\mathfrak{v}_1 = \mathfrak{v}_2))])$,
where $\mathfrak{v}_1$ (and thus $\mathfrak{v}_2$ also) is either a $\mathfrak{p}$ or an $\mathfrak{f}$.

(i) Primitive sentences of *extensionality*.

PSII 22. Every sentence of the form
$$(\mathfrak{v}_1) \ldots (\mathfrak{v}_n)(\mathfrak{p}_1(\mathfrak{v}_1, \ldots \mathfrak{v}_n) \equiv \mathfrak{p}_2(\mathfrak{v}_1, \ldots \mathfrak{v}_n)) \supset (\mathfrak{p}_1 = \mathfrak{p}_2)$$

PSII 23. Every sentence of the form
$$(\mathfrak{v}_1)(\mathfrak{v}_2) \ldots (\mathfrak{v}_n)(\mathfrak{f}_1(\mathfrak{v}_1, \ldots \mathfrak{v}_n) = \mathfrak{f}_2(\mathfrak{v}_1, \ldots \mathfrak{v}_n)) \supset (\mathfrak{f}_1 = \mathfrak{f}_2)$$

The variables which are named in the schemata may belong to

any type whatsoever; the stipulation that the whole expression must be a sentence is sufficient to secure the correct relationship to one another of the types of the different variables. [For instance, if, in PSII 21, v_1 belongs to the type t_1 (of any kind except 0), then it follows that p_2, p_3, and p_4 must belong to the type (t_1) and p_1 to the type $((t_1))$.]—PSII 4–6 are substitutes for definitions of the *junction-symbols* 'V', '.', and ' = ' (between ⊆); they correspond to RI 2 *a–c*. PSII 6 need only be put down as an implication; the converse implication follows with the help of PSII 11.—PSII 16 and 17 are the most important rules for the *unlimited universal operator*; by means of these schemata simple substitution and substitution with arguments respectively are rendered possible.—PSII 18 replaces an explicit definition of the *unlimited existential operator.*—PSII 19 makes possible the so-called shifting of the universal operator.—PSII 20 is the Principle of Complete Induction; in Language I it was formulated (RI 4) as a rule of inference, but here, with the help of the unlimited operator, it can be formulated as a primitive sentence.—PSII 21 is Zermelo's *Principle of Selection* (corresponding to Russell's Multiplicative Axiom) in a more generalized form (applied to types of any kind whatsoever); it means: " If M is a class (of the third or higher levels), and the classes which are elements of M are not empty and are mutually exclusive, then there exists at least one selective class, H, of M—that is to say, a class H which has exactly one element in common with every class which is an element of M." If this sentence is applied to numbers as elements, then it is demonstrable without PSII 21. (In such a case it is possible, for instance, to construct the selective class by taking the smallest number out of every class which is an element of M.) Therefore in PSII 21 it is established that v_1 and v_2 are not 3, but are either p or f.—The formulation of PSII 22 (in conjunction with PSII 11) effects the result that two pr which are co-extensive are everywhere interchangeable. Thus all sentences of Language II are *extensional* with respect to $\mathfrak{Pr}$ (see § 66). PSII 23 effects a corresponding result for the $\mathfrak{Fu}$. It should be noted that an equation of the form $\mathfrak{Z}_1 = \mathfrak{Z}_2$, or $\mathfrak{Pr}_1 = \mathfrak{Pr}_2$, or $\mathfrak{Fu}_1 = \mathfrak{Fu}_2$ does not mean that the two terms of the equations are equivalent in meaning. The two expressions are equivalent in meaning (synonymous) when and only when the equation is analytic.

§ 31. THE RULES OF INFERENCE OF LANGUAGE II

The rules of inference of Language II are very simple:

RII 1. Rule of *implication*. $\mathfrak{S}_3$ is called *directly derivable* from $\mathfrak{S}_1$ and $\mathfrak{S}_2$ when $\mathfrak{S}_2$ has the form $\mathfrak{S}_1 \supset \mathfrak{S}_3$.

RII 2. Rule of the *universal operator*. $\mathfrak{S}_3$ is called *directly derivable* from $\mathfrak{S}_1$ when $\mathfrak{S}_3$ has the form $(v)\,(\mathfrak{S}_1)$.

Only RI 3 (= RII 1) of the four rules of inference of Language I (§ 12) is here retained. RI 1 is replaced by PSII 16 and 17 and RII 2: from $\mathfrak{S}_1$, according to RII 2, is derivable $(v_1)\,(\mathfrak{S}_1)$ or $(\mathfrak{p}_1)\,(\mathfrak{S}_1)$; and from this, by PSII 16 or 17 and RII 1, are derivable $\mathfrak{S}_1\!\begin{pmatrix} v_1 \\ \mathfrak{A} \end{pmatrix}$ or $\mathfrak{S}_1\!\begin{pmatrix} \mathfrak{p}_1\,(\mathfrak{A}_1) \\ \mathfrak{S}_2 \end{pmatrix}$ respectively. RI 2 is replaced by PSII 4–6; RI 4 by PSII 20.

In the construction of a language, it is frequently a matter of choice whether to give a certain rule the form of a *Primitive Sentence* or that of a *Rule of Inference*. If it is possible without too much complication, the first form is the one usually chosen. [*Example:* In Language I the principle of complete induction can only be formulated as a rule of inference; in Language II it may be either a primitive sentence or a rule of inference. We have chosen the former. Further examples emerge from a comparison with other systems, see § 33.]   It is, however, incorrect to hold that there is a difference in principle, namely that for the establishment of a rule the language of syntax (usually a word-language) is necessary, while for the establishment of a primitive sentence it is not. Actually, the latter must also be formulated in the language of syntax, namely by means of the stipulation "... is a primitive sentence" (or "... is directly derivable from the null-class", compare p. 171).

The terms '*derivation*', '*derivable*', '*proof*', '*demonstrable*' have the same definition here as they have in the syntax of Language I (p. 29). If $v_1, v_2, \ldots v_n$ are the free variables of $\mathfrak{S}_1$ in the order of their appearance, then '$(\ )\,(\mathfrak{S}_1)$' will designate the closed sentence $(v_1)(v_2)\ldots(v_n)\,(\mathfrak{S}_1)$; if $\mathfrak{S}_1$ is closed, then $(\ )\,(\mathfrak{S}_1)$ is $\mathfrak{S}_1$ itself. $\mathfrak{S}_1$ is called **refutable** when $\sim(\ )\,(\mathfrak{S}_1)$ is demonstrable. $\mathfrak{S}_1$ is called **resoluble** when $\mathfrak{S}_1$ is either demonstrable or refutable; otherwise it is called **irresoluble**. The terms 'analytic', 'consequence', and so on will be defined later (§§ 34 d, f).

§ 32. DERIVATIONS AND PROOFS IN LANGUAGE II

We will now give some simple theorems about demonstrability and derivability in Language II. The proof and derivation schemata are shortened.

Theorem 32.1. Every sentence having one of the following forms is *demonstrable* in Language II:

(a) $\mathfrak{S}_1 \begin{pmatrix} \mathfrak{v}_1 \\ \mathfrak{A} \end{pmatrix} \supset (\exists \mathfrak{v}_1)(\mathfrak{S}_1).$

Proof schema. PSII 16 $(\mathfrak{v}_1)(\sim \mathfrak{S}_1) \supset (\sim \mathfrak{S}_1)\begin{pmatrix} \mathfrak{v}_1 \\ \mathfrak{A}_1 \end{pmatrix}$ (1)

(1) $(\mathfrak{v}_1)(\sim \mathfrak{S}_1) \supset \sim (\mathfrak{S}_1)\begin{pmatrix} \mathfrak{v}_1 \\ \mathfrak{A}_1 \end{pmatrix}$ (2)

(2), Sentential Calculus (transposition)

$\mathfrak{S}_1 \begin{pmatrix} \mathfrak{v}_1 \\ \mathfrak{A}_1 \end{pmatrix} \supset \sim (\mathfrak{v}_1)(\sim \mathfrak{S}_1)$ (3)

(3), PSII 18 $\mathfrak{S}_1 \begin{pmatrix} \mathfrak{v}_1 \\ \mathfrak{A}_1 \end{pmatrix} \supset (\exists \mathfrak{v}_1)(\mathfrak{S}_1)$ (4)

(b) $(\mathfrak{v}_1)(\mathfrak{S}_1) \supset (\exists \mathfrak{v}_1)(\mathfrak{S}_1)$. From PSII 16, Theorem 1 a.

(c) $(\exists \mathfrak{z}_1)(\mathfrak{z}_1 = \mathfrak{z}_1)$. From PSII 10, RII 2, Theorem 1 b.

Theorem 32.2. In Language II is *derivable*:

(a) from $\mathfrak{S}_1 \supset \mathfrak{S}_2$, where $\mathfrak{v}_1$ does not occur freely in $\mathfrak{S}_1$: $\mathfrak{S}_1 \supset (\mathfrak{v}_1)(\mathfrak{S}_2)$.

Schema of derivation. Premiss: $\mathfrak{S}_1 \supset \mathfrak{S}_2$, $\mathfrak{v}_1$ does not occur freely in $\mathfrak{S}_1$;   (1)

(1), Sentential Calculus $\sim \mathfrak{S}_1 \vee \mathfrak{S}_2$ (2)

(2), RII 2 $(\mathfrak{v}_1)(\sim \mathfrak{S}_1 \vee \mathfrak{S}_2)$ (3)

(3), PSII 19 $\sim \mathfrak{S}_1 \vee (\mathfrak{v}_1)(\mathfrak{S}_2)$ (4)

(4), Sentential Calculus $\mathfrak{S}_1 \supset (\mathfrak{v}_1)(\mathfrak{S}_2)$ (5)

(b) from $\mathfrak{S}_1 \supset \mathfrak{S}_2$, where $\mathfrak{v}_1$ does not occur freely in $\mathfrak{S}_2$: $(\exists \mathfrak{v}_1)(\mathfrak{S}_1) \supset \mathfrak{S}_2$.

Schema of derivation. Premiss: $\mathfrak{S}_1 \supset \mathfrak{S}_2$, $\mathfrak{v}_1$ does not occur freely in $\mathfrak{S}_2$;   (1)

(1), Sentential Calculus $\mathfrak{S}_2 \vee \sim \mathfrak{S}_1$ (2)

(2), RII 2 $(\mathfrak{v}_1)(\mathfrak{S}_2 \vee \sim \mathfrak{S}_1)$ (3)

(3), PSII 19	$\mathfrak{S}_2 \vee (\mathfrak{v}_1)(\sim \mathfrak{S}_1)$	(4)
(4), Sentential Calculus	$\sim (\mathfrak{v}_1)(\sim \mathfrak{S}_1) \supset \mathfrak{S}_2$	(5)
(5), PSII 18	$(\exists \mathfrak{v}_1)(\mathfrak{S}_1) \supset \mathfrak{S}_2$	(6)

(c) from $\mathfrak{S}_1 \supset (\mathfrak{v})(\mathfrak{S}_2)$: $\mathfrak{S}_1 \supset \mathfrak{S}_2$.

Schema of derivation. Premiss:	$\mathfrak{S}_1 \supset (\mathfrak{v}_1)(\mathfrak{S}_2)$	(1)
PSII 16	$(\mathfrak{v}_1)(\mathfrak{S}_2) \supset \mathfrak{S}_2$	(2)
(1), (2), Sentential Calculus	$\mathfrak{S}_1 \supset \mathfrak{S}_2$	(3)

Theorem 32.3. In Language II are *mutually derivable*:

(a) $\mathfrak{S}_1$ and $(\mathfrak{v}_1)(\mathfrak{S}_1)$; hence also $\mathfrak{S}_1$ and $()(\mathfrak{S}_1)$. By RII 2 and PSII 16.

(b) $(\mathfrak{v}_1)(\mathfrak{v}_2)(\mathfrak{S}_1)$ and $(\mathfrak{v}_2)(\mathfrak{v}_1)(\mathfrak{S}_1)$.

Schema of derivation. Premiss:	$(\mathfrak{v}_1)(\mathfrak{v}_2)(\mathfrak{S}_1)$	(1)
(1), twice PSII 16	$\mathfrak{S}_1$	(2)
(2), twice RII 2	$(\mathfrak{v}_2)(\mathfrak{v}_1)(\mathfrak{S}_1)$	(3)

§ 33. Comparison of the Primitive Sentences and Rules of Language II with those of other Systems

1. The method of giving *schemata* of primitive sentences instead of stating the primitive sentences themselves originated with von Neumann [*Beweisth.*] and has also been applied by both Gödel [*Unentscheidbare*] and Tarski [*Widerspruchsfr.*].

2. *Sentential calculus.* Russell [*Princ. Math.*] had five primitive sentences; these were reduced to four by Bernays [*Aussagenkalkül*]. Our system of three primitive sentences PSII 1–3 is due to Lukasiewicz [*Aussagenkalkül*].

3. *Functional calculus.* By this is usually understood a system which corresponds approximately to our rules PSII (1–3), 16–19, and RII 1 and 2. We will now compare these rules with the corresponding ones in a number of other systems, with the object of showing briefly that to the primitive sentences and rules of the other systems which are not amongst those of Language II correspond (on the basis of a suitably chosen translation) demonstrable syntactical sentences about demonstrability and derivability in II. Thus for all demonstrable sentences of the other systems, there are corresponding demonstrable sentences in II; and for every relation of derivability in one of the other systems, there is a corresponding relation in II. In the earlier systems (not only in those which are mentioned here) substitution with arguments was for the most part

admitted and undertaken in practice; apparently, however, exact rules for carrying it out (see p. 90) have never been stated.

(a) Russell ([*Princ. Math.*] *10, second version of the calculus of functions) gives PSII 16 as a primitive sentence $(*10·1:'(x)(F(x))\supset F(y)')$ and not as a schema. This necessitates a rule of substitution which, however, is not formulated but merely tacitly applied. Further, PSII 19 is given as a primitive sentence (*10·12), PSII 18 as a definition (*10·01), and RII 1 and 2 as rules (*1·1, *10·11). For our Theorem 32.3b (*11·2) Russell requires a primitive sentence (*11·07) which is not necessary in II.

(b) Hilbert [*Logik*], like Russell, states PSII 16 as a primitive sentence and adds the necessary substitution rule (α). Hilbert's second primitive sentence corresponds to our Theorem 32.1a. Hilbert gives three more rules: Rule (β) corresponds to RII 1, the rules (γ) to Theorems 32.2a and b. PSII 18 is proved in Hilbert (Formula 33a) and he obtains RII 2 as a derived rule (γ').

(c) Gödel [*Unentscheidbare*] does not use the existential operator, and therefore PSII 18 is not necessary. Gödel's schemata of primitive sentences III 1 and 2 correspond to PSII 16 and 19. RII 1 and 2 are laid down as rules of inference (definition of 'direct consequence').

(d) Tarski [*Widerspruchsfr.*] does not erect primitive sentences for the calculus of functions but only lays down rules of inference (Def. 9 'consequence'). 9 (2) is a rule of substitution; substitution with arguments is not admitted, so that PSII 17 disappears. 9(3) corresponds to RII 1; 9(4) and 9(5) to Theorems 32.2a and c respectively. RII 2 is replaced by 9(5), and PSII 16 by 9(5) together with 9(2). Since he does not make use of an existential operator, PSII 18 is unnecessary.

4. *Arithmetic.* Like Peano ([*Formulaire*] II, § 2) we take '0' and a successor symbol ('1') as primitive symbols. We do not make use of Peano's undefined pr 'number', because Languages I and II are co-ordinate languages and consequently all expressions of the lowest type are numerical expressions. Therefore (1) and (2) of Peano's five axioms are eliminated. To his axioms (3), (4) and (5) correspond PSII 13, 12, and 20.—On real numbers, see § 39.

5. *Theory of aggregates.* Since we represent aggregates or classes by pr (compare § 37), sentences containing variables p correspond to the axioms of the Theory of Aggregates.—(a) An *Axiom of Infinity* (Russell [*Princ. Math.*] II, p. 203; Fraenkel [*Mengenlehre*] p. 267, Ax. VII, p. 307) is not necessary in II; the corresponding sentence, $('(x)(\exists y)(y=x^1)')$, is demonstrable. The reason for this is that, in Peano's method of designating numbers, given a numerical expression, an expression for the next higher number can be formed. (On this point compare Bernays [*Philosophie*] p. 364.)—(b) To Zermelo's *Axiom of Selection* (Russell [*Princ. Math.*] I, pp. 561 ff.

7

and [*Math. Phil.*]; Fraenkel Ax. VI, pp. 283 ff.) corresponds PSII 21.—(c) PSII 22 is an *Axiom of Extensionality* (Fraenkel Def. 2, p. 272; Gödel [*Unentscheidbare*] Ax. V, 1; Tarski [*Widerspruchsfr.*] Def. 7 (3)).—(d) An *Axiom of Reducibility* (Russell [*Princ. Math.*] I, p. 55) is not necessary in II, because in the syntax of II only the so-called simple classification of types, and not Russell's 'branched' theory, is carried out (compare p. 86).—(e) An *Axiom of Comprehension* (akin to the Axiom of Reducibility) (von Neumann [*Beweisth.*] Ax. V, 1; Gödel Ax. IV, 1; Tarski Def. 7 (2); it corresponds approximately to Fraenkel's Axiom of *Aussonderung*, v, p. 281) is not necessary in II, since, according to the syntactical rules of definition, a pr^n can be defined by every sentence having n free variables, not excluding even the so-called impredicative definitions (concerning the legitimateness of which, see § 44).—(f) Finally, let us examine the axioms of Fraenkel which have not previously been mentioned ([*Mengenlehre*] § 16). The Axiom of Determinateness (Fraenkel Ax. I) is in II a special case of PSII 11. Fraenkel's Axioms of Pairing, of Summation, of the Aggregate of Sub-aggregates, of *Aussonderung*, of Replacement (II–V or VI, and VIII) are not necessary in Language II, because the aggregates (pr) postulated by these axioms can always be defined. Predicate-functors for the general formation of these aggregates can likewise be defined (compare the examples 'sm' and 'clsm', pp. 86 f.).

C. RULES OF CONSEQUENCE FOR LANGUAGE II

§ 34a. INCOMPLETE AND COMPLETE CRITERIA OF VALIDITY

One of the chief tasks of the logical foundation of mathematics is to set up a formal criterion of validity, that is, to state the necessary and sufficient conditions which a sentence must fulfil in order to be valid (correct, true) in the sense understood in classical mathematics. Since Language II is constructed in such a way that classical mathematics may be formulated in it, we can state the problem as that of setting up a formal criterion of validity for the sentences of Language II. In general, it is possible to distinguish *three kinds of criteria of validity*.

1. We may aim at discovering a *definite criterion of validity*— that is to say, a criterion of a kind such that the question of its fulfilment or non-fulfilment could in every individual instance be decided in a finite number of steps by means of a strictly estab-

lished method. If a criterion of this kind were discovered we should then possess a *method of solution* for mathematical problems; we could, so to speak, calculate the truth or falsehood of every given sentence, for example, of the celebrated Theorem of Fermat. Some time ago Weyl ([*Philosophie*] p. 20) asserted—without, however, giving a proof—"A touchstone of this kind has not yet been discovered and never will be discovered." And according to the more recent findings of Gödel [*Unentscheidbare*] the search for a definite criterion of validity for the whole mathematical system seems to be a hopeless endeavour. Nevertheless, the task of solving this so-called problem of resolution for certain classes of sentences remains both an important and a productive one; and in this direction many significant advances have already been made and many more may be expected. But if we seek a criterion which applies to more than a limited domain, then we must abandon the idea of definiteness.

2. We may set up a criterion of validity which, although itself indefinite, is yet based upon definite rules. Of this kind is the method that is used in all modern systems which attempt to create a logical foundation for mathematics (for example, the systems of Frege, Peano, Whitehead and Russell, Hilbert, and others). We shall designate it as the *method of derivation* or the *d-method*. It consists of setting up primitive sentences and rules of inference, such as have already been formulated for Language II. The primitive sentences are either given as finite in number, or they emerge by substitution from a finite number of schemata of primitive sentences. In the rules of inference only a finite number of premisses (usually only one or two) appear. The construction of primitive sentences and rules of inference may be understood as the definition of the term 'directly derivable (from a class of premisses)'; in the case of a primitive sentence, the class of premisses is null. It is usual to construct the rules in such a way that the term 'directly derivable' is always a definite term; that is to say, that in every individual case it can be decided whether or not we have an instance of a primitive sentence—or of the application of a rule of inference, respectively. We have already seen how the terms 'derivable', 'demonstrable', 'refutable', 'resoluble', and 'irresoluble' are defined on the basis of this d-method. Since no upper limit to the length of a derivation-chain is determined, the

terms mentioned, although they are based upon the definite term 'directly derivable', are themselves indefinite. It was at one time thought possible to construct a complete criterion of validity for classical mathematics with the help of a method of derivation of this kind; that is to say, it was believed, either that all valid mathematical theorems were already demonstrable in a certain existing system, or that, should a hiatus be discovered, at any rate in the future the system could be transformed into a complete one of the kind required by the addition of further suitable primitive sentences and rules of inference. Now, however, Gödel has shown that not only all former systems, but all systems of this kind in general, are incomplete. In every sufficiently rich system for which a method of derivation is prescribed, sentences can be constructed which, although they consist of symbols of the system, are yet not resoluble in accordance with the method of the system—that is to say, are neither demonstrable nor refutable in it. And, in particular, for every system in which mathematics can be formulated, sentences can be constructed which are valid in the sense of classical mathematics but not demonstrable within the system. In spite of this necessary incompleteness of the method of derivation (on this point, see § 60 d), the method retains its fundamental significance; for every strict proof of any sentence in any domain must, in the last resort, make use of it. But, for our particular task, that of constructing a *complete criterion* of validity for mathematics, this procedure, which has hitherto been the only one attempted, is useless; we must endeavour to discover another way.

3. In order to attain completeness for our criterion we are thus forced to renounce definiteness, not only for the criterion itself but also for the individual steps of the deduction. (For a general discussion of the admissibility of indefinite syntactical concepts see § 45.) A method of deduction which depends upon indefinite individual steps, and in which the number of the premisses need not be finite, we call a *method of consequence* or a *c-method*. In the case of a method of this kind, we operate, not with sentences but with sentential classes, which may also be infinite. We have already laid down rules of consequence of this kind for Language I (in § 14) and in what follows we shall state similar ones for Language II. In this way a *complete criterion of validity for mathematics* is obtained. We shall define the term 'analytic' in such a

way that it is applicable to all those sentences, and only to those sentences, of Language II that are valid (true, correct) on the basis of logic and classical mathematics. We shall define the term 'contradictory' in such a way that it applies to those sentences that are false in the logico-mathematical sense. We shall call $\mathfrak{S}_1$ *L-determinate* if it is either analytic or contradictory; otherwise we shall call it *synthetic*. The synthetic sentences are the (true or false) sentences about facts. An important point is that Language II includes descriptive symbols and hence also synthetic sentences. As we sha.! see, this influences certain details in the form of the definition of 'analytic'.

The following table shows which terms used in the two methods correspond to one another:

d-terms	*c-terms*
(depending upon the method of derivation)	(depending upon the method of consequence)
derivable	consequence
demonstrable	analytic
refutable	contradictory
resoluble	L-determinate
irresoluble	synthetic

In every one of these pairs of terms with the exception of the last, the d-term is narrower than the corresponding c-term.

The completeness of the criterion of validity which we intend to set up, as opposed to that which is dependent upon a d-method, will be proved by showing that every logical sentence of the system is L-determinate, whereas, in accordance with what was said earlier, no d-method can be so constructed that every logical sentence is resoluble.

When Wittgenstein says [*Tractatus*, p. 164]: "It is possible...to give at the outset a description of all 'true' logical propositions. Hence there can never be surprises in logic. Whether a proposition belongs to logic can be determined", he seems to overlook the *indefinite* character of the term 'analytic'—apparently because he has defined 'analytic' ('tautology') only for the elementary domain of the sentential calculus, where this term is actually a definite term. The same error seems to occur in Schlick [*Fundament*, p. 96] when he says that directly a sentence is understood, it is also known whether or not the sentence is analytic. "In the case of an analytic judgment, to understand its meaning and to see its *a priori* validity are one and the same process." He tries to justify this opinion by quite rightly pointing out that the analytic character of a sentence depends solely upon the rules of application of the words concerned, and that a sentence is only understood when the rules of application are clear. But the crux of the matter is that it is possible to be clear about the rules of application without at the same time being able to envisage all their consequences and connections. The rules of application of the symbols which occur in Fermat's theorem can easily be made clear to any beginner, and accordingly he understands the theorem; but nevertheless no one knows to this day whether it is analytic or contradictory.

§ 34b. REDUCTION

Our procedure in laying down the consequence-rules for Language I (§ 14) was first to define the term 'consequence' by means of the expansion of the rules of inference and then, with its help, the terms 'analytic' and 'contradictory'. In laying down the consequence-rules for Language II, we shall, for technical reasons, do just the reverse: first we shall define 'analytic' and 'contradictory' and then, with the help of these terms, the term 'consequence'. We shall frame these definitions in such a way that, in spite of the different methods, within the domain of those sentences of Language II which are at the same time sentences of I, the c-terms concerning the two languages coincide: if a sentence of I is analytic, or contradictory, or synthetic, or a consequence of $\Re_1$ in I, then the consonant sentence of II has the same property in II.

In consequence of the richer structure of Language II, and particularly of the occurrence of variables $\mathfrak{p}$ and $\mathfrak{f}$ and primitive symbols $\mathfrak{pr}_\mathfrak{b}$ and $\mathfrak{fu}_\mathfrak{b}$ of infinitely many levels, the definitions of the c-terms are considerably more complicated for II than they are for I. By way of preparation for these definitions, we shall first lay down rules for the reduction of sentences. By means of reduction, every sentence of II is univocally transformed into a certain (usually simpler) standard form. The *rules of reduction* RR 1-9 are to be understood in this way: to any sentence under consideration, the first of these rules whose application is possible must always be applied. Thus, the order of the rules must be taken into account (especially in the case of RR 9e). If the application of one of the rules (even out of turn, except in the case of RR 9e) leads from $\mathfrak{S}_1$

to $\mathfrak{S}_2$, then $\mathfrak{S}_1$ and $\mathfrak{S}_2$—as may easily be established—are always mutually derivable.

Let '$\mathfrak{S}_1$' designate any sentence in question. "$\mathfrak{A}_2$ results from $\mathfrak{A}_1$" means "$\mathfrak{S}_1$ is transformed in such a way that the (proper or improper) partial expression of $\mathfrak{S}_1$, $\mathfrak{A}_1$, is replaced by $\mathfrak{A}_2$."

RR 1. Every *defined symbol* is *eliminated* with the help of its definition. (In Language II, all definitions are explicit.)

RR 2. Construction of the *conjunctive standard form*:

a. $(\mathfrak{S}_2 \supset \mathfrak{S}_3) \cdot (\mathfrak{S}_3 \supset \mathfrak{S}_2)$ results from $\mathfrak{S}_2 \equiv \mathfrak{S}_3$.

b. $\sim \mathfrak{S}_2 \vee \mathfrak{S}_3$ results from $\mathfrak{S}_2 \supset \mathfrak{S}_3$.

c. $\sim \mathfrak{S}_2 \cdot \sim \mathfrak{S}_3$ results from $\sim (\mathfrak{S}_2 \vee \mathfrak{S}_3)$.

d. $\sim \mathfrak{S}_2 \vee \sim \mathfrak{S}_3$ results from $\sim (\mathfrak{S}_2 \cdot \mathfrak{S}_3)$.

e. $(\mathfrak{S}_2 \vee \mathfrak{S}_3) \cdot (\mathfrak{S}_2 \vee \mathfrak{S}_4)$ results from $\mathfrak{S}_2 \vee (\mathfrak{S}_3 \cdot \mathfrak{S}_4)$ or from $(\mathfrak{S}_3 \cdot \mathfrak{S}_4) \vee \mathfrak{S}_2$.

f. $\mathfrak{S}_2$ results from $\sim \sim \mathfrak{S}_2$.

RR 3. *Disjunction and conjunction.* Here disjunctions and conjunctions not merely of two, but of many, terms are meant; for instance, $(\mathfrak{S}_2 \vee \mathfrak{S}_3) \vee \mathfrak{S}_4$ or $\mathfrak{S}_2 \vee (\mathfrak{S}_3 \vee \mathfrak{S}_4)$ is called a three-termed disjunction having the three terms $\mathfrak{S}_2, \mathfrak{S}_3, \mathfrak{S}_4$. The cancellation of a term is understood to include the cancellation of the appertaining symbol of disjunction—or of conjunction—and of the brackets which thus become superfluous.

a. If two terms of a disjunction (or of a conjunction) are equal, then the first is cancelled.

b. If $\mathfrak{S}_2$ is a disjunction (or a conjunction) of which two terms have the form $\mathfrak{S}_3$ and $\sim \mathfrak{S}_3$, then $\mathfrak{N}$ (or $\sim \mathfrak{N}$ respectively) results from $\mathfrak{S}_2$. [$\mathfrak{N}$ is '$0 = 0$'.]

c. If $\mathfrak{S}_2$ is a disjunction of which one member is $\mathfrak{N}$, then $\mathfrak{N}$ results from $\mathfrak{S}_2$.

d. A term $\sim \mathfrak{N}$ of a disjunction is cancelled.

e. A term $\mathfrak{N}$ of a conjunction is cancelled.

f. If $\mathfrak{S}_2$ is a conjunction of which one member is $\sim \mathfrak{N}$. then $\sim \mathfrak{N}$ results from $\mathfrak{S}_2$.

RR 4. Every limited $\exists$-operator is eliminated with the help of PSII 9.

RR 5. *Equations.*

a. $\mathfrak{N}$ results from $\mathfrak{A}_1 = \mathfrak{A}_1$.

b. $\mathfrak{Z}_1 = \mathfrak{Z}_2$ results from $\mathfrak{Z}_1{}' = \mathfrak{Z}_2{}'$.

c. $\sim \mathfrak{N}$ results from $\mathfrak{nu} = \mathfrak{Z}_1{}^{\mathfrak{l}}$ or from $\mathfrak{Z}_1{}^{\mathfrak{l}} = \mathfrak{nu}$.

d. $\mathfrak{Z}_{\mathfrak{b}} = \mathfrak{Z}_1$ results from $\mathfrak{Z}_1 = \mathfrak{Z}_{\mathfrak{b}}$.

RR 6. *Elimination of the sentential variables* $\mathfrak{f}$.

a. Let $\mathfrak{f}_1$ be the first free $\mathfrak{f}$ in $\mathfrak{S}_1$; $\mathfrak{S}_1\!\left(\dfrac{\mathfrak{f}_1}{\mathfrak{N}}\right) \cdot \mathfrak{S}_1\!\left(\dfrac{\mathfrak{f}_1}{\sim\mathfrak{N}}\right)$ results from $\mathfrak{S}_1$.

b. $\mathfrak{S}_2\!\left(\dfrac{\mathfrak{f}_1}{\mathfrak{N}}\right) \cdot \mathfrak{S}_2\!\left(\dfrac{\mathfrak{f}_1}{\sim\mathfrak{N}}\right)$ results from $(\mathfrak{f}_1)\,(\mathfrak{S}_2)$.

c. $\mathfrak{S}_2\!\left(\dfrac{\mathfrak{f}_1}{\mathfrak{N}}\right) \vee \mathfrak{S}_2\!\left(\dfrac{\mathfrak{f}_1}{\sim\mathfrak{N}}\right)$ results from $(\exists \mathfrak{f}_1)\,(\mathfrak{S}_2)$.

RR 7. A K-operator is eliminated:

a. When it is limited, by means of PSII 14;

b. When it is unlimited, by means of PSII 15.

RR 8. Let $\mathfrak{S}_2$ be a sentence with a *limited universal operator* $(\mathfrak{Z}_1)\,\mathfrak{Z}_1(\mathfrak{S}_3)$.

a. Let $\mathfrak{Z}_1$ not occur as a free variable in $\mathfrak{S}_3$; $\mathfrak{S}_3$ results from $\mathfrak{S}_2$.

b. Let $\mathfrak{Z}_1$ be $\mathfrak{nu}$; $\mathfrak{S}_3\!\left(\dfrac{\mathfrak{Z}_1}{\mathfrak{nu}}\right)$ results from $\mathfrak{S}_2$.

c. Let $\mathfrak{Z}_1$ have the form $\mathfrak{Z}_2{}^{\mathfrak{l}}$; $(\mathfrak{Z}_1)\,\mathfrak{Z}_2(\mathfrak{S}_3) \cdot \mathfrak{S}_3\!\left(\dfrac{\mathfrak{Z}_1}{\mathfrak{Z}_2{}^{\mathfrak{l}}}\right)$ results from $\mathfrak{S}_2$.

d. $(\mathfrak{Z}_1)\,(\mathfrak{Z}_2)\,(\mathfrak{f}_1)\,(\exists\,\mathfrak{Z}_3)\,(\exists\,\mathfrak{Z}_4)\,\big[\sim (\mathfrak{f}_1\,(\mathfrak{nu}, \mathfrak{Z}_4) = \mathfrak{Z}_4)\vee \sim (\mathfrak{f}_1\,(\mathfrak{Z}_3{}^{\mathfrak{l}}, \mathfrak{Z}_4) = \mathfrak{f}_1\,(\mathfrak{Z}_3, \mathfrak{Z}_4){}^{\mathfrak{l}})\vee \sim (\mathfrak{f}_1\,(\mathfrak{Z}_1, \mathfrak{Z}_2) = \mathfrak{Z}_1)\vee \mathfrak{S}_3\big]$ results from $\mathfrak{S}_2$. (This sentence is equivalent in meaning to $(\mathfrak{Z}_1)\,[(\mathfrak{Z}_1 \leqq \mathfrak{Z}_1) \supset \mathfrak{S}_3]$; see definition of 'Grgl' on p. 59, and the transformation described in §29.)

RR 9. Construction of the so-called *standard form of the functional calculus* (see Hilbert [*Logik*] p. 63). Only *unlimited sentential operators* now occur as operators. Such an operator is called an *initial operator* of $\mathfrak{S}_1$ when either nothing, or only unlimited operators occur before it in $\mathfrak{S}_1$ (apart from brackets), and its operand (apart from brackets) extends to the end of $\mathfrak{S}_1$.

a. $\mathfrak{S}_2$ results from $(\mathfrak{v}_1)\,(\mathfrak{S}_2)$ or from $(\exists\,\mathfrak{v}_1)\,(\mathfrak{S}_2)$ if $\mathfrak{v}_1$ does not occur as a free variable in $\mathfrak{S}_2$.

b. Let the first operator variable in $\mathfrak{S}_1$ which is equal either to another operator variable, or to a variable which occurs as a free variable in $\mathfrak{S}_1$, be $\mathfrak{v}_1$. This operator variable together with all variables which are bound by it (that is to say all variables $\mathfrak{v}_1$ which occur as free variables in its operand) are replaced by variables which are equal to one another, but which are not equal to the other variables occurring in $\mathfrak{S}_1$.

c. $(\exists\, v_1)\,(\sim \mathfrak{S}_2)$ results from $\sim (v_1)\,(\mathfrak{S}_2)$.

d. $(v_1)\,(\sim \mathfrak{S}_2)$ results from $\sim (\exists\, v_1)\,(\mathfrak{S}_2)$.

e. The first operator in $\mathfrak{S}_1$ that is not an initial operator, together with the appertaining operand-brackets, is so transposed that it becomes the last initial operator.

A sentence is called *reduced* when none of the rules of reduction can be applied to it. The application of the rules to a sentence $\mathfrak{S}_1$ always leads by means of a finite number of steps to the ultimate form, namely to a reduced sentence; this we call the *reductum* of $\mathfrak{S}_1$, and the syntactical designation of it is: '$^{\mathfrak{R}}\mathfrak{S}_1$'.

Theorem 34b.1. $\mathfrak{S}_1$ and $^{\mathfrak{R}}\mathfrak{S}_1$ are always mutually derivable.

Theorem 34b.2. If $\mathfrak{S}_1$ is reduced, then:

A. $\mathfrak{S}_1$ has one of the following forms: 1. $(v_1)(\mathfrak{S}_2)$ or $(\exists\, v_1)(\mathfrak{S}_2)$, where v_1 occurs as a free variable in $\mathfrak{S}_2$ and where $\mathfrak{S}_2$ has one of the forms 1 to 9. —2. $\sim \mathfrak{S}_2$, where $\mathfrak{S}_2$ has one of the forms 5 to 9. —3. $\mathfrak{S}_2 \vee \mathfrak{S}_3$, where each of the two terms has one of the forms 2, 3, 5 to 9. —4. $\mathfrak{S}_2 \bullet \mathfrak{S}_3$, where each of the two terms has one of the forms 2 to 9. —5. $\mathfrak{Z}_1 = \mathfrak{Z}_2$, where both $\mathfrak{Z}$ are $\mathfrak{Z}_1$ and where at least one has the form d or e (see under B). —6. $\mathfrak{Z}_b = \mathfrak{Z}$. —7. $\mathfrak{Pr}_1 = \mathfrak{Pr}_2$. —8. $\mathfrak{Fu}_1 = \mathfrak{Fu}_2$. —9. $\mathfrak{Pr}(\mathfrak{Arg})$. —10. $\mathfrak{N}$. —11. $\sim \mathfrak{N}$; only in the case of this form does $\mathfrak{N}$ occur as a proper partial sentence.

B. Every $\mathfrak{Z}$ in $\mathfrak{S}_1$ has one of the following forms:

a. $\mathfrak{nu}$.—b. $\mathfrak{Z}_1{}^{\prime}$, where $\mathfrak{Z}_1$ has either the form a or the form b. (a and b are $\mathfrak{St}$.)—c. $\mathfrak{Z}_1{}^{\prime}$, where $\mathfrak{Z}_1$ has one of the forms c, d or e. —d. $\mathfrak{z}$.—e. $\mathfrak{Fu}(\mathfrak{Arg})$.—Every $\mathfrak{Z}_b$ in $\mathfrak{S}_1$ has the form c or e.

C. Every $\mathfrak{Pr}$ in $\mathfrak{S}_1$ is either an undefined $\mathfrak{pr}_b$, or a $\mathfrak{p}$, or of the form $\mathfrak{Fu}(\mathfrak{Arg})$.

D. Every $\mathfrak{Fu}$ in $\mathfrak{S}_1$ is either an undefined $\mathfrak{fu}_b$, or an $\mathfrak{f}$, or of the form $\mathfrak{Fu}(\mathfrak{Arg})$.

Theorem 34b.3. If $\mathfrak{S}_1$ is logical, reduced, and closed, then $\mathfrak{S}_1$ has one of the following forms: 1. $\mathfrak{A}_1, \mathfrak{A}_2, \dots \mathfrak{A}_n (\mathfrak{S}_2)$, where $n \geqq 1$, $\mathfrak{A}_i (i = 1$ to $n)$ is either (v_i) or $(\exists v_i)$, and $\mathfrak{S}_2$ contains no operators, but does contain the free variables $v_1, \dots v_n$; 2. $\mathfrak{N}$; 3. $\sim \mathfrak{N}$.

Theorem 34b.4. If $\mathfrak{S}_1$ is logical and definite, then $^{\mathfrak{R}}\mathfrak{S}_1$ is either $\mathfrak{N}$ or $\sim \mathfrak{N}$.

Theorem 34b.5. If by the application of a rule of reduction (even out of turn, except in the case of RR 9 e) a sentence of the form $\mathfrak{S}_2 \equiv \mathfrak{S}_2$ results from $\mathfrak{S}_1$, then $^\mathfrak{R}\mathfrak{S}_1$ is $\mathfrak{N}$.

Theorem 34b.6. Every *atomic* (but not every molecular) sentence is reduced (see p. 88).

Theorem 34b.7. If $\mathfrak{S}_1$ is reduced and contains no proper partial sentence, no variable, and at the most one $^1\mathfrak{pr}$ or one $^1\mathfrak{fu}$, but neither $^n\mathfrak{pr}$ nor $^n\mathfrak{fu}$ for $n > 1$, then $\mathfrak{S}_1$ is an atomic sentence.

§ 34c. EVALUATION

We shall not define the term 'analytic' explicitly, but instead we shall lay down rules to the effect that a sentence of a certain form is to be called an analytic sentence when such and such other sentences fulfil certain conditions—for instance, when they are analytic. We must do this in such a way that this process of successive reference comes to an end in a finite number of steps. We shall therefore proceed from a sentence to simpler sentences, for instance from $\mathfrak{S}_1$ to $^\mathfrak{R}\mathfrak{S}_1$, or from a reduced sentence to sentences which contain a lesser number of variables. If $\mathfrak{z}_1$, for example, occurs as a free variable in $\mathfrak{S}_1$, then we shall call $\mathfrak{S}_1$ analytic when and only when all sentences of the form $\mathfrak{S}_1\left(\begin{smallmatrix}\mathfrak{z}_1 \\ \mathfrak{St}\end{smallmatrix}\right)$ are analytic; thus we refer for instance from '$P_1(x)$' to the sentences of the infinite sentential class $\{$'$P_1(0)$', '$P_1(0^\mathsf{I})$', '$P_1(0^\mathsf{II})$',...$\}$. In this manner, the numerical variable is eliminated. In the case of a predicate- or functor-variable, however, the analogous method does not succeed; a fact which has been pointed out by Gödel. Let $\mathfrak{S}_1$ be, for example, '$M(F)$' (in words: "M is true for all properties"). Now, if from $\mathfrak{S}_1$ we refer back to the sentences '$M(P_1)$', '$M(P_2)$', and so on, which result from $\mathfrak{S}_1$ by substituting for 'F' each of the predicates of the type in question which are definable in II, in turn, then it may happen that, though all these sentences are true, '$M(F)$' is nevertheless false—in so far as M does not hold for a certain property for which no predicate can be defined in II. As a result of Gödel's researches it is certain, for instance, that for every arithmetical system there are *numerical properties which are not definable*, or, in other words, indefinable real numbers (see Theorem 60d.1, p. 221). Obviously it would not be consistent with the concept of validity of classical mathematics if we were to call the sentence: "All real numbers have the property M" an analytic sentence, when a real number can be stated (not, certainly, in the linguistic system concerned, but in a richer system) which does not possess this property. Instead we will follow Gödel's suggestions and define 'analytic' in such a way that '$M(F)$' is only called analytic if M holds for every numerical property irrespective of the limited domain of definitions which are possible in II.

Thus, in the case of a $\mathfrak{p}$, we cannot refer to substitutions but must proceed in a different way. Let 'F' occur in $\mathfrak{S}_1$ as the only free variable, a $^1\mathfrak{p}^1$ for instance. Then we shall not examine the defined predicates of this type, but instead all the possible valuations (*Bewertungen*) for 'F'. By a possible *valuation* (syntactical designation, $\mathfrak{B}$) for 'F' (i.e. a value assigned to 'F') we shall here understand a class (that is to say, a syntactical property) of accented expressions. Now if $\mathfrak{B}_1$ is a particular valuation for 'F' of this kind, and if at any place in $\mathfrak{S}_1$ 'F' occurs with $\mathfrak{St}_1$ as its argument (for example, in the partial sentence '$F(0^{II})$'), then this partial sentence is—so to speak—true on account of $\mathfrak{B}_1$, if $\mathfrak{St}_1$ is an element of $\mathfrak{B}_1$, and otherwise false. Now, by the evaluation of $\mathfrak{S}_1$ on the basis of $\mathfrak{B}_1$, we understand a transformation of $\mathfrak{S}_1$ in which the partial sentence mentioned is replaced by $\mathfrak{N}$ if $\mathfrak{St}_1$ is an element of $\mathfrak{B}_1$, and otherwise by $\sim \mathfrak{N}$. The definition of 'analytic' will be so framed that $\mathfrak{S}_1$ will be called analytic if and only if every sentence is analytic which results from $\mathfrak{S}_1$ by means of evaluation on the basis of any valuation for 'F'. And $\mathfrak{S}_1$ will be called contradictory when at least one of the resulting sentences is a contradictory sentence. We shall lay down analogous rules for the other $\mathfrak{p}$-types.

A valuation for a free $^1\mathfrak{f}_1^{\,1}$ will consist in a correlation by means of which to every $\mathfrak{St}$ an $\mathfrak{St}$ is univocally correlated. In the case of the evaluation of a sentence on the basis of a certain valuation $\mathfrak{B}_1$ for $\mathfrak{f}_1$, we shall replace a partial expression $\mathfrak{f}_1(\mathfrak{St}_1)$ by that $\mathfrak{St}_2$ which by means of $\mathfrak{B}_1$ is correlated to $\mathfrak{St}_1$. We shall lay down analogous rules for the other $\mathfrak{f}$-types.

Let $\mathfrak{pr}_1$ be descriptive; here a valuation of the same kind as for a $\mathfrak{p}$ is possible. Here also, $\mathfrak{S}_1$, in which $\mathfrak{pr}_1$ occurs, will be called analytic if the evaluation on the basis of any valuation for $\mathfrak{pr}_1$

leads to an analytic sentence. In contradistinction to the case of a p, however, $\mathfrak{S}_1$ will here only be called contradictory if the evaluation on the basis of any valuation for $\mathfrak{pr}_1$ leads to a contradictory sentence. For, in the case of a p, $\mathfrak{S}_1$ means: "So and so is true for every property", and this is false if it does not hold for even one instance. Here, in the case of the $\mathfrak{pr}_1$, however, $\mathfrak{S}_1$ means: "So and so is true for the particular property expressed by $\mathfrak{pr}_1$" where we have a $\mathfrak{pr}_b$ and therefore an empirically and not a logically determinable property; and this sentence is only contradictory—that is to say, false on logical grounds—if there exists no property for which $\mathfrak{S}_1$ is true.

On the basis of the foregoing considerations, we shall now proceed to lay down first the **rules of valuation, VR,** and then the *rules of evaluation,* EvR. Later, in connection with these, we shall formulate the definitions of 'analytic' and 'contradictory'. Symbols to which a valuation can be assigned are called convaluable [*bewertbare*] symbols (syntactical designation, '$\mathfrak{b}$'). The convaluable symbols in $\mathfrak{S}_1$ are all descriptive $\mathfrak{pr}_b$ and $\mathfrak{fu}_b$, and are also all $\mathfrak{z}$, $\mathfrak{p}$, and $\mathfrak{f}$ in those places where they occur as free variables in $\mathfrak{S}_1$.

VR 1. As the *valuation for a convaluable symbol* $\mathfrak{b}_1$, any valuation may be chosen which, in accordance with the following rules, is of the same type as $\mathfrak{b}_1$.

a. A valuation of the type 0 is an $\mathfrak{St}$.

b. A valuation of the type $t_1, t_2, \ldots t_n$ is an ordered n-ad of valuations which belong to the types t_1 to t_n respectively.

c. A valuation of the type (t_1) is a class of valuations of the type t_1.

d. A valuation of the type $(t_1 : t_2)$ is a many-one correlation by means of which, to every valuation of the type t_1, exactly one valuation of the type t_2 is correlated.

VR 2. Let $\mathfrak{S}_1$ be a *reduced sentence without operators*; for all $\mathfrak{b}$ of $\mathfrak{S}_1$, let valuations be chosen according to VR 1, and, in particular, let equal valuations be chosen for equal symbols. Then, by the following rules, a univocally determined valuation results for every partial expression in $\mathfrak{S}_1$ of the form $\mathfrak{z}$, $\mathfrak{Arg}$, $\mathfrak{Pr}$, or $\mathfrak{Fu}$.

a. $\mathfrak{nu}$ itself shall be taken as the valuation for $\mathfrak{nu}$.

b. Let $\mathfrak{St}_1$ be the valuation for $\mathfrak{z}_1$; then $\mathfrak{St}_1{}'$ shall be taken as the valuation for $\mathfrak{Z}_1{}^!$. (Thus, as the valuation for an $\mathfrak{St}$, the $\mathfrak{St}$ itself is always to be taken.)

c. Let the valuations $\mathfrak{B}_1$ to $\mathfrak{B}_n$ be assigned to the terms $\mathfrak{A}_1$ to $\mathfrak{A}_n$ of $\mathfrak{Arg}_1$. Then the ordered n-ad $\mathfrak{B}_1, \mathfrak{B}_2, \ldots \mathfrak{B}_n$ shall be taken as the valuation of $\mathfrak{Arg}_1$.

d. Let $\mathfrak{A}_1$ be an expression, $\mathfrak{Z}$, $\mathfrak{Pr}$, or $\mathfrak{Fu}$, of the form $\mathfrak{Fu}_2(\mathfrak{Arg}_1)$; and let the valuations $\mathfrak{B}_1$ and $\mathfrak{B}_2$ be assigned to $\mathfrak{Arg}_1$ and $\mathfrak{Fu}_2$ respectively. Then that valuation which is correlated by $\mathfrak{B}_2$ to the valuation $\mathfrak{B}_1$ shall be taken as the valuation for $\mathfrak{A}_1$.

According to these rules, the valuation of an expression $\mathfrak{A}_1$ is always of the same type as $\mathfrak{A}_1$ itself.

Examples. 1. In connection with VR 1 *a*: A $\mathfrak{B}$ for a free $\mathfrak{Z}$ belongs to the type 0, and is therefore an $\mathfrak{St}$, for example '0''' '.—2. In connection with VR 1 *c*: A $\mathfrak{B}$ for a $^1\mathfrak{pr}^1$, for example, for '*F*' in '*F(x)*', belongs to the type (0), and is therefore a class of $\mathfrak{St}$, that is to say, a syntactical property of expressions which only applies to accented expressions.—3. In connection with VR 1 *b*, *c*: A $\mathfrak{B}$ for a $^1\mathfrak{pr}^3$, for instance, for '*G*' in '*G(x, y, z)*', belongs to the type $(0, 0, 0)$ and is therefore a class of ordered triads (or a three-termed relation) of $\mathfrak{St}$—that is to say, a three-termed syntactical relation between accented expressions.—4. In connection with VR 1 *c*: A $\mathfrak{B}$ for a $^2\mathfrak{pr}^1$, for example, for '*M*' in '*M(F)*' belongs to the type $((0))$, and is therefore a class of classes of $\mathfrak{St}$.—5. In connection with VR 1 *d*: A $\mathfrak{B}$ for an $^1\mathfrak{fu}^2$, for instance, for '*f*' in '*f(x, y) = z*' belongs to the type $(0, 0 : 0)$, and is therefore a correlation by means of which an $\mathfrak{St}$ is univocally correlated to every ordered pair of $\mathfrak{St}$, and is therefore a many-many-one syntactical relation between $\mathfrak{St}$.—6. In connection with VR 2 *a*, *b*, *c*: Let the $\mathfrak{St}$ '0' ' and '0' be chosen as the valuations for '*x*' and '*y*' respectively, in accordance with VR 1 *a*. Then, in accordance with VR 2 *a*, *b*, *c*, the expression '0', 0, 0''' ' is the valuation for '*x, y*, 0''' '.—7. In connection with VR 2 *d*: We have already (p. 86) considered the sentence 'sm$(F, G)(x)$' ("*x* belongs to the sum of the classes *F* and *G*"). Instead of 'sm', we will now put a variable '*m*' of the same type $((0), (0) : (0))$: '*m*$(F, G)(x)$'. As an example of $\mathfrak{Fu}_2(\mathfrak{Arg}_1)$, let us take from this the $\mathfrak{Pr}$, '*m*(F, G)', which has the form $^2\mathfrak{f}^2(^1\mathfrak{p}^1, {}^1\mathfrak{p}^1)$ and is of the type (0). Let the class of the $\mathfrak{St}$ from '0' ' to '0'''' ' be chosen as the valuation of '*F*' (according to VR 1 *c*) and the class of the $\mathfrak{St}$ from '0''' ' to '0'''''' ' as the valuation of '*G*'. Then, according to VR 2 *c*, the valuation $\mathfrak{B}_1$ for $\mathfrak{Arg}_1$ ('*F, G*'; type (0), (0)) is the ordered pair consisting of the two aforesaid classes in the aforesaid order. For $\mathfrak{Fu}_2$ (i.e. '*m*'), let $\mathfrak{B}_2$ be arbitrarily chosen. According to VR 1 *d*, $\mathfrak{B}_2$ belongs to the type $((0), (0) : (0))$ and is a correlation by means of which a valuation of the type (0) is univocally correlated to every valuation of the type $((0), (0) : (0))$, and therefore also to $\mathfrak{B}_1$. We will assume that $\mathfrak{B}_2$ is chosen in such a way that the class of $\mathfrak{St}$ from '0|' to '0|||||' is correlated to $\mathfrak{B}_1$. (This would, for instance, correspond to the constant 'sm' as a value for 'm'.) Then according to VR 2 d, this class is the valuation for '$m(F, G)$'.

Let $\mathfrak{S}_1$ be a reduced sentence without operators; and let valuations for all $\mathfrak{b}$ in $\mathfrak{S}_1$ be chosen according to VR 1 and valuations for further expressions be determined in accordance with VR 2. Then the evaluation of $\mathfrak{S}_1$, on the basis of the valuations, consists in the transformation according to the following **rules of evaluation**, EvR 1, 2. If a non-reduced sentence results from a transformation, it must first be reduced and then transformed further.

EvR 1. Let a partial sentence $\mathfrak{S}_2$ have the form $\mathfrak{Pr}_2(\mathfrak{Arg}_1)$; and let the valuations for $\mathfrak{Arg}_1$ and $\mathfrak{Pr}_2$ be $\mathfrak{B}_1$ and $\mathfrak{B}_2$, respectively. If $\mathfrak{B}_1$ is an element of $\mathfrak{B}_2$ then $\mathfrak{S}_2$ is replaced by $\mathfrak{N}$; otherwise by $\sim\mathfrak{N}$.

EvR 2. Let a partial sentence $\mathfrak{S}_2$ have the form $\mathfrak{A}_1=\mathfrak{A}_2$, but not $\mathfrak{N}$; and let the valuations for $\mathfrak{A}_1$ and $\mathfrak{A}_2$ be $\mathfrak{B}_1$ and $\mathfrak{B}_2$ respectively. If $\mathfrak{B}_1$ and $\mathfrak{B}_2$ are identical, $\mathfrak{S}_2$ is replaced by $\mathfrak{N}$; otherwise by $\sim\mathfrak{N}$.

Theorem 34c.1. Let $\mathfrak{S}_1$ be a reduced sentence without operators. The evaluation of $\mathfrak{S}_1$, on the basis of any valuations for the $\mathfrak{b}$ which occur, leads in every case, in a finite number of steps, to the final result; this is either $\mathfrak{N}$ or $\sim\mathfrak{N}$.—For every $\mathfrak{a}_\mathfrak{b}$ and $\mathfrak{v}$ occurring in $\mathfrak{S}_1$ we have a valuation. From these valuations there results a valuation for every $\mathfrak{Z}$, $\mathfrak{Arg}$, $\mathfrak{Pr}$, and $\mathfrak{Fu}$ which occurs. Thus every partial sentence of the form $\mathfrak{Pr}(\mathfrak{Arg})$ is replaced either by $\mathfrak{N}$ or by $\sim\mathfrak{N}$; and likewise every partial sentence of the form $\mathfrak{A}_1=\mathfrak{A}_2$, since $\mathfrak{A}_1$ and $\mathfrak{A}_2$ have the form $\mathfrak{Z}$, $\mathfrak{Pr}$, or $\mathfrak{Fu}$. In this way, we get a concatenation of sentences $\mathfrak{N}$ by means of symbols of negation, disjunction, and conjunction, from which, by the application of RR 2 and 3, either $\mathfrak{N}$ or $\sim\mathfrak{N}$ results.

§ 34d. DEFINITION OF 'ANALYTIC IN II' AND 'CONTRADICTORY IN II'

The definitions of '*analytic*' and '*contradictory*' with reference to Language II are, as we have already mentioned, considerably more complicated than they are with reference to Language I. On the basis of the foregoing stipulations concerning reduction and evaluation, these definitions for II can now be embodied in the following rules DA 1–3. ('A' and 'C' are here used as abbreviations for "the necessary and sufficient condition under which $\Re_1$ or $\mathfrak{S}_1$ is analytic" and "...contradictory", respectively.)

DA 1. Definition of '**analytic**' and '**contradictory**' (in II) for a *sentential class* $\Re_1$. We distinguish the following cases.

A. *Not* all sentences of $\Re_1$ are *reduced*. A (or C): The class of the reducta of the sentences of $\Re_1$ is analytic (or contradictory, respectively).

B. All sentences of $\Re_1$ are *reduced* and *logical*. A: Every sentence of $\Re_1$ is analytic; C: At least one sentence of $\Re_1$ is contradictory.

C. The sentences of $\Re_1$ are *reduced*, and at least one of them is *descriptive*.

a. An *open* sentence occurs in $\Re_1$. Let $\Re_2$ be the class which results from $\Re_1$ by replacing every sentence $\mathfrak{S}_i$ by $(\,)\,(\mathfrak{S}_i)$ (see p. 94). A (or C): $\Re_2$ is analytic (or contradictory, respectively).

b. The sentences of $\Re_1$ are *closed*. A: For every sentence $\mathfrak{S}_i$ of $\Re_1$ the logical sentence is analytic that results from $\mathfrak{S}_i$ by replacing every descriptive symbol by a variable of the same type, whose design does not occur in $\mathfrak{S}_i$, equal symbols being replaced by equal variables and unequal symbols by unequal variables. C: For the arbitrary choice of one valuation for every descriptive symbol occurring in $\Re_1$ (the same valuation being taken for equal symbols) there is at least one sentence in $\Re_1$ which is contradictory in respect of this valuation (see DA 3).

DA 2. Definition of 'analytic' and 'contradictory' (in II) for a *sentence* $\mathfrak{S}_1$.

A. $\mathfrak{S}_1$ is *not reduced*. A (or C): $^{\Re}\mathfrak{S}_1$ is analytic (or contradictory, respectively).

B. $\mathfrak{S}_1$ is *reduced* and *open*. A (or C): $(\,)\,(\mathfrak{S}_1)$ is analytic (or contradictory, respectively).

C. $\mathfrak{S}_1$ is reduced, *closed* and *logical*.

a. $\mathfrak{S}_1$ has the form $(\mathfrak{v}_1)\,(\mathfrak{S}_2)$. A: $\mathfrak{S}_2$ is analytic in respect of every valuation of $\mathfrak{v}_1$; C: $\mathfrak{S}_2$ is contradictory in respect of at least one valuation of $\mathfrak{v}_1$.

b. $\mathfrak{S}_1$ has the form $(\exists \mathfrak{v}_1)\,(\mathfrak{S}_2)$. A: $\mathfrak{S}_2$ is analytic in respect of at least one valuation of $\mathfrak{v}_1$; C: $\mathfrak{S}_2$ is contradictory in respect of every valuation of $\mathfrak{v}_1$.

c. $\mathfrak{S}_1$ has the form $\mathfrak{N}$ or $\sim \mathfrak{N}$. A: Form $\mathfrak{N}$; C: Form $\sim \mathfrak{N}$.

D. $\mathfrak{S}_1$ is reduced, *closed* and *descriptive*. A (or C): the class $\{\mathfrak{S}_1\}$ is analytic (or contradictory, respectively).

DA 3. Definition of "analytic (or contradictory) in respect of certain valuations" for a reduced sentence $\mathfrak{S}_1$. (These terms only serve as auxiliary terms for DA 1, 2.) 'A – $\mathfrak{B}_1$' and 'C – $\mathfrak{B}_1$' here mean: "necessary and sufficient condition under which $\mathfrak{S}_1$ is analytic (or contradictory, respectively) in respect of $\mathfrak{B}_1$", where $\mathfrak{B}_1$ is a series of valuations, namely, that consisting of one valuation for each symbolic design $\mathfrak{b}$ occurring in $\mathfrak{S}_1$ (hence not for the bound variables).

A. $\mathfrak{S}_1$ has the form $(\mathfrak{v}_2)\,(\mathfrak{S}_2)$. A – $\mathfrak{B}_1$: for every valuation $\mathfrak{B}_2$ for $\mathfrak{v}_2$, $\mathfrak{S}_2$ is analytic in respect of $\mathfrak{B}_1$ and $\mathfrak{B}_2$. C – $\mathfrak{B}_1$: for at least one valuation $\mathfrak{B}_2$ for $\mathfrak{v}_2$, $\mathfrak{S}_2$ is contradictory in respect of $\mathfrak{B}_1$ and $\mathfrak{B}_2$.

B. $\mathfrak{S}_1$ has the form $(\exists \mathfrak{v}_2)\,(\mathfrak{S}_2)$. A – $\mathfrak{B}_1$: for at least one valuation $\mathfrak{B}_2$ for $\mathfrak{v}_2$, $\mathfrak{S}_2$ is analytic in respect of $\mathfrak{B}_1$ and $\mathfrak{B}_2$. C – $\mathfrak{B}_1$: for every valuation $\mathfrak{B}_2$ for $\mathfrak{v}_2$, $\mathfrak{S}_2$ is contradictory in respect of $\mathfrak{B}_1$ and $\mathfrak{B}_2$.

C. $\mathfrak{S}_1$ contains *no operator*. A – $\mathfrak{B}_1$ (or C – $\mathfrak{B}_1$): The result of the evaluation of $\mathfrak{S}_1$ on the basis of $\mathfrak{B}_1$ is $\mathfrak{N}$ (or $\sim \mathfrak{N}$, respectively).

Let $\mathfrak{S}_1$ (or $\mathfrak{R}_1$) be arbitrarily given; and let it be asked whether $\mathfrak{S}_1$ (or $\mathfrak{R}_1$, respectively) is either analytic, or contradictory, or neither, i.e. synthetic. Then in the first place one and only one of the rules DA is applicable (for DA 2 *Ca–c* this results from Theorem 34 *b*.3). If this rule is DA 2 *Cc* or DA 3 *C* the question will be decided by means of this rule. Every one of the remaining rules, on the other hand, will refer back univocally to a second question concerning one or more other $\mathfrak{S}$ or a $\mathfrak{R}$. Thus for $\mathfrak{S}_1$ or $\mathfrak{R}_1$, the univocal result is a sequence of questions which is always finite and which terminates with one of those two final rules. For an arbitrarily given sentence or sentential class, a sufficient and necessary criterion for 'analytic'—and likewise for 'contradictory'—can be formulated on the basis of this sequence of questions. (An example of this is to be found in the proof of Theorem 34 *h*.1.) These terms are thus univocally defined for all cases by means of the rules DA. But there is *no general method of resolution* for the individual questions, far less for the whole criterion. The terms 'analytic' and 'contradictory' are *indefinite*.

We have formulated the definition of 'analytic' in a word-language which does not possess a strictly determined syntax. The following questions now present themselves. 1. Can this definition be translated into a strictly formalized syntax-language, S_1? 2. Can Language II itself be used as the syntax-language for this purpose? Later we shall show (Theorem 60 *c*.1) that for no (non-contradictory) language S can the definition of 'analytic in S' be formulated in S itself as the syntax-language. Hence the second question must be answered in the negative. On the other hand, the first question can be answered in the affirmative provided that S_1 has adequate means at its disposal, especially variables p and f of certain types which do not occur in II.

If we take as our object-language not the whole of Language II but the single concentric regions (see p. 88), then for our syntax-language we have no need to go outside the domain of II. It is true that the concept 'analytic in II_n' is not definable for any *n* in II_n itself as syntax-language, but it is always definable in a more extensive region II_{n+m} (perhaps always in II_{n+1}). Hence every definition of one of the concepts 'analytic in II_n' (for the various *n*), and also every criterion for 'analytic in II' with respect to a particular sentence of II, is formulable in II as syntax-language.

A certain point in the given definition of 'analytic in II' may appear dubious. For the sake of simplicity we will consider the corresponding definition of 'analytic in II_1'. Let a language S be used as a formalized syntax-language (for example, a more extensive region of II, or II itself). Since in II_1 free ^{1}p and undefined ^{1}pr$_b$ occur, the definition of 'analytic in II_1' (corresponding to DA 1 *Cb*, 2 *Ca*) will contain phrases such as "for every valuation for a ^{1}p^1 ..."; this, according to VR 1 *a* and VR 1 *c*, is the same as saying "for all syntactical properties of accented expressions...". Now what is meant by this phrase and how is it to be formulated in the symbolic language S? If we said instead merely "for all syntactical properties which are definable in S ...", then the definition of 'analytic in II₁' would not effect what is required of it. For just as for every language there are numerical properties which are not definable in it (see p. 106), so there are also syntactical properties which are not definable in S. Thus it might happen that the sentence '$\mathfrak{S}_1$ is analytic in II₁' was true (analytic) in the syntax-language S, and yet false (contradictory) in a richer syntax-language S', namely if the phrase, "for all definable syntactical properties...", contained in the criterion for that sentence, although valid for all the properties definable in S, was not valid for a certain property which is only definable in S'. Thus the definition must not be limited to the syntactical properties which are definable in S, but must refer to all syntactical properties whatsoever. But do we not by this means arrive at a Platonic absolutism of ideas, that is, at the conception that the totality of all properties, which is non-denumerable and therefore can never be exhausted by definitions, is something which subsists in itself, independent of all construction and definition? From our point of view, this metaphysical conception—as it is maintained by Ramsey for instance (see Carnap [*Logizismus*] p. 102)—is definitely excluded. We have here absolutely nothing to do with the metaphysical question as to whether properties exist in themselves or whether they are created by definition. The question must rather be put as follows: can the phrase "for all properties..." (interpreted as "for all properties whatsoever" and not "for all properties which are definable in S") be formulated in the symbolic syntax-language S? This question may be answered in the affirmative. The formulation is effected by the help of a universal operator with a variable p, i.e. by means of '$(F)(...)$', for example. (That this phrase has in the language S the meaning intended is formally established by the fact that the definition of 'analytic in S' is formulated in the wider syntax-language S_2, again in accordance with previous considerations (pp. 106 f.), not by substitutions of the pr of S, but with the help of valuations.) This is correspondingly true for the valuations of higher types in the wider language regions.

§ 34*e*. On Analytic and Contradictory Sentences of Language II

$\mathfrak{S}_1$ (or $\mathfrak{R}_1$) is called *L-determinate* if $\mathfrak{S}_1$ (or $\mathfrak{R}_1$, respectively) is either analytic or contradictory. $\mathfrak{S}_1$ (or $\mathfrak{R}_1$) is called **synthetic** if $\mathfrak{S}_1$ (or $\mathfrak{R}_1$, respectively) is not L-determinate, and therefore is neither analytic nor contradictory.

Theorem 34e.1. (*a*) $\mathfrak{S}_1$ and $^{\mathfrak{R}}\mathfrak{S}_1$ are either both analytic, or both contradictory, or both synthetic.—(*b*) Likewise $\mathfrak{S}_1$ and $(\,)\,(\mathfrak{S}_1)$.—(*c*) Likewise $\mathfrak{S}_1$ and $\{\mathfrak{S}_1\}$.

Theorem 34e.2. (*a*) If $\mathfrak{S}_1$ is analytic, then $\sim\mathfrak{S}_1$ is contradictory.—(*b*) If $\mathfrak{S}_1$ is contradictory and closed, then $\sim\mathfrak{S}_1$ is analytic.

Theorem 34e.3. If every sentence of $\mathfrak{R}_1$ is analytic, then $\mathfrak{R}_1$ also is analytic; and conversely.

Theorem 34e.4. A $\mathfrak{R}_I$ is contradictory if and only if at least one sentence belonging to it is contradictory. A $\mathfrak{R}_b$ can be contradictory even if no sentence belonging to it is contradictory. (See the remarks concerning Theorem 14.4.)

Theorem 34e.5. A closed sentence $\mathfrak{S}_1$ is analytic (or contradictory) if (but not only if) the truth-value table (§ 5) of $\mathfrak{S}_1$, in respect of partial sentences from which $\mathfrak{S}_1$ is constructed with the help of symbols of negation and junction, always yields 'T' (or 'F', respectively) for all admissible distributions of 'T' and 'F'. In this connection, a distribution is called admissible if it always assigns 'T' to an analytic partial sentence, 'F' to a contradictory partial sentence and 'T' or 'F' to a synthetic partial sentence.

Theorem 34e.6. (*a*) $\mathfrak{S}_1 \vee \mathfrak{S}_2$ is analytic if (but not only if) $\mathfrak{S}_1$ or $\mathfrak{S}_2$ is analytic.—(*b*) $\mathfrak{S}_1 \vee \mathfrak{S}_2$ is contradictory if (and only if) $\mathfrak{S}_1$ and $\mathfrak{S}_2$ are contradictory.

Theorem 34e.7. $\mathfrak{A}_1 = \mathfrak{A}_1$ is always analytic.

Theorem 34e.8. Let $\mathfrak{R}_1$ be a sub-class of $\mathfrak{R}_2$. (*a*) If $\mathfrak{R}_2$ is analytic, then $\mathfrak{R}_1$ is likewise analytic.—(*b*) If $\mathfrak{R}_1$ is contradictory then $\mathfrak{R}_2$ is likewise contradictory.

Theorem 34e.9. If $\mathfrak{R}_1 + \mathfrak{R}_2$ is contradictory and $\mathfrak{R}_1$ is analytic, then $\mathfrak{R}_2$ is contradictory.

We have already seen that the concepts 'demonstrable' and 'refutable' do not fulfil the requirement that they constitute an exhaustive distribution of all logical sentences (which also include all mathematical sentences) into mutually exclusive classes. This circumstance provided the reason for the introduction of the concepts 'analytic' and 'contradictory'. We must now determine whether such a classification is effected by these new concepts; the result of this test is given in Theorems 10 and 11.

Theorem 34e.10. No sentence (and no sentential class) is at the same time both analytic and contradictory.—A testing of the single rules DA one by one shows that the conditions for 'analytic' and those for 'contradictory' are mutually exclusive in every case provided that they are mutually exclusive in that case to which further reference is made. In the last stage, namely DA 2 Cc or 3 C, they are definitely mutually exclusive; and therefore they are so in general. [In contradistinction to the analogous theorem concerning 'demonstrable' and 'refutable', Theorem 10 does not require the assumption that Language II is non-contradictory.]

Theorem 34e.11. Every logical sentence is L-determinate, that is to say it is either analytic or contradictory. (There is, however, no general method of resolution.)—For the purpose of indirect proof, let us assume that $\mathfrak{S}_1$ were both logical and synthetic. Then according to DA 2 A, $^{\mathfrak{R}}\mathfrak{S}_1$ would be both logical and synthetic; and, according to DA 2 B, ( ) $\left(^{\mathfrak{R}}\mathfrak{S}_1\right)$ also would be both logical and synthetic. Let this be $\mathfrak{S}_2$. Then $\mathfrak{S}_2$ would be logical, reduced, and closed, and therefore, by Theorem 34 b.3, it would have one of the following forms: 1. $\mathfrak{A}_1\mathfrak{A}_2...\mathfrak{A}_n(\mathfrak{S}_3)$, where $n \geqq 1, \mathfrak{A}_i$ ($i = 1$ to n) is either ($\mathfrak{v}_i$) or ($\exists \mathfrak{v}_i$), and $\mathfrak{S}_3$ contains no operators; 2. $\mathfrak{R}$; 3. $\sim \mathfrak{R}$. According to DA 2 Cc, the forms $\mathfrak{R}$ and $\sim \mathfrak{R}$ are excluded here, since $\mathfrak{S}_2$ is supposed to be synthetic. Hence $\mathfrak{S}_2$ would have the first-mentioned form. Then, in accordance with DA 2 Ca and b, in respect of at least one series of valuations for $\mathfrak{v}_1, ... \mathfrak{v}_n$, $\mathfrak{S}_3$ must be neither analytic nor contradictory. The evaluation of $\mathfrak{S}_3$ on the basis of such a series of valuations would, in accordance with DA 3 C, lead to a sentence which is neither $\mathfrak{R}$ nor $\sim \mathfrak{R}$. But, by Theorem 34 c.1, that is impossible.

According to Theorem 11 synthetic sentences are only to be found amongst the descriptive sentences.

Theorem 34e.12. If a definite $\mathfrak{S}_l$ is analytic, then it is also demonstrable.—(By DA 2 A, Theorem 34 b.4 and 34 b.1.) On the other hand a definite $\mathfrak{S}_b$ may be analytic without being demonstrable.—Amongst the indefinite $\mathfrak{S}_I$ there are analytic ones which are non-demonstrable, also some of the simple form $\mathfrak{pr}_1(\mathfrak{z}_1)$, where $\mathfrak{pr}_1$ is a definite $\mathfrak{pr}_I$ (compare the examples in § 36). In a case like this, $\mathfrak{pr}_1\left(\mathfrak{fu}_1(\mathfrak{nu})\right)$, where $\mathfrak{fu}_1$ is any undefined $\mathfrak{fu}_b$, is a definite $\mathfrak{S}_b$ which is analytic but not demonstrable.

Theorem 34e.13. Every definite $\mathfrak{S}_I$ is resoluble, that is to say, it is either demonstrable or refutable. For this case a general method of resolution exists.

§ 34*f*. CONSEQUENCE IN LANGUAGE II

Two or more sentences are called **incompatible** with one another if the class constituted by them is contradictory; otherwise they are called mutually **compatible.**

A sentence is (in material interpretation) a logical consequence of certain other sentences if, and only if, its antithesis is incompatible with these sentences. Hence we define as follows: $\mathfrak{S}_1$ is called a **consequence** of $\mathfrak{R}_1$ in II, if $\mathfrak{R}_1+\left\{\sim()\left(\mathfrak{S}_1\right)\right\}$ is contradictory. $\mathfrak{S}_1$ is called **independent** of $\mathfrak{R}_1$, if $\mathfrak{S}_1$ is neither a consequence of $\mathfrak{R}_1$ nor incompatible with $\mathfrak{R}_1$. We shall use the defined terms not only in the case of a sentential class $\mathfrak{R}_1$ but also in the case of one or more sentences (as premisses). For instance, we call $\mathfrak{S}_3$ a consequence of $\mathfrak{S}_1$ and $\mathfrak{S}_2$ if $\mathfrak{S}_3$ is a consequence of $\left\{\mathfrak{S}_1, \mathfrak{S}_2\right\}$.

It happens sometimes that $\mathfrak{S}_1$ is a consequence of an infinite sentential class $\mathfrak{R}_1$, without being a consequence of any proper sub-class of $\mathfrak{R}_1$. [*Example.* Let $\mathfrak{pr}_1$ be an undefined $\mathfrak{pr}_b$, $\mathfrak{R}_1$ be the class of the sentences $\mathfrak{pr}_1(\mathfrak{St})$, and $\mathfrak{S}_1$ be $\mathfrak{pr}_1(\mathfrak{z}_1)$.] It is thus essential that the definition of 'consequence', as opposed to that of 'derivable', should refer not only to finite but also to infinite classes.

The concept 'consequence' is related to the concept 'derivable' as 'analytic' is to 'demonstrable'; that is to say, it is more comprehensive, but on the other hand it has the disadvantage of possessing a much more complicated definition and a higher degree of indefiniteness. 'Derivable' is defined as a finite chain of the relation 'directly derivable'. 'Consequence' might be analogously defined as a chain of a simpler relation 'direct consequence'.

'Analytic' would then be defined as 'consequence of the sentential null class' and 'contradictory' as 'sentence of which every sentence is a consequence'. In this way the definitions for Language I were previously formulated (§ 14). In the case of the definitions just given for Language II we took a different course, and for the sake of simplifying the technical process first defined 'analytic' and 'contradictory' and from them the term 'consequence'. The question now is whether the term 'consequence' as so defined is related to the terms 'analytic' and 'contradictory' in the way described; that this is the case is expressed in Theorems 5 and 7. Further, it must be shown that the relation 'consequence' possesses a certain kind of *transitivity*. This would be obvious in the case of the first method of definition, but here the proof is not so simple (Theorem 8).

Theorem 34f.1. If $\mathfrak{S}_1$ is an element of $\mathfrak{R}_1$, then $\mathfrak{S}_1$ is a consequence of $\mathfrak{R}_1$. $\mathfrak{S}_1$ is always a consequence of $\mathfrak{S}_1$.

Theorem 34f.2. If $\mathfrak{R}_1$ is analytic, and $\mathfrak{S}_1$ a consequence of $\mathfrak{R}_1$, then $\mathfrak{S}_1$ is also analytic.—$\mathfrak{R}_1 + \left\{ \sim()(\mathfrak{S}_1) \right\}$ is contradictory; therefore, by Theorems 34e.9 and 34e.1c, $\sim()(\mathfrak{S}_1)$ is contradictory, and hence, by Theorem 34e.2b, $\mathfrak{S}_1$ analytic.

Theorem 34f.3. If $\mathfrak{S}_1$ is contradictory and a consequence of $\mathfrak{R}_1$, then $\mathfrak{R}_1$ is also contradictory.—According to Theorem 34e.1b and 2b, $\sim()(\mathfrak{S}_1)$ is analytic, and hence, by Theorem 34e.9, $\mathfrak{R}_1$ is contradictory.

Theorem 34f.4. Let $\mathfrak{S}_2$ be a consequence of $\mathfrak{S}_1$; if $\mathfrak{S}_1$ is analytic, then $\mathfrak{S}_2$ is likewise analytic; if $\mathfrak{S}_2$ is contradictory, then $\mathfrak{S}_1$ is likewise contradictory.

Theorem 34f.5. If $\mathfrak{S}_1$ is a consequence of the sentential null class, then $\mathfrak{S}_1$ is analytic; and conversely.—This follows from Theorem 34e.2.

Theorem 34f.6. If $\mathfrak{S}_1$ is analytic, then $\mathfrak{S}_1$ is a consequence of every sentence; and conversely.

Theorem 34f.7. If $\mathfrak{R}_1$ (or $\mathfrak{S}_1$) is contradictory, then every sentence is a consequence of $\mathfrak{R}_1$ (or of $\mathfrak{S}_1$, respectively); and conversely.—By Theorem 34e.8b. Converse by Theorem 3.

Theorem 34f.8. If $\mathfrak{S}_3$ is a consequence of $\mathfrak{R}_2$, and every sentence of $\mathfrak{R}_2$ is a consequence of $\mathfrak{R}_1$, then $\mathfrak{S}_3$ is a consequence of $\mathfrak{R}_1$.

Proof. Let $\mathfrak{R}_4$ be the class of the sentences $()\left(^{\mathfrak{R}}\mathfrak{S}_i\right)$ for every $\mathfrak{S}_i$ of $\mathfrak{R}_1$; likewise $\mathfrak{R}_5$ for every $\mathfrak{S}_i$ of $\mathfrak{R}_2$; and let $\mathfrak{S}_6$ be $()\left(^{\mathfrak{R}}\mathfrak{S}_3\right)$.

Then $\mathfrak{S}_6$ and all sentences of $\mathfrak{R}_4$ and $\mathfrak{R}_5$ are reduced and closed. Let a series of valuations for the $\mathfrak{b}$ (here descriptive symbols) of a sentence or a sentential class be designated by '$\mathfrak{B}$' with the corresponding suffix. Assumptions: 1. $\mathfrak{R}_2 + \{\sim()(\mathfrak{S}_3)\}$ is contradictory; hence also $\mathfrak{R}_5 + \{\sim\mathfrak{S}_6\}$. 2. For every $\mathfrak{S}_i$ of $\mathfrak{R}_2$, $\mathfrak{R}_1 + \{\sim()(\mathfrak{S}_i)\}$ is contradictory; accordingly for every $\mathfrak{S}_j$ of $\mathfrak{R}_5$, $\mathfrak{R}_4 + \{\sim\mathfrak{S}_j\}$ is contradictory. Assertion: $\mathfrak{R}_1 + \{\sim()(\mathfrak{S}_3)\}$ is contradictory; that is to say, $\mathfrak{R}_4 + \{\sim\mathfrak{S}_6\}$ is contradictory. This, according to DA 1 *Cb*, means: for any choice of $\mathfrak{B}_4$ and $\mathfrak{B}_6$, either $\sim\mathfrak{S}_6$ or a sentence of $\mathfrak{R}_4$ is contradictory in respect of $\mathfrak{B}_4$ or $\mathfrak{B}_6$, respectively. For the purpose of indirect proof, let us suppose the contrary, namely: $\mathfrak{B}_4$ and $\mathfrak{B}_6$ are given in such a way that neither $\sim\mathfrak{S}_6$ nor any sentence of $\mathfrak{R}_4$ is contradictory in respect of $\mathfrak{B}_4 + \mathfrak{B}_6$. Assumption 1 means: for any $\mathfrak{B}_5$ and $\mathfrak{B}_6$, either $\sim\mathfrak{S}_6$ or a sentence of $\mathfrak{R}_5$ is contradictory in respect of $\mathfrak{B}_5$ or of $\mathfrak{B}_6$, respectively. Assumption 2 means: for every $\mathfrak{S}_j$ of $\mathfrak{R}_5$ in the case of any choice of $\mathfrak{B}_4$ and $\mathfrak{B}_j$, either $\sim\mathfrak{S}_j$ or a sentence of $\mathfrak{R}_4$ is contradictory in respect of $\mathfrak{B}_j$ or $\mathfrak{B}_4$, respectively. Hence, on our supposition, on the one hand, for any arbitrary $\mathfrak{B}_5$, a sentence of $\mathfrak{R}_5$, say $\mathfrak{S}_7$, would be contradictory in respect of $\mathfrak{B}_5$; and on the other hand, as for every $\mathfrak{S}_j$ of $\mathfrak{R}_5$, so also for $\mathfrak{S}_7$ in the case of an arbitrary $\mathfrak{B}_7$ (contained in $\mathfrak{B}_5$), $\sim\mathfrak{S}_7$ would be contradictory in respect of $\mathfrak{B}_7$. But this is impossible; for since $\mathfrak{S}_7$ is closed, $\mathfrak{S}_7$ and $\sim\mathfrak{S}_7$ cannot both be contradictory in respect of the same valuation (see Theorem 34*e*.2*b*).

Theorem 34f.9. (*a*) If $\mathfrak{S}_1 \supset \mathfrak{S}_2$ is analytic, then $\mathfrak{S}_2$ is a consequence of $\mathfrak{S}_1$.—(*b*) If $\mathfrak{S}_1$ is closed and if $\mathfrak{S}_2$ is a consequence of $\mathfrak{S}_1$, then $\mathfrak{S}_1 \supset \mathfrak{S}_2$ is analytic.

Proof of 9a. For a closed $\mathfrak{S}_1$ the proof is simple. For an open $\mathfrak{S}_1$ the procedure is as follows. Since $\mathfrak{S}_1 \supset \mathfrak{S}_2$ is analytic, $()(\sim\mathfrak{S}_1 \vee \mathfrak{S}_2)$ also is analytic; further, $\sim()(\mathfrak{S}_1) \vee ()(\mathfrak{S}_2)$ also (the proof is too long to be given here). According to Theorem 34*e*.2*b* the negation of the last-named sentence is contradictory; hence $()(\mathfrak{S}_1) \cdot \sim()(\mathfrak{S}_2)$ is likewise contradictory; hence also the class $\{()(\mathfrak{S}_1), \sim()(\mathfrak{S}_2)\}$, and hence $\{\mathfrak{S}_1, \sim()(\mathfrak{S}_2)\}$. Therefore $\mathfrak{S}_2$ is a consequence of $\mathfrak{S}_1$.

Proof of 9b. $\{\mathfrak{S}_1, \sim()(\mathfrak{S}_2)\}$ is contradictory, hence $\mathfrak{S}_1 \cdot \sim()(\mathfrak{S}_2)$ is also contradictory. Since this sentence is closed, according to Theorem 34*e*.2*b* its negation is analytic, and consequently $\sim \mathfrak{S}_1 \vee (\,) (\mathfrak{S}_2)$ is likewise analytic. Therefore, since $\mathfrak{S}_1$ is closed, $\sim \mathfrak{S}_1 \vee \mathfrak{S}_2$ is analytic, hence also $\mathfrak{S}_1 \supset \mathfrak{S}_2$.

Theorem 34f.10. $\mathfrak{S}_1$ and $(\mathfrak{z}_1)(\mathfrak{S}_1)$ are consequences of the class of the sentences $\mathfrak{S}_1\left(\dfrac{\mathfrak{z}_1}{\mathfrak{S}t}\right)$.—This corresponds to the rule DC 2 for Language I (p. 38).

§ 34g. Logical Content

We call the class of the non-analytic sentences (of II) which are consequences of $\mathfrak{S}_1$ or $\mathfrak{R}_1$ (in II) the **content** of $\mathfrak{S}_1$ or $\mathfrak{R}_1$, respectively (in II). (For the reason for this definition see pp. 41 f.) Let '*equipollent*' and '*synonymous*' be given definitions for II analogous to those for I (see p. 42). These formally defined terms correspond exactly to what is usually designated in material interpretation as 'equivalent in sense', or 'equivalent in meaning', respectively, so long as 'equivalent in meaning' is understood as "of equivalent logical meaning" and not as "designating the same object". In order that two object- (or number-) designations $\mathfrak{A}_1$ and $\mathfrak{A}_2$ may be synonymous, $\mathfrak{A}_1 = \mathfrak{A}_2$ not only must be true but must also be analytic. (See § 75, examples 6 and 7.)

We say that $\mathfrak{S}_1$ or $\mathfrak{R}_1$ has *null content* if its content is the null class. By *total content*, we understand the class of all non-analytic sentences.

Theorem 34g.1. If two sentences are consequences of one another, then they are also equipollent; and conversely.

Theorem 34g.2. If two sentences are equipollent, then they are synonymous; and conversely.

Theorem 34g.3. (*a*) If $\mathfrak{A}_1 = \mathfrak{A}_2$ is analytic, then $\mathfrak{A}_1$ and $\mathfrak{A}_2$ are synonymous.—(*b*) If $\mathfrak{A}_1$ and $\mathfrak{A}_2$ are synonymous, and if $\mathfrak{A}_1 = \mathfrak{A}_2$ is a sentence, then this sentence is analytic.

Theorem 34g.4. If $\mathfrak{S}_1 \equiv \mathfrak{S}_2$ is analytic, then $\mathfrak{S}_1$ and $\mathfrak{S}_2$ are equipollent; and conversely.

Theorem 34g.5. If $\mathfrak{S}_1$ (or $\mathfrak{R}_1$) is analytic, then $\mathfrak{S}_1$ (or $\mathfrak{R}_1$, respectively) has *null content*; and conversely.

Theorem 34g.6. If $\mathfrak{S}_1$ (or $\mathfrak{R}_1$) is contradictory, then $\mathfrak{S}_1$ (or $\mathfrak{R}_1$, respectively) has *total content*; and conversely.

Theorem 34g.7. $\mathfrak{S}_1 \cdot \mathfrak{S}_2 \cdot \ldots \mathfrak{S}_n$ and $\{\mathfrak{S}_1, \mathfrak{S}_2, \ldots \mathfrak{S}_n\}$ are equipollent.

Theorem 34g.8. The content of a disjunction is the product of the contents of the terms of the disjunction.— If the product of the contents of several sentences is null (and consequently, according to Theorem 8, the disjunction of the sentences is analytic), we say that the sentences have mutually *exclusive contents*.

§ 34*h*. THE PRINCIPLES OF INDUCTION AND SELECTION ARE ANALYTIC

We shall now prove that the Principle of Complete Induction and the Principle of Selection are both analytic. These principles are included amongst the primitive sentences which were previously stated for Language II (PSII 20 and 21, § 30). By the example of the Principle of Induction, we shall show how the criterion of whether a certain particular sentence is analytic or not is developed step by step by means of the DA rules. The proofs of Theorems 1 and 2 are interesting because they involve a fundamental question: in each one of these proofs, there is used a theorem of the syntax-language which corresponds with the theorem of the object-language whose analytic character is to be proved.

Theorem 34h.1. *The Principle of Complete Induction* (PSII 20) is analytic.

Construction of the criterion. Let us call PSII 20 $\mathfrak{S}_1$. The necessary and sufficient criterion of the analytic character of $\mathfrak{S}_1$ may be transformed in the following manner, each step being univocally established by means of the DA rules. By DA 2 A the criterion is: $\mathfrak{R}\mathfrak{S}_1$ must be analytic. Let this be $\mathfrak{S}_2$. We find $\mathfrak{S}_2$ by means of reduction:

'$(\exists x)(y) \left[(\sim F(0) \lor F(x) \lor F(y)) \cdot (\sim F(0) \lor \sim F(x^!) \lor F(y)) \right]$'.

Further, according to DA 2 B: '$(F)(\exists x)(y) [\ldots]$' must be analytic. Let this be $\mathfrak{S}_3$. For this to be analytic by DA 2 Ca, $\mathfrak{S}_2$ must be analytic in respect of every valuation for 'F'. By DA 3 B: for every valuation $\mathfrak{B}_1$ for 'F', and for at least one valuation $\mathfrak{B}_2$ for 'x', '$(y) [\ldots]$' must be analytic in respect of $\mathfrak{B}_1$ and $\mathfrak{B}_2$. By DA 3 A: in the case of every $\mathfrak{B}_1$ for 'F', for at least one valuation $\mathfrak{B}_2$ for

'x', and for every $\mathfrak{B}_3$ for 'y', the operand which occurs in the square brackets—let it be $\mathfrak{S}_4$—must be analytic in respect of $\mathfrak{B}_1$, $\mathfrak{B}_2$, and $\mathfrak{B}_3$. By DA 3 C: in the case of every $\mathfrak{B}_1$ for 'F', for at least one $\mathfrak{B}_2$ for 'x', and for every $\mathfrak{B}_3$ for 'y', the evaluation of $\mathfrak{S}_4$ on the basis of $\mathfrak{B}_1$, $\mathfrak{B}_2$, and $\mathfrak{B}_3$ must lead to $\mathfrak{N}$. In this way the criterion is constructed.

Proof that the criterion is fulfilled. Let $\mathfrak{S}_5$ be '$\sim F(0) \vee F(x) \vee F(y)$', and $\mathfrak{S}_6$ be '$\sim F(0) \vee \sim F(x^\text{I}) \vee F(y)$'; $\mathfrak{S}_4$ is then $\mathfrak{S}_5 \cdot \mathfrak{S}_6$. $\mathfrak{B}_1$ is of the same type as 'F', i.e. of the type (0); and therefore, according to VR 1 a and c it is a class of $\mathfrak{S}t$. With regard to $\mathfrak{B}_1$, three cases are to be distinguished: 1. The $\mathfrak{S}t$ '0' does not belong to $\mathfrak{B}_1$; 2. '0' and every other $\mathfrak{S}t$ belongs to $\mathfrak{B}_1$; 3. '0' belongs to $\mathfrak{B}_1$ but an $\mathfrak{S}t$ exists—say $\mathfrak{S}t_1$—which does not belong to $\mathfrak{B}_1$.— 1. In case 1, the evaluation of $\mathfrak{S}_4$, independently of $\mathfrak{B}_2$ and $\mathfrak{B}_3$, always leads to $\mathfrak{N}$. For here, in accordance with VR 2 a and EvR 1, '$F(0)$' is replaced by $\sim \mathfrak{N}$; and thus '$\sim F(0)$' leads to $\sim \sim \mathfrak{N}$, from which, by reduction in accordance with RR 2f, $\mathfrak{N}$ results. Then, by RR 3 c, $\mathfrak{N}$ results from $\mathfrak{S}_5$ and from $\mathfrak{S}_6$, and hence, by RR 3 a, also from $\mathfrak{S}_4$.—2. In case 2, $\mathfrak{S}_4$ independently of $\mathfrak{B}_2$, for any $\mathfrak{B}_3$, leads to $\mathfrak{N}$. For, since every $\mathfrak{S}t$ belongs to $\mathfrak{B}_1$, so also does the valuation for 'y', $\mathfrak{B}_3$. Therefore, in accordance with EvR 1, the evaluation of '$F(y)$' leads to $\mathfrak{N}$. Thence, as before, $\mathfrak{S}_5, \mathfrak{S}_6, \mathfrak{S}_4$ all yield $\mathfrak{N}$.—3. In case 3, it is possible to state, for any $\mathfrak{B}_1$, a $\mathfrak{B}_2$ such that the evaluation of $\mathfrak{S}_4$ leads independently of $\mathfrak{B}_3$ to $\mathfrak{N}$. Since, namely, '0' belongs to $\mathfrak{B}_1$, but $\mathfrak{S}t_1$ does not, as step by step we erase from $\mathfrak{S}t_1$ a stroke 'I', we get an $\mathfrak{S}t_2$ such that it belongs to $\mathfrak{B}_1$, while $\mathfrak{S}t_2\text{I}$ does not. (In this inference, complete induction is applied in the syntax-language.) Now let us take $\mathfrak{S}t_2$ as $\mathfrak{B}_2$ (which, by VR 1 a, is an $\mathfrak{S}t$). Then, in accordance with EvR 1, '$F(x)$' will become $\mathfrak{N}$. By VR 2 b, $\mathfrak{S}t_2\text{I}$ is the valuation for 'x^I'. Hence, according to EvR 1, '$F(\dot{x}^\text{I})$' becomes $\sim \mathfrak{N}$, and hence '$\sim F(x^\text{I})$' becomes $\sim \sim \mathfrak{N}$, from which we get $\mathfrak{N}$. And hence, as before, $\mathfrak{S}_5$, $\mathfrak{S}_6$, and $\mathfrak{S}_4$ issue in $\mathfrak{N}$.—The criterion is fulfilled in all three cases; and $\mathfrak{S}_1$ (PSII 20) is accordingly analytic.

Theorem 34h.2. Every sentence of the form PSII 21 (*Principle of Selection*) is analytic.

The proof is easy but too long to be given here in full. For the sake of a fundamental question which is involved, we shall, however, at least indicate its form. Let us assume that $\mathfrak{S}_1$ is a sentence of the form PSII 21. $^{\mathfrak{R}}\mathfrak{S}_1$ is then:

$$(\exists\, p_2)\,(v_7)\,(\exists\, p_3)\,(\exists\, p_4)\,(\exists\, v_8)\,(\exists\, p_5)\,(p_6)\,(\exists\, v_9)\,(v_{10})\,(v_{11})\,[\mathfrak{S}_2];$$

where $\mathfrak{S}_2$ is:

$$\big(p_1\,(p_2)\vee p_1\,(p_3)\vee \sim p_1\,(p_6)\vee p_6\,(v_9)\big)\bullet(\ldots)\bullet\ldots\bullet\big(\sim p_2\,(v_7)\vee$$
$$\sim(p_3=p_4)\vee\sim p_1\,(p_6)\vee\sim p_6\,(v_{10})\vee\sim p_5\,(v_{10})\vee\sim p_6\,(v_{11})\vee$$
$$\sim p_5\,(v_{11})\vee(v_{10}=v_{11})\big).$$

$\mathfrak{S}_2$ is a conjunction with 30 terms, every term of which is a disjunction having 4 or 8 terms. Let $\mathfrak{B}_i$ ($i=1$ to 11) be the valuation for v_i or p_i, respectively. According to DA, $\mathfrak{S}_1$ is analytic if the following condition is fulfilled: for every $\mathfrak{B}_1$ there is a $\mathfrak{B}_2$ of a kind such that, for every $\mathfrak{B}_7$, there is a $\mathfrak{B}_3,\mathfrak{B}_4,\mathfrak{B}_8,\mathfrak{B}_5$ of a kind such that, for every $\mathfrak{B}_6$, there is a $\mathfrak{B}_9$ of a kind such that for every $\mathfrak{B}_{10}$ and $\mathfrak{B}_{11}$, the evaluation of $\mathfrak{S}_2$ based on $\mathfrak{B}_1$ to $\mathfrak{B}_{11}$ leads to $\mathfrak{R}$. Let $\mathfrak{B}_1$ be given arbitrarily. We may classify the possibilities with regard to $\mathfrak{B}_1$ as follows: $\mathfrak{B}_1$ is either null or it is not; $\mathfrak{B}_1$ contains a null class as an element or it does not; there are two classes belonging to $\mathfrak{B}_1$ and having an element in common, or there are not. Then it is easy to show that, in each one of these cases, the criterion is fulfilled. Here we shall only examine the most important case, namely the last: $\mathfrak{B}_1$ and the classes belonging to $\mathfrak{B}_1$ are not null and no two of the classes belonging to $\mathfrak{B}_1$ have an element in common. Then—assuming that the *Principle of Selection* holds in the syntax-language—there is a selective class of $\mathfrak{B}_1$, that is to say, a class such that it has exactly one element in common with every class belonging to $\mathfrak{B}_1$. Let us take this selective class as $\mathfrak{B}_5$. Then, as it is easy to show (classification of cases: $\mathfrak{B}_6$ is either an element of $\mathfrak{B}_1$ or it is not), the given criterion can be fulfilled in every case.

The Principle of Selection itself is used in the foregoing proof. It must be noted, however, that this principle does not appear here as a sentence of the object-language, but *as a sentence of the syntax-language which we use in our syntactical investigations*. It is clear that the possibility of proving a certain syntactical sentence depends upon the richness of the syntax-language which is used, and especially upon what is regarded as valid in this language. In the present case, the situation is as follows: we can work out in our syntax-language S (for which we have here taken a not strictly determined word-language) the proof that a certain sentence, $\mathfrak{S}_1$, of the object-language II is analytic, if, in S, we have a certain sentence at our disposal, namely, that particular sentence of S which (in ordinary translation) is translatable into the sentence $\mathfrak{S}_1$ of II. From this it follows that our proof is not in any way a circular one. An exact analogue holds for the application of the Principle of Induction of the syntax-language in the proof of Theorem 1. The proofs of Theorems 1 and 2 must not be interpreted as though by means of them it were proved that the Principle of Induction and the Principle of Selection were materially true. They only show that our definition of 'analytic' effects on this point what it is intended to effect, namely, the characterization of a sentence as analytic if, in material interpretation, it is regarded as logically valid.

The question as to whether the Principle of Selection should be admitted into the whole of the language of science (including also all syntactical investigations) as logically valid or not is not decided thereby. That is a matter of choice, as are all questions concerning the language-form which is to be chosen (cf. the Principle of Tolerance, § 17 and § 78). In view of our present knowledge of the syntactical nature of the Principle of Selection, its admission should be regarded as expedient. The fact that by means of its admission the construction of the mathematical calculus is obviously considerably simplified speaks for it. Against it, there is hardly anything to be said, so long as the existence of any contradiction in it has not been proved (and seems, on the contrary, highly improbable).

§ 34*i.* Language II is Non-Contradictory

We have already attempted to represent the inexact concept of logical validity (in II) by means of two different terms: the d-term '*demonstrable*' and the c-term '*analytic*'. The relation subsisting between these two terms must now be examined more closely. We shall show that the second term is an extension of the first: every demonstrable sentence is analytic, but not conversely. In the same way we shall show that if $\mathfrak{S}_1$ is derivable from $\mathfrak{R}_1$, $\mathfrak{S}_1$ is also always a consequence of $\mathfrak{R}_1$. In connection with this, we shall show that Language II is *non-contradictory*—that is to say, that two sentences $\mathfrak{S}_1$ and $\sim\mathfrak{S}_1$ are never demonstrable in II.

In order to show that every demonstrable sentence is analytic
(Theorem 21) we must prove that every one of the primitive sentences PSII 1–23 of Language II (§ 30) is analytic. The individual
primitive sentences will be tested one after the other in the following paragraphs (Theorems 2–14).

Theorem 34i.1. All sentences which are demonstrable in the
ordinary sentential calculus—hence, for example, the *Principle
of Excluded Middle*, the Principle of Contradiction, and the
Principle of Double Negation—are analytic.—This follows from
RR 2, 3.

Theorem 34i.2. The primitive sentences PSII 1–6 are analytic.—This follows from Theorem 1.

Theorem 34i.3. The primitive sentences PSII 7–9 are analytic.—This follows from RR 8 *b*, *c*, 4 and Theorem 34 *b*.5.

Theorem 34i.4. Every sentence of the form PSII 10 is analytic.
—This follows from RR 5 *a*.

Theorem 34i.5. Every sentence of the form PSII 11 is analytic.
—The proof is a simple one based upon a differentiation of cases:
v_1 and v_2 either have or have not the same valuation.

Theorem 34i.6. PSII 12 is analytic.—This follows from
RR 5 *c*, 2 *f*.

Theorem 34i.7. PSII 13 is analytic.—This follows from
RR 2 *b*, 5 *b*, 3 *b*.

Theorem 34i.8. PSII 14 and 15 are analytic.—This follows
from RR 7 *a*, *b*, and Theorem 34 *b*.5.

Theorem 34i.9. Every sentence of the form PSII 16 is analytic.

Proof. By (partial) reduction we get: $(\exists v_1)\left[\sim \mathfrak{S}_1 \vee \mathfrak{S}_1\!\left(\begin{array}{c} v_1 \\ \mathfrak{A}_1 \end{array}\right)\right]$.
This is analytic since the operand is analytic in respect of at least
one valuation, $\mathfrak{B}_1$, for v_1, inasmuch as $\mathfrak{A}_1$, or any arbitrary valuation for $\mathfrak{A}_1$, may be taken as $\mathfrak{B}_1$.

Theorem 34i.10. Every logical sentence of the form PSII 17 is
analytic.—The primitive sentence PSII 17, the *Principle of
Substitution with arguments*, represents one of the critical points
in the logico-mathematical system, especially in the case where
so-called *surplus variables* occur.

Proof. Let $\mathfrak{S}_3$ be a logical sentence of the form PSII 17; and
let $\mathfrak{Arg}_1$ be $v_1, v_2, \ldots v_k$. We will assume that in addition to these
variables (which do not necessarily occur at all) $\mathfrak{S}_2$ contains the

surplus free variables $\mathfrak{v}_{k+1}, \ldots \mathfrak{v}_m$ (by surplus variables are understood those that do not occur in $\mathfrak{Arg}_1$). Let the variables which occur as free variables in $\mathfrak{S}_1$, in addition to $\mathfrak{p}_1$, be $\mathfrak{v}_{m+1}, \ldots \mathfrak{v}_p$. In order to show that $\mathfrak{S}_3$ is analytic, we will show that $^{\mathfrak{R}}\mathfrak{S}_3$ is analytic in respect of any given series $\mathfrak{B}$ of valuations for the variables $\mathfrak{v}_{k+1}, \ldots \mathfrak{v}_m, \mathfrak{v}_{m+1}, \ldots \mathfrak{v}_p$. By partial reduction we get for $^{\mathfrak{R}}\mathfrak{S}_3$ $^{\mathfrak{R}}[\mathfrak{S}_4 \vee \mathfrak{S}_5]$, wherein $\mathfrak{S}_4$ is $(\exists \mathfrak{p}_1)(\sim\mathfrak{S}_1)$ and $\mathfrak{S}_5$ is $\mathfrak{S}_1\begin{pmatrix} \mathfrak{p}_1(\mathfrak{Arg}_1) \\ \mathfrak{S}_2 \end{pmatrix}$. Two cases may be distinguished:

1. Let there be a valuation $\mathfrak{B}_1$ for $\mathfrak{p}_1$ such that $^{\mathfrak{R}}(\sim\mathfrak{S}_1)$ is analytic in respect of $\mathfrak{B}_1$ and $\mathfrak{B}$. Then, according to DA 3 B, $(\exists \mathfrak{p}_1)^{\mathfrak{R}}(\sim\mathfrak{S}_1)$ is analytic in respect of $\mathfrak{B}$; hence, so also is $^{\mathfrak{R}}\mathfrak{S}_4$, and further $^{\mathfrak{R}}\mathfrak{S}_3$.

2. Let there be no valuation for $\mathfrak{p}_1$ of the kind described. Then, for every arbitrary valuation $\mathfrak{B}_i$ for $\mathfrak{p}_1$, $^{\mathfrak{R}}(\sim\mathfrak{S}_1)$ is not analytic in respect of $\mathfrak{B}_i$ and $\mathfrak{B}$, and therefore, since it is logical, in accordance with Theorem 34e.11, it is contradictory. Thus, $^{\mathfrak{R}}\mathfrak{S}_1$ is analytic in respect of $\mathfrak{B}_i$ and $\mathfrak{B}$. Now, on the basis of the given valuations $\mathfrak{B}$ we will choose a certain valuation $\mathfrak{B}_1$ for $\mathfrak{p}_1$ in the following manner. According to VR 1 c, a possible valuation for $\mathfrak{p}_1$ is a class of possible valuations for $\mathfrak{Arg}_1$: now let $\mathfrak{B}_1$ be determined by the condition that a possible valuation $\mathfrak{B}_j$ for $\mathfrak{Arg}_1$ shall be an element of $\mathfrak{B}_1$ if, and only if, $^{\mathfrak{R}}\mathfrak{S}_2$ is analytic in respect of $\mathfrak{B}_j$ and $\mathfrak{B}$. $\mathfrak{p}_1$ is always followed in $\mathfrak{S}_1$ by an argument-expression. Let a certain partial sentence in $\mathfrak{S}_1$ containing $\mathfrak{p}_1$ be $\mathfrak{p}_1(\mathfrak{A}_1, \mathfrak{A}_2, \ldots \mathfrak{A}_k)$. Assume that $\mathfrak{B}'$ is the series of valuations for $\mathfrak{A}_1, \ldots \mathfrak{A}_k$ which, according to VR 2, result from the valuations $\mathfrak{B}$ (of which here only the valuations for the free variables occurring in $\mathfrak{A}_1, \ldots \mathfrak{A}_k$ come into consideration); here, when partial sentences occur in those expressions, we take $\mathfrak{R}$ as the valuation for an analytic partial sentence and $\sim\mathfrak{R}$ as the valuation for a contradictory partial sentence. Then $^{\mathfrak{R}}\mathfrak{p}_1(\mathfrak{A}_1, \ldots \mathfrak{A}_k)$, since it is logical, is either analytic (Case a) or contradictory (Case b) in respect of $\mathfrak{B}_1$ and $\mathfrak{B}'$. In Case a, according to EvR 1, $\mathfrak{B}'$ is an element of $\mathfrak{B}_1$; in Case b it is not. Now, $\mathfrak{B}'$ is also a possible valuation for $\mathfrak{Arg}_1$. In Case a, in accordance with our choice of $\mathfrak{B}_1$, $^{\mathfrak{R}}\mathfrak{S}_2$ is analytic in respect of $\mathfrak{B}'$ (for $\mathfrak{v}_1, \ldots \mathfrak{v}_k$) and $\mathfrak{B}$; in Case b, it is contradictory. Thus, in

Case a, $^{\Re}\mathfrak{S}_2\left(\begin{matrix}v_1\\\mathfrak{A}_1\end{matrix}\right)\dots\left(\begin{matrix}v_k\\\mathfrak{A}_k\end{matrix}\right)$ is analytic in respect of $\bar{\mathfrak{B}}$, and in Case b it is contradictory.—$\mathfrak{S}_5$ is obtained from $\mathfrak{S}_1$ by replacing, at the substitution-positions, a partial sentence of the form $\mathfrak{p}_1(\mathfrak{A}_1,\dots\mathfrak{A}_k)$ by the corresponding partial sentence $\mathfrak{S}_2\left(\begin{matrix}v_1\\\mathfrak{A}_1\end{matrix}\right)\dots\left(\begin{matrix}v_k\\\mathfrak{A}_k\end{matrix}\right)$. As we have already seen, any two corresponding partial sentences of this kind are either both analytic or both contradictory in respect of $\mathfrak{B}_1$ and $\bar{\mathfrak{B}}$. Hence, if $^{\Re}\mathfrak{S}_1$ is analytic in respect of $\mathfrak{B}_1$ and $\bar{\mathfrak{B}}$, then $^{\Re}\mathfrak{S}_5$ is also analytic in respect of $\bar{\mathfrak{B}}$. It has been shown earlier that $^{\Re}\mathfrak{S}_1$ is analytic in respect of $\bar{\mathfrak{B}}$ and every arbitrary valuation for $\mathfrak{p}_1$, and therefore it is also analytic in respect of $\bar{\mathfrak{B}}$ and $\mathfrak{B}_1$. Accordingly $^{\Re}\mathfrak{S}_5$ is analytic in respect of $\bar{\mathfrak{B}}$, and hence so also is $^{\Re}\mathfrak{S}_3$.

Theorem 34i.11. Every sentence of the form PSII 18 is analytic.—This follows from RR 9c, 2f, and Theorem 34b.5.

Theorem 34i.12. Every sentence of the form PSII 19 is analytic.—By means of partial reduction, we get

$$(\exists\,v_1)(v_2)\left[\sim\mathfrak{S}_1\vee\mathfrak{S}_1\left(\begin{matrix}v_1\\v_2\end{matrix}\right)\right];$$

the rest of the proof is analogous to that of Theorem 9.

Theorem 34i.13. Every sentence of the form PSII 22 is analytic.

Proof. Let $\mathfrak{S}_1$ have the form PSII 22. $^{\Re}\mathfrak{S}_1$ is

$$(\exists v_3)\left[\left(\mathfrak{p}_1(v_3)\vee\mathfrak{p}_2(v_3)\vee(\mathfrak{p}_1=\mathfrak{p}_2)\right)\bullet\left(\sim\mathfrak{p}_2(v_3)\vee\sim\mathfrak{p}_1(v_3)\vee(\mathfrak{p}_1=\mathfrak{p}_2)\right)\right].$$

For this to be analytic, there must exist for any arbitrary valuations $\mathfrak{B}_1$ and $\mathfrak{B}_2$ for $\mathfrak{p}_1$ and $\mathfrak{p}_2$ respectively, a valuation $\mathfrak{B}_3$ for v_3 such that the evaluation of the operand on the basis of these valuations leads to $\mathfrak{N}$. By means of a classification of cases, it is easy to show that this condition is fulfilled.

Theorem 34i.14. Every sentence of the form PSII 23 is analytic.

Proof. Reduction leads to:

$$(\exists\,v_1)\dots(\exists\,v_n)\left[\sim\left(\mathfrak{f}_1(v_1,\dots v_n)=\mathfrak{f}_2(v_1,\dots v_n)\right)\vee(\mathfrak{f}_1=\mathfrak{f}_2)\right].$$

For this to be analytic, there must exist for any arbitrary valuations for $\mathfrak{f}_1$ and $\mathfrak{f}_2$ a series of valuations for $v_1,\dots v_n$ such that the evaluation of the operand leads to $\mathfrak{N}$. It is easy to demonstrate that this condition is fulfilled. If any arbitrary valuations for $\mathfrak{f}_1$ and $\mathfrak{f}_2$ are given, then either they agree with one another or they do not. In the first case, the second term of the disjunction, and hence, the whole operand, becomes $\mathfrak{N}$. In the second case, we take a series of valuations for $\mathfrak{v}_1, \ldots \mathfrak{v}_n$, such that, with it, by means of the valuations for $\mathfrak{f}_1$ and $\mathfrak{f}_2$, two different valuations are correlated. Then the first term of the disjunction becomes $\mathfrak{N}$ and hence the whole operand becomes $\mathfrak{N}$.

Theorem 34i.15. Every logical primitive sentence of II is analytic.—This follows from Theorems 2–14, 34 h.1 and 2.

Theorem 34i.16. If $\mathfrak{S}_1$ is analytic, then $\mathfrak{S}_1\begin{pmatrix} \mathfrak{v} \\ \mathfrak{a}_\mathfrak{b} \end{pmatrix}$ is also analytic.

Theorem 34i.17. Every primitive sentence of II is analytic.—This follows from Theorems 15 and 16.

Theorem 34i.18. Every definition in II is analytic.—By RR 1 and Theorem 34 e.7.

Theorem 34i.19. (a) $\mathfrak{S}_2$ is a consequence of $\mathfrak{S}_1$ and $\mathfrak{S}_1 \supset \mathfrak{S}_2$.— (b) $(\mathfrak{v})(\mathfrak{S}_1)$ is a consequence of $\mathfrak{S}_1$.

Theorem 34i.20. If, according to RII 1 and 2 (§ 31), $\mathfrak{S}_3$ is directly derivable from $\mathfrak{S}_1$ or from $\mathfrak{S}_1$ and $\mathfrak{S}_2$, then $\mathfrak{S}_3$ is a consequence of $\mathfrak{S}_1$ or of $\mathfrak{S}_1$ and $\mathfrak{S}_2$, respectively. This follows from Theorem 19.

Theorem 34i.21. *Every demonstrable sentence* (in II) *is analytic.* —From Theorems 17, 18 and 20, and Theorem 34 f.2. The converse is not true (example: Theorems 36.2 and 5). (See the second diagram on p. 185.)

Theorem 34i.22. If $\mathfrak{S}_n$ is *derivable* (in II) from $\mathfrak{S}_1, \mathfrak{S}_2, \ldots \mathfrak{S}_m$, then $\mathfrak{S}_n$ is a *consequence* of $\mathfrak{S}_1, \ldots \mathfrak{S}_m$.—This follows from Theorems 17, 18, 20, and 34 f.8.

Theorem 34i.23. $\sim \mathfrak{N}$ is not demonstrable in II.—This follows from Theorem 21 and DA 2 Cc.

A language S is called **contradictory** if every sentence of S is demonstrable in S; otherwise it is called **non-contradictory**. (See § 59.)

Theorem 34i.24. Language II (as the system of the d-rules PSII 1–23 and RII 1–2) is a *non-contradictory* language.—This follows from Theorem 23.

Hilbert set himself the task of proving "with finite means" *the non-contradictoriness of classical mathematics.* What is meant by 'finite means' is not stated exactly in any work of Hilbert's which has been published up to now (including [*Grundl.* 1934]), but presumably what we call 'definite syntactical concepts' is intended. Whether with such a restriction, or anything like it, Hilbert's aim can be achieved at all, must be regarded as at best very doubtful in view of Gödel's researches on the subject (see § 36). Even in the achievement of the partial results which are attainable, there are very considerable difficulties to be overcome. The proof which we have just given of the non-contradictoriness of Language II, in which classical mathematics is included, by no means represents a solution of Hilbert's problem. Our proof is essentially dependent upon the use of such syntactical terms as 'analytic', which are indefinite to a high degree, and which, in addition, go beyond the resources at the disposal of Language II. Hence, the significance of the presented proof of non-contradictoriness must not be over-estimated. Even if it contains no formal errors, it gives us no absolute certainty that contradictions in the object-language II cannot arise. For, since the proof is carried out in a syntax-language which has richer resources than Language II, we are in no wise guaranteed against the appearance of contradictions in this syntax-language, and thus in our proof.

§ 35. Syntactical Sentences which Refer to Themselves

If the syntax of a language is formulated in that language itself, then a syntactical sentence may sometimes speak about itself, or more exactly, it may speak about its own design—for pure syntax, of course, cannot speak of individual sentences as physical things, but only of designs and forms. For instance, $\mathfrak{S}_1$ states: "a sentence of the design ... is closed (or: open, demonstrable, synthetic, and the like)"; and here $\mathfrak{S}_1$ itself possesses the design which is described in it. For every syntactical property, it is possible so to construct a sentence that it attributes to itself—whether rightly or wrongly—just this property. We shall state the method of doing this, since it leads to important consequences for the questions of the completeness of languages and the possibility of a proof of non-contradictoriness. We have already formulated the syntax of Language I in that language itself. In the same way *the syntax of Language II can be formulated in II itself*, and to an even wider extent, since in Language II indefinite syntactical concepts can also be defined. Our further investigations will have reference to Language II, but they can easily be transferred to Language I, since in them we use only definite symbols of the kinds which have already occurred in I.

'str(n)' means: "the ^{SN}𝔖t, which has the value n". [For example, str(4) is the ^{SN}𝔖t '0¹¹¹¹'.] Regressive definition:

$$\text{str}(0) = \text{reihe}(4) \tag{1}$$

$$\text{str}(n') = \text{zus}[\text{str}(n), \text{reihe}(14)] \tag{2}$$

Let any syntactical property of expressions be chosen—for instance, 'descriptive' or 'non-demonstrable (in II)'. Let $\mathfrak{S}_1$ be that sentence with the free variable 'x' (for which we will take the term-number 3) which expresses this property [in the examples: 'DeskrA(x)', '~BewSatzII(r, x)'; compare p. 76]. Let $\mathfrak{S}_2$ be that sentence which results from $\mathfrak{S}_1$ if for 'x' 'subst $[x, 3, \text{str}(x)]$' is substituted. [In the second example, $\mathfrak{S}_2$ is '~BewSatzII $(r, \text{subst}[x, 3, \text{str}(x)])$'.] By means of the rule which has been stated earlier (p. 68), the term-number for every defined symbol is univocally determined. Thus, if $\mathfrak{S}_2$ is given, the series-number of $\mathfrak{S}_2$ can be calculated; let it be designated by 'b' ('b' is a defined 𝔷𝔷). Let the ^{SN}sentence subst $[b, 3, \text{str}(b)]$ be $\mathfrak{S}_3$; thus $\mathfrak{S}_3$ is the sentence which results from $\mathfrak{S}_2$ when the 𝔖t with the value b is substituted for 'x'. It is easy to see that, syntactically interpreted, $\mathfrak{S}_3$ means that $\mathfrak{S}_3$ itself has the chosen syntactical property.

We will explain this point by the example of the property 'non-demonstrable (in II)'. Here instead of '$\mathfrak{S}_3$' we will write '𝔊'. [This sentence forms the analogue in II to the sentence constructed by Gödel [*Unentscheidbare*], the only difference being that in it we use a free instead of a bound variable.] Let b_2 be the series-number of the $\mathfrak{S}_2$ (given above) of this example. str(b_2) is an ^{SN}𝔖t; to make the following discussion clearer, we will indicate this 𝔖t by '0¹¹··' (this 𝔖t consists of '0' and b_2 accents and is thus far too long for anyone to write out in full). Hence, $0^{||}\cdots = b_2$. Let 𝔊 be the sentence which has the series-number subst $[b_2, 3, \text{str}(b_2)]$ (or subst $[0^{||}\cdots, 3, \text{str}(0^{||}\cdots)]$). Hence, 𝔊 is the sentence which results from $\mathfrak{S}_2$ if '0¹¹··' is substituted for 'x'; 𝔊 is accordingly the sentence '~BewSatzII $(r, \text{subst}[0^{||}\cdots,$

3, str $(0^{II} \cdot \cdot)]) $'. In this way, we have determined the wording of
$\mathfrak{G}$. Syntactically interpreted, it means that that sentence which
has the series-number subst $[0^{II} \cdot \cdot, 3, str(0^{II} \cdot \cdot)]$ is not demonstrable. But that sentence is $\mathfrak{G}$ itself. Thus $\mathfrak{G}$ means that $\mathfrak{G}$ is
not demonstrable.

Incidentally, it is to be noted that a sentence of *descriptive*
syntax can refer to itself in an even more direct manner, namely,
not merely to its design but also to itself as a physical thing consisting of printer's ink. A sentence which occurs at a certain place
can, in material interpretation, mean that that sentence which
occurs at that place, i.e. itself, possesses such and such a syntactical property. And here it is even easier than in the case of
sentences of pure syntax to construct for every given syntactical
property a sentence which—whether rightly or wrongly—attributes that property to itself. Suppose the property in question
is expressed by the pr 'Q'; then the sentence 'Q [ausdr (b, a)]'
means: "The expression occurring at the positions a to a + b has
the property Q" (compare p. 78). [*Example:* At the places a to
a + 8 (indicated, say, by numbered positions on a piece of paper)
let the sentence $\mathfrak{S}_1$ 'DeskrA [ausdr (8, a)]' occur. Syntactically
interpreted, $\mathfrak{S}_1$ means that the expression which occurs at the
places a to a + 8 is a descriptive expression. But this expression
is $\mathfrak{S}_1$ itself. Incidentally, $\mathfrak{S}_1$ is true (empirically valid) since $\mathfrak{S}_1$
contains the $\mathfrak{fu}_b$ 'ausdr'.]

§ 36. IRRESOLUBLE SENTENCES

We will now show (following Gödel's line of thought [*Unentscheidbare*]) that *the sentence $\mathfrak{G}$ constructed in the preceding Section
is irresoluble in II.*

We have built up Language II in such a way that the syntactical
rules of formation and transformation are in agreement with a
material interpretation of the symbols and expressions of II which
we had in view. [From the systematic standpoint, the converse
relationship holds: logically arbitrary syntactical rules are laid
down, and from these formal rules the interpretation can be
deduced. Compare § 62.] In particular, the definition of
'analytic (in II)' is so constructed that all those sentences and
only those sentences which are logically valid in their material

interpretation are called analytic. Further, in the construction of the arithmetized syntax of I in I (D 1–125), we proceeded in such a way that a sentence of this syntax—and hence a syntactically interpretable, logical sentence, namely, an arithmetical sentence of I—turns out to be true arithmetically when and only when on a syntactical interpretation it is a true syntactical sentence. [For instance: 'BewSatz(a, b)' is arithmetically true when and only when a is the series-series-number of a proof in accordance with the rules laid down, and b the series-number of the last sentence in this proof.] Now let us suppose that in the same way the arithmetized syntax of II is stated in II. [For instance, 'BewSatzII (r, x)' is defined so that it means: "r is an ^{SN}proof of the ^{SN}sentence x". Here, 'BewSatzII' is a definite pr.] Then a syntactically interpretable arithmetical sentence of Language II will here be logically valid, and therefore also analytic, when and only when, materially interpreted, it turns out to be a true syntactical sentence. Thus we have here a shorter method (which is, because of its clarity, easy to use) of proving with respect to certain $\mathfrak{S}_I$ (a proof which is otherwise very tedious) that they are analytic (or contradictory); this proof arises from a non-formal consideration of the truth or falsity of the sentence in question in its syntactical interpretation. [In the above example: if we can show that the ^{SSN}sentence-series a is a proof of the ^{SN}sentence b, it is thereby demonstrated that the sentence 'BewSatzII (a, b)' is analytic in II.]

$\mathfrak{G}$ was the sentence '$\sim$ BewSatzII $(r, \text{subst} [...])$'; for the sake of brevity we will write here 'subst [...]' instead of 'subst $[0^{II}\cdot\cdot, 3, \text{str}(0^{II}\cdot\cdot)]$'. The series-number of $\mathfrak{G}$ was subst [...].

Theorem 36.1. If Language II is non-contradictory, $\mathfrak{G}$ is not demonstrable in II.—Suppose that there were an ^{SSN}proof a of $\mathfrak{G}$. Then the sentence of II which means this, namely 'BewSatzII (a, subst [...])', would be true, and thus analytic, and, since it is definite, also demonstrable. Now if $\mathfrak{G}$ were demonstrable, so also would be $\mathfrak{G}\left(\dfrac{'r'}{'a'}\right)$, which is '$\sim$ BewSatzII (a, subst [...])'. But this sentence is the negation of the previous sentence. Thus II would be contradictory.

Theorem 36.2. $\mathfrak{G}$ is *not demonstrable* in II.—From Theorems 1 and 34 *i*.24.

Theorem 36.3. ⑤ is *not refutable* in II.—Suppose that ⑤ were refutable, and therefore (compare p. 94) '∼(r)(∼BewSatzII (r, subst [...]))' demonstrable. Then '(∃r)(BewSatzII (r, subst [...]))' would be demonstrable, and, by Theorem 34*i*.21, analytic, and therefore true; that means that a proof for the sentence with the series-number subst [...] would exist, and therefore for ⑤. But according to Theorem 2 this is not the case.

Theorem 36.4. ⑤ is *irresoluble* in II.—By Theorems 2 and 3.

Theorem 36.5. ⑤ is analytic.—In syntactical interpretation, ⑤ means the same as Theorem 2, is therefore true, and consequently analytic. Thus ⑤ is an example of an analytic but non-demonstrable sentence of II (see diagram, p. 185). Every sentence of the form $⑤\left(\dfrac{\mathfrak{z}_1}{\mathfrak{St}}\right)$, where $\mathfrak{z}_1$ is '*r*', is analytic and definite and therefore, according to Theorem 34*e*.12, also demonstrable; but the universal sentence ⑤ itself is not demonstrable.

Let $\mathfrak{W}_{II}$ be the closed sentence '(∃x)(r)(∼BewSatzII (r, x))'. In syntactical interpretation it means that there exists in II a non-demonstrable sentence and that therefore Language II is non-contradictory.

Theorem 36.6. $\mathfrak{W}_{II}$ is analytic.—$\mathfrak{W}_{II}$ is true, according to Theorem 34*i*.23.

Theorem 36.7. $\mathfrak{W}_{II}$ is not demonstrable in II.—Theorem 7 can be proved by applying the proof given by Gödel ([*Unentscheidbare*] p. 196). We will indicate the argument very briefly. The proof of Theorem 36.1 can be effected by the means at the disposal of Language II; that is to say, the sentence $\mathfrak{W}_{II} \supset ⑤$ is demonstrable in II. Now were $\mathfrak{W}_{II}$ demonstrable, then, according to RII 1, ⑤ would also be demonstrable. But this, by Theorem 2, is impossible. *The non-contradictoriness of II cannot be proved by the means at the disposal of II.* $\mathfrak{W}_{II}$ is a new example of an analytic but at the same time non-demonstrable sentence.

Theorem 7 does not mean that a proof of the non-contradictoriness of II would not be possible at all; indeed we have already indicated such a proof. The theorem means rather that this proof is only possible with the resources of a syntax formulated in a language richer than II. The proof which we stated earlier makes a very essential use of the term 'analytic (in II)'; but this term (as we shall see later) cannot be defined in any syntax formulated in Language II.

Corresponding results are true *for Language I also*: if $\mathfrak{G}_I$ is the analogously constructed sentence to $\mathfrak{G}$ in I (' $\sim$ BewSatz $(r$, subst $[\ldots])$ '), $\mathfrak{G}_I$ is analytic but irresoluble in Language I. Let $\mathfrak{W}_I$ be a sentence of I which approximately corresponds to the sentence $\mathfrak{W}_{II}$ (such as ' $\sim$ BewSatz (r, c) ', where c is the series-number of $\sim \mathfrak{N}$). Then $\mathfrak{W}_I$ is analytic but irresoluble in I. The non-contradictoriness of Language I (the non-demonstrability of some sentences in I) cannot be proved by the means at the disposal of I.

The fact that the non-contradictoriness of the language cannot be proved in a syntax which limits itself to the resources of that language is not due to any particular weaknesses in Languages I and II. This property, as Gödel [*Unentscheidbare*] has shown, is an attribute of a large class of languages, to which belong all the systems known hitherto (and possibly all systems whatever) which contain within themselves the arithmetic of the natural numbers. (On this point compare also Herbrand [*Non-contrad.*] pp. 5 f.)

D. FURTHER DEVELOPMENT OF LANGUAGE II

§ 37. Predicates as Class-Symbols

Frege and Russell both introduce *class-expressions* in such a way that, from every expression which designates a property (for instance, from a pr^1 or from a so-called one-termed sentential function—that is to say, a sentence having exactly one free variable) a class-expression is constructed which designates the class of those objects possessing the property in question. In Language II we do not intend to introduce any special class-expressions; in their place we use the predicates themselves. In what follows we shall indicate how a shorter method of writing can be introduced in which arguments and operators can, under certain circumstances, be left out. The result of this is a symbolism that is perfectly analogous to Russell's symbolism of classes. A sentence in this symbolism can be paraphrased in the word-language in terms either of "properties" or of "classes", as one wishes.

A property (or class) is called *null* [*leer*] when it does not apply to (or contain) any object whatsoever; and *universal* when it applies to (or contains) every object. Thus our definitions are as follows:

Def. 37.1. $\text{Leer}_{(0)}(F) \equiv \sim (\exists x)(F(x))$

Def. 37.2. $\text{Un}_{(0)}(F) \equiv (x)(F(x))$

Analogous definitions can be framed for other types; the type of the argument (here: '(0)' for 'F') may be attached in the form of a suffix, for instance:

Def. 37.3. $\text{Leer}_{(0,\,0)}(F) \equiv \sim (\exists x)(\exists y)(F(x,y))$

Now with the help of the symbols of negation, disjunction, and conjunction we will form some combined $\mathfrak{Pr}$:

Def. 37.4. $(\sim F)(x) \equiv \sim F(x)$

Def. 37.5. $(F \vee G)(x) \equiv (F(x) \vee G(x))$

Def. 37.6. $(F \bullet G)(x) \equiv (F(x) \bullet G(x))$

Corresponding definitions may be framed for any other types, including many-termed $\mathfrak{pr}$. Analogous $\mathfrak{Pr}$ can be constructed with the help of the other junction-symbols; they are, however, seldom applied in practice.

We define the $\mathfrak{pr}$ 'Λ' and 'V' for the *null property* and for the *universal property* as follows:

Def. 37.7. $\Lambda_0(x) \equiv \sim (x = x)$

Def. 37.8. $V_0(x) \equiv (x = x)$

Corresponding definitions can be framed for all the remaining $\mathfrak{pr}$-types in which the designation of the type of the appertaining $\mathfrak{Arg}$ is attached as a suffix.

Theorem 37.9. '$(F = G) \equiv (x)(F(x) \equiv G(x))$' is demonstrable (with the help of PSII 22 and 11).—Analogously we now define as follows:

Def. 37.10. $(F \subset G) \equiv (x)(F(x) \supset G(x))$

Corresponding definitions may be framed for any two $\mathfrak{pr}$ of the same type, and therefore, specifically, also for many-termed $\mathfrak{pr}$.

[According to the previously stated syntax of Language II, instead of '$F \vee G$' we should write '$V(F, G)$' or '$\text{sm}(F, G)$', where 'sm' (as in the example, p. 86) is an $\mathfrak{fu}$ of the type $((0),(0):(0))$ or, in general, of the type $((t),(t):(t))$ for any type t whatsoever. And instead of '$F \subset G$', we should write '$\subset(F, G)$' or '$\text{Sub}(F, G)$', where 'Sub' is a $\mathfrak{pr}$ of the type $((0),(0))$ (compare p. 86), or, more generally, of the type $((t),(t))$. But we will here write '$F \vee G$' and '$F \subset G$' in order not to deviate too far from the usual Russellian symbolism.] According to Theorem 9 and Def. 10, for a sentence of the form $(v_1)(v_2)\dots(v_n)\big(\mathrm{pr}_1(v_1,\dots v_n)\equiv$ $\mathrm{pr}_2(v_1,\dots v_n)\big)$ we can always write $\mathrm{pr}_1=\mathrm{pr}_2$; and for a sentence of the form $(v_1)\dots(v_n)\big(\mathrm{pr}_1(v_1,\dots v_n)\supset\mathrm{pr}_2(v_1,\dots v_n)\big)$ we can always write $\mathrm{pr}_1\subset\mathrm{pr}_2$. For this mode of symbolization without arguments, two different translations into word-language are possible. For instance, let 'P' and 'Q' be pr^1; then we can translate 'P⊂Q' as: "The property P implies the property Q", or, if we wish, as: "The class P is a sub-class of the class Q"; correspondingly "sub-relation", when it is a question of many-termed pr. Further, we can interpret the 𝔓r 'P∨Q' when it is used without arguments as the "*sum* of the classes P and Q", and 'P•Q' as the "*product* of the classes P and Q"; analogously also the "sum" and "product of relations" in the case of many-termed pr. 'Λ' and 'V' used without arguments can be interpreted as "*null class*" and "*universal class*" (or as "null relation" and "universal relation", respectively). As an example of an application of the class symbolism, the Axiom of Selection PSII 21 may be used (the p which occur are to be taken from suitable types of at least the second order):

$$[(M\subset\sim\text{Leer})\bullet(F)(G)\,([M(F)\bullet M(G)\bullet\sim\text{Leer}(F\bullet G)]\supset$$
$$(F=G))]\supset(\exists H)(F)\,[M(F)\supset\text{A1}\,(F\bullet H)]$$

Hereby 'A1' ("cardinal number 1") is to be defined as follows (compare § 38 b):

$$\text{A1}\,(F)\equiv(\exists x)(y)\big(F(y)\equiv(y=x)\big)$$

The mode of symbolization whose introduction is indicated in the foregoing is completely analogous to Russell's symbolism of classes; the whole theory of classes and relations of the [*Princ. Math.*] can easily be put into this simplified form. But we shall not go into this here, as it raises no further fundamental problems.

§ 38. THE ELIMINATION OF CLASSES

The historical development of the use of class symbols in modern logic contains several noteworthy phases, the examination of which is fruitful for the study even of present-day problems. We select for our consideration the two most important steps in this development, which are due to Frege and Russell. Frege [*Grundgesetze*] was the first to give an exact form to the traditional differentiation between the *content* and the *extent of a concept*. According to his view, the content of a concept is represented by the sentential function (that is to say, by an open sentence in which the free variables serve to express indeterminateness and not universality). The extent (for instance, in the case of a property concept, i.e. of a one-termed sentential function, the corresponding class) is represented either by a special expression containing the sentential function, or else by a new symbol which is introduced as an abbreviation for this expression. An identity-sentence with class expressions here means the coextensiveness of the corresponding properties (if, for instance, 'k_1' and 'k_2' are the class symbols belonging to the pr 'P_1' and 'P_2', then '$k_1 = k_2$' is equivalent in meaning to '$(x)[P_1(x) \equiv P_2(x)]$'). Later on, Russell proceeded in the same manner. Following the traditional modes of thought, however, Frege made a mistake at a certain point; and this mistake was discovered by Russell and subsequently corrected.

It was a decisive moment in the history of logic when, in the year 1902, a letter from Russell drew Frege's attention to the fact that there was a contradiction in his system. After years of laborious effort, Frege had established the sciences of logic and arithmetic on an entirely new basis. But he remained unknown and unacknowledged. The leading mathematicians of his time, whose mathematical foundations he attacked with unsparing criticism, ignored him. His books were not even reviewed. Only by means of the greatest personal sacrifices did he manage to get the first volume of his chief work [*Grundgesetze*] published, in the year 1893. The second volume followed after a long interval in 1903. At last there came an echo—not from the German mathematicians, much less the German philosophers, but from abroad: Russell in England attributed the greatest importance to Frege's work. In the case of certain problems Russell himself, many years after Frege, but still in ignorance of him, had hit upon the same or like solutions; in the case of some others, he was able to use Frege's results in his own system. But now, when the second volume of his work was almost printed, Frege learned from Russell's letter that his concept of class led to a contradiction. Behind the dry statement of this fact which Frege gives in the Appendix to his second volume, one senses a deep emotion. But, at all events, he could comfort himself with the thought that the error which had been brought to light was not a peculiarity of his system; he only shared the fate of all who had hitherto occupied themselves with the problems of the extension of concepts, of classes, and of aggregates—amongst them both Dedekind and Cantor.

The contradiction which was discovered by Russell is the antinomy which has since become famous, namely that of the class of those classes which are not members of themselves. In his Appendix, Frege examined various possibilities for a way out of the difficulty, but without discovering a suitable one. Then Russell, in an Appendix to his work [*Principles*] which appeared in the same year (1903), suggested a solution in the form of the *theory of types*, according to which only an individual can be an element of a class of the first level, and only a class of the *n*th level can be an element of a class of the $n+1$th level. According to this theory, a sentence of the form '$k \epsilon k$' or '$\sim(k \epsilon k)$' is neither true nor false; it is merely meaningless. Later on Russell showed that this antinomy can also be so formulated as to apply not only to classes but to properties as well (the antinomy of 'impredicable', see § 60a). Here, also, the contradiction is eliminated by means of the rule of types; applied to $\mathfrak{pr}^1$ (as symbols for properties) it runs thus: the argument of a $^1\mathfrak{pr}$ can only be an individual symbol, and the argument of an $^{n+1}\mathfrak{pr}$ can only be an $^n\mathfrak{pr}$.

Now it is a very remarkable fact that Frege himself had already made a similar classification of all sentential functions into levels and kinds which also were arranged according to the kinds of their arguments ([*Grundgesetze*] Vol. I, pp. 37 ff.). In this he had done important preliminary work for Russell's classification of types. But on two points—like traditional logic and Cantor's Theory of Aggregates—he made errors, which were corrected by means of Russell's rule of types. It is because of these errors that, in spite of the perfectly correct classification of functions, the antinomies arise. Frege's first error consisted in the fact that in his system all expressions (or more exactly, all expressions which begin with the assertion symbol) are either true or false. He was thus obliged to count as false, expressions in which an unsuitable argument was attributed to some predicate. It was Russell who first introduced the triple classification into true, false, and meaningless expressions —a classification which was to prove so important for the further development of logic and its application to empirical science and philosophy. According to Russell, those expressions which have unsuitable arguments are neither true nor false; they are meaningless (in our terminology: they are not sentences at all). When this first error of Frege is corrected, then the antinomy of the term 'impredicable' can no longer be set up in his system—for the definition would have to contain the contra-syntactical expression '$F(F)$'. The antinomy which relates to classes, however, can still be constructed in his system. For Frege made a second mistake in not applying the type-classification of the predicates (sentential functions), which he had constructed with such insight and clarity, to the classes corresponding to the predicates; instead of that, he counted the classes—and similarly the many-termed extensions—simply as individuals (objects) quite independently of the level and kind of the sentential function which defined the class in question. And even after the discovery of the contradiction, he still thought that he need not alter his procedure (Vol. II, pp. 254 f.), because he believed the names of objects and the names of functions to be differentiated by the fact that the former have a meaning of their own while the latter remain incomplete symbols which only become significant after being completed by means of other symbols. Now, since Frege held the numerals '0', '1', '2', etc., to be significant in themselves, and since, on the other hand, he defined these symbols as class symbols of the second level, he was compelled to regard class

symbols, as opposed to predicates, as individual names. Today we
have the tendency to regard all the partial expressions of a sentence
which are not sentences in their turn as dependent; and to attribute
independent meaning at most to sentences.

In order to define a cardinal number in Frege's sense without
making use of classes, we have only to replace Frege's class of properties by a property of properties (designated by a $^2\mathfrak{pr}$). It is remarkable that Frege at an earlier stage expressed this view himself
([*Grundlagen*] 1884, p. 80, Note): "I think that [in the definition of
'cardinal number'], instead of 'extent of the concept', we might
say simply 'concept'. But then two kinds of objections would be
raised : .... I am of the opinion that both these objections could be
removed; but that might lead too far at this stage." Later he
apparently abandoned this view altogether. Then again—as it
appears when one looks back—Russell seemed to be very close to
the decisive point of abandoning classes altogether. While for Frege
it was important to introduce the class symbols as well as the predicates—since in his system they obey different rules—the whole
question had a different aspect for Russell. In order to avoid
Frege's error, Russell did not adopt the class symbols as individual symbols but instead he divided them into types which
correspond exactly to the types of the predicates. But by this means
a quite unnecessary duplication was introduced. Russell himself
recognized that it was of no importance for logic whether "classes"
—that is to say, anything which is designated by the class symbols
—"really exist" or not ("no-class theory"). The further development proceeded ever more definitely in the direction of the standpoint that class symbols are superfluous. In connection with
Wittgenstein's statements, Russell himself later discussed the view
that classes and properties are the same, but he did not as yet acknowledge it (1925: [*Princ. Math.*], 2nd edition of Vol. I). The
whole question is connected with the problem of the Thesis of
Extensionality (see § 67). Behmann [*Logik*] introduces the class
symbolism merely as an abbreviated method of writing, in which the
predicates are given without arguments; he insists, however, on
differentiating between extensional and intensional sentences, holding that this method of writing is only admissible for the former.
Von Neumann [*Beweistheorie*] and Gödel [*Unentscheidbare*] do not
even symbolically make any difference between predicates and the
corresponding class symbols; in the place of the latter, they simply
use the former. The critique of Kaufmann ([*Unendliche*], [*Bemerkungen*]) concerning Russell's concept of class is also worthy of note.
But this criticism is really directed less against the Russellian system
itself than against the philosophical discussions by Russell and others
of the concept of class, which do not properly belong to the system.

We will summarize briefly the development which we have
just been considering. Frege introduced the class expressions in

order to have, besides the predicates, something which could be treated like an object-name. Russell recognized the inadmissibility of such a treatment, but, nevertheless, retained the class expressions. The former reason for their introduction having been removed, however, they are now superfluous and therefore have been finally discarded.

§ 38a. On Existence Assumptions in Logic

If logic is to be independent of empirical knowledge, then it must assume nothing concerning the *existence of objects*. For this reason Wittgenstein rejected the Axiom of Infinity, which asserts the existence of an infinite number of objects. And, for kindred reasons, Russell himself did not include this axiom amongst the primitive sentences of his logic. But in Russell's system [*Princ. Math.*] as well as in that of Hilbert [*Logik*], sentences such as '$(\exists x)(F(x) \vee \sim F(x))$' and '$(\exists x)(x=x)$', and others like them, in which the existence of at least one object is stated, are (logically) demonstrable. Later on, Russell himself criticized this point ([*Math. Phil.*], Chap. XVIII, Footnote). In the above-mentioned systems, not only the sentences which are true in every domain, independently of the number of objects in that domain, but also sentences (for example, the one just given) which are true, not in every domain, but in every *non-empty* domain, are demonstrable. In practice, this distinction is immaterial, since we are usually concerned with non-empty domains. But if, in order to separate logic as sharply as possible from empirical science, we intend to exclude from the logical system any assumptions concerning the existence of objects, we must make certain alterations in the forms of language used by Russell and Hilbert.

We may proceed somewhat as follows: No free variables are admitted in sentences and therefore universality can only be expressed by means of universal operators. The schemata of primitive sentences PSII 18 and 19 are retained (see § 30); PSII 16 and 17 are replaced by rules of substitution: $(v_1)(\mathfrak{S}_1)$ can be transformed into $\mathfrak{S}_1\!\left(\dfrac{v_1}{\mathfrak{A}}\right)$, and $(\mathfrak{p}_1)(\mathfrak{S}_1)$ into $\mathfrak{S}_1\!\left(\dfrac{\mathfrak{p}_1(\mathfrak{Arg}_1)}{\mathfrak{S}_2}\right)$. RII 2 disappears; but certain other rules must be laid down instead. In the language thus altered, when an object-name such as 'a' is given, '$P(a)$' can be derived from '$(x)(P(x))$'; and again, '$(\exists x)(P(x))$' from '$P(a)$'.

The important point is that the existential sentence can only be derived from the universal one when a proper name is available; that is to say, only when the domain is really non-empty. In the altered language, as opposed to the languages of Russell and Hilbert, the sentence '$(x)\,(\mathrm{P}\,(x))\supset(\exists\,x)\,(\mathrm{P}\,(x))$' is not demonstrable without the use of a proper name.

In our object-languages I and II, the matter is quite different owing to the fact that they are not *name-languages* but *coordinate-languages*. The expressions of the type 0 here designate not objects but positions. The Axiom of Infinity (see § 33, 5a) and sentences like '$(\exists\,x)\,(x=x)$' are demonstrable in Language II, as are similar sentences in Language I. But the doubts previously mentioned are not relevant here. For here, those sentences only mean, respectively, that for every position there is an immediately succeeding one, and that at least one position exists. But whether or not there are objects to be found at these positions is not stated. That such is or is not the case is expressed in a co-ordinate language, on the one hand, by the fact that the fu$_b$ at the positions concerned have a value which appertains to the normal domain, or, on the other, by the fact that they have merely a trivially degenerate value. But this is stated not by analytic but by synthetic sentences.

Example. In the system of the *physical language*, the sentence which states that quadruples of real numbers (as quadruples of co-ordinates) exist is analytic. In its material interpretation it means that spatio-temporal positions exist. Whether something (matter or an electro-magnetic field) is to be found at a particular position is expressed by the fact that at the position in question the value of the density—or of the field-vector, respectively—is not zero. But whether anything at all exists—that is to say, whether there is such a non-trivially occupied position—can only be expressed by means of a synthetic sentence.

If it is a question not of the existence of objects but of the *existence of properties or classes* (expressed by means of predicates), then it is quite another matter. Sentences like '$(\exists\,F)\,(F=F)$' ("There exists a property (or class)") and '$(\exists\,F)\,(\mathrm{Leer}\,(F))$' ("There exists a null property (or class)") are true in every possible domain, including the null-domain; they are also analytic and logically demonstrable in the aforesaid system without existence assumptions.

There are, however, also sentences about the existence of properties the legitimacy of which is disputed; the most important
examples being the Axiom of Reducibility and the Axiom of
Selection. We need not here go into the question of the *Axiom of
Reducibility*. In Russell's form of language, it was a necessary
axiom on account of his branched classification of types (see
p. 86); but in Language II it is superfluous. [On the *Axiom of
Comprehension*, which is closely related to it, see § 33, 5*e*.] The so-
called *Axiom of Selection* (PSII 21) maintains the existence of a
selective class even in those cases where no such class can be
defined; and it is therefore a so-called pure (non-constructive)
existence statement. As such it is rejected by Intuitionism. In
Language II we have stated it as a primitive sentence, and we
regard the question of its assumption as purely one of expedience
(see pp. 97f.). That is true not only within the bounds of the
formalistic view of language as a calculus but also from the standpoint of material interpretation. For, in such an interpretation,
only the atomic $\mathfrak{S}_b$ are given a meaning directly; the remaining
$\mathfrak{S}_b$ then acquire one indirectly. The $\mathfrak{S}_I$ (and with them all sentences of mathematics) are, from the point of view of material
interpretation, expedients for the purpose of operating with the
$\mathfrak{S}_b$. Thus, in laying down an $\mathfrak{S}_I$ as a primitive sentence, only use-
fulness for this purpose is to be taken into consideration.

§ 38*b*. CARDINAL NUMBERS

In the material interpretation of Languages I and II, the $\mathfrak{Z}$ are
to be interpreted for the most part as designations of positions or
of values of an $\mathfrak{fu}_b$. Concerning the possibility of formulating
statements of cardinal numbers ("There are so and so many ...")
we have so far said nothing. We will now proceed to show several
possibilities of doing so, which lie partly within and partly without
the syntactical framework set up for Language II.

The *first method* consists in defining every cardinal number
(*Anzahl*) as a ²pr. For example, 'A5 (P)' (where 'A5' counts as
one symbol) means: "The property P has the cardinal number 5,
that is to say there are exactly 5 numbers (positions) which have
this property." Taking as an auxiliary term 'Am5 (P)' (*Mindest-*

Anzahl; 'Am5' is one symbol) which means: "There are at least 5 numbers which have the property P", we define as follows:

$$\text{Am1}(F) \equiv (\exists x)(F(x))$$
$$\text{Am2}(F) \equiv (\exists x)(\exists y)(\sim(x=y) \cdot F(x) \cdot F(y))$$
$$\text{Am3}(F) \equiv (\exists x)(\exists y)(\exists z)(\sim(x=y) \cdot \sim(x=z) \cdot \sim(y=z) \cdot F(x) \cdot F(y) \cdot F(z))$$

and so on. On the basis of these minimum numbers, the exact numbers are defined:

$$\text{A0}(F) \equiv \qquad\qquad \sim \text{Am1}(F)$$
$$\text{A1}(F) \equiv (\text{Am1}(F) \cdot \sim \text{Am2}(F))$$
$$\text{A2}(F) \equiv (\text{Am2}(F) \cdot \sim \text{Am3}(F))$$

and so on.

These definitions of the cardinal numbers correspond to those of Frege and Russell; only here the second-level class expressions are replaced, for the reasons discussed in § 38, by second-level predicates. These ^{2}pr are here not written, as in Russell, simply as '0', '1', and so on, because we already use these symbols in our languages as symbols of the type 0, and therefore may not use them also as symbols of the type $((0))$.

The *second method* employs special number-operators which were not provided for in the previously stated syntax. Here, for example, '$(0''' \exists x)(P(x))$' means: "There are exactly 3 numbers (or positions) having the property P." ['u' in '$(u \exists x)$' is not an operator-variable and is not bound.] In this case we can either, on the lines of the first method, define every individual number-operator, or, more simply, construct *two primitive sentences* to represent a general regressive definition:

(1) $(0 \exists x)(F(x)) \equiv \sim(\exists x)(F(x))$
(2) $(u' \exists x)(F(x)) \equiv (\exists x)(\exists G)[F(x) \cdot (y)(G(y) \equiv [F(y) \cdot \sim(y=x)]) \cdot (u \exists x)(G(x))]$

The *third method* expresses "There are 3 ..." by means of '$\text{Anz}(3, P)$'. As in the second method, analogous primitive sentences can be constructed for the pr 'Anz'.

The *fourth method* is perhaps the *most useful*. It is like the first, but in the place of a ^{2}pr it uses a ^{2}fu, and writes '$\text{anz}(P) = 3$'. As in the second method, two primitive sentences which take the place of a regressive definition can be constructed for the functor 'anz' of the type $((0):0)$. But instead of the primitive sentences, an *explicit definition* can also be constructed (according to the method stated on pp. 88 f.):

$$\text{anz}(F) = (Kv)(\exists f)(G)\,\big[\,([f(G)=0] \equiv \sim(\exists x)[G(x)])\bullet$$
$$(u)([f(G)=u^1] \equiv (\exists x)(\exists H)[G(x)\bullet(y)(H(y)\equiv[G(y)\bullet$$
$$\sim(y=x)])\bullet(f(H)=u)]\,)\bullet(v=f(F))\big]$$

In a precisely analogous way an ^{n+1}fu 'anz' of the type $((t_1):0)$ can be defined for the $^{n}pr^1$ of the type (t_1) and $n>1$.

A definite cardinal-number term referring to a *limited domain* can similarly be introduced in accordance with the four methods just given. The sentence: "There are 3 places up to the place 8 which have the property P" may be expressed, for example, as follows: 1. 'A 3 (8, P)'.—2. '(3 $\exists x$) 8 $(P(x))$'.—3. 'Anz (3, 8, P)'. —4. 'anz (8, P) = 3'.

All the cardinal-number terms which have been mentioned can be applied to logical as well as to descriptive properties (for example, to the number of the prime numbers less than 100, as well as to the number of red positions).

§ 38c. Descriptions

By a *description* we understand an expression which (in material interpretation) does not designate an object (in the widest sense) by a name, but characterizes it univocally in a different way, namely, by means of the statement of a property which belongs only to that object.

Examples. Description of a number: "The smallest prime number which is greater than 20"; of a thing: "The son of A"; of a property: "The logical sum of the properties P and Q". In the word-language a description is effected by the use of the definite article in the singular number ("the so-and-so").

Profiting by the attempts of Frege and Peano, Russell has produced a detailed theory of descriptions: [*Princ. Math.*] Vol. I, pp. 66 ff. and 173 ff.; and [*Math. Phil.*].

Following Russell's method one could (in an extension of the syntax of Language II) symbolize a description with the help of a special *descriptional operator* 'ιx'. "That number (or position) which has the property P" would then be written as follows: '$(\iota x)(P(x))$'. We call a description of this kind an *empty* or a *univocal* or an *ambiguous* description, respectively, if there is no number, or exactly one number, or several numbers having the property. A numerical description is used like a 3, for example as an argument. '$Q\left[(\imath x)\,(P(x))\right]$' means: "The number having the property P has also the property Q." This sentence is to be taken as true when, and only when, the description is univocal and the described number has the property Q. It is obviously necessary to make clearly recognizable the partial sentence (narrower or wider) which is to express the property to be ascribed to the described object. This can be done (as by Russell) by means of an auxiliary operator: the whole description (consisting of descriptional operator and bracketed operand) is put in square brackets in front of the partial sentence in question. In accordance with the material interpretation previously given, we can now construct the following schema of primitive sentences which applies to descriptions of any type whatsoever (3, $\mathfrak{Pr}$, or $\mathfrak{Fu}$):

$$[(\imath\,\mathfrak{v}_1)\,(\mathrm{pr}_1(\mathfrak{v}_1))]\,[\mathrm{pr}_2\,[(\imath\,\mathfrak{v}_1)\,(\mathrm{pr}_1(\mathfrak{v}_1))]] \equiv [(\imath\,\exists\,\mathfrak{v}_1)\,(\mathrm{pr}_1(\mathfrak{v}_1))\bullet$$
$$(\mathfrak{v}_1)\,(\mathrm{pr}_1(\mathfrak{v}_1)\supset\mathrm{pr}_2(\mathfrak{v}_1))]$$

The necessity for the use of the auxiliary operator may be seen by a comparison between the following two sentences [analogy: the necessity of the universal operator in order to be able to differentiate between $(\mathfrak{z}_1)\,(\sim\mathfrak{S}_1)$ and $\sim(\mathfrak{z}_1)\,(\mathfrak{S}_1)$]:

$$[(\imath\,x)\,(P(x))]\,[\sim Q\,[(\imath\,x)\,(P(x))]] \tag{1}$$
$$\sim[(\imath\,x)\,(P(x))]\,[Q\,[(\imath\,x)\,(P(x))]] \tag{2}$$

(1) means: "There is exactly one P-number, and every P-number (and therefore this one) is not a Q-number"; (2), on the other hand, means: "It is not true that there is exactly one P-number and that every P-number is a Q-number." If the description is not univocal (that is to say, if there are either no P-numbers at all or several P-numbers) then (1) is false but (2) is true. To simplify the symbolism it is possible (as Russell does) to rule that the clumsy auxiliary operator may be left out when its operand is the smallest partial sentence in which the description in question occurs. In this case, for instance in (2), we speak of a "primary occurrence" of the description; otherwise, for instance in (1), of a "secondary occurrence". According to this rule, (2), but not (1), may be written briefly thus: '$\sim[Q\,[(\imath\,x)\,(P(x))]]$'.

Descriptions are expressions of a special kind which cannot in all cases be treated in exactly the same manner as the other expressions ($\mathfrak{Z}$, $\mathfrak{Pr}$, or $\mathfrak{Fu}$) of the type concerned. While, for instance, according to PSII 16, $(\mathfrak{Z}_1)\,(\mathrm{pr}_2(\mathfrak{Z}_1))\supset\mathrm{pr}_2(\mathfrak{Z}_1)$ is true for every ordinary $\mathfrak{Z}_1$, it is not always true when a numerical description is used for $\mathfrak{Z}_1$. For example, the sentence $(\mathfrak{Z}_1)\,(\mathrm{pr}_2(\mathfrak{Z}_1))\supset\mathrm{pr}_2\,[(\imath\,\mathfrak{Z}_1)\,(\mathrm{pr}_1(\mathfrak{Z}_1))]$ may be falsified on account of the fact that the description is not univocal. The sentence which here holds in its place is: $(\mathfrak{Z}_1)\,(\mathrm{pr}_2(\mathfrak{Z}_1))\supset[(\mathrm{1}\exists\,\mathfrak{Z}_1)\,(\mathrm{pr}_1(\mathfrak{Z}_1))\supset\mathrm{pr}_2\,[(\imath\,\mathfrak{Z}_1)\,(\mathrm{pr}_1(\mathfrak{Z}_1))]]$; this sentence is demonstrable with the help of the schema of primitive sentences already given.

If we wish to use definite descriptions, we must write the descriptional operator with a limit; '$(\imath\,x)\,5\,(\mathrm{P}(x))$' then means: "That number up to 5 which has the property P."

The K-operator is a descriptional operator of a very special kind; and the clumsy auxiliary operator is not necessary for its use. The K-descriptions, since they are always univocal, can be treated like ordinary $\mathfrak{Z}$. This univocality is, however, only achieved by laying down the convention that when no number exists which has the property in question, the value of the description is zero. Herein lies the disadvantage of the K-operator; however, it might prove expedient in many cases. The K-operator itself is only applicable to numbers; nevertheless, with its help very often $\mathfrak{pr}$ and $\mathfrak{fu}$ of higher levels can also be defined. Let 'f' and 'g' be $^1\mathfrak{f}^1$; and let 'Q' be a $^2\mathrm{pr}^2$ of the type $((0:0),(0:0))$ (so that '$Q(f,g)$' is a sentence). Suppose that we wish to define the functor 'k' so that '$k(g)$' is equivalent in meaning to "that functor f for which $Q(f,g)$ is true". The definition can make use either of an ordinary descriptional operator (with an operator variable $\mathfrak{f}$):

$$k(g)=(\imath f)(Q(f,g))$$

or else of a K-operator (with an operator-variable $\mathfrak{z}$):

$$k(g)(x)=(Ky)(\exists f)\,[Q(f,g)\bullet(y=f(x))].$$

If the first definition is set up, then the defined symbol 'k' cannot be used everywhere like an ordinary $\mathfrak{fu}$ of the type in question; this disadvantage does not occur in the case of the second definition.

§ 39. REAL NUMBERS

The real numbers, together with their properties, relations, and functions, can be represented within the framework of the given syntax of Language II. If a particular (absolute) *real number* consists of the integral part a and the real number b (<1), this number can be represented by means of a *functor* 'k' which is defined so that k (0) = a, and, for $n > 0$, k (n) = 0 or 1 respectively, according to whether at the *n*th place in the development of the dual fraction of b, '0' or '1' occurs. In order that the development of the dual fraction may be univocal, we exclude those dual fractions in which, from some point onwards, only '0' occurs. The real numbers with sign (positive or negative) can be represented in a like manner.

The method of representation of real numbers indicated here was stated by Hilbert [*Grundlagen*, 1923] (see also von Neumann [*Beweisth.*]). Hilbert has planned a construction of the theory of real numbers on this basis, but up to now he has not produced it.

A *real number* is thus represented by means of a $^1\mathfrak{fu}^1$ of the type (0:0); we shall designate this type briefly by 'r'. Then a *property* (or aggregate) of real numbers (for example, "algebraic" or "transcendental" numbers) is expressed by means of a $^2\mathfrak{pr}^1$ of the type (r); a relation between two real numbers (for example: "is greater than" or "is a square root of") by means of a $^2\mathfrak{pr}^2$ of the type (r, r); a function of a real number (such as: "square root" or "sine") by means of a $^2\mathfrak{fu}^1$ of the type (r:r); a function of two real numbers (for instance: "product" or "power") by means of a $^2\mathfrak{fu}^2$ of the type (r, r : r); and so on. The arithmetical *equality* of two real numbers $\mathfrak{fu}_1$ and $\mathfrak{fu}_2$ is expressed by $\mathfrak{fu}_1 = \mathfrak{fu}_2$; for this sentence (according to PSII 23 and 11) is true when and only when the values of the two functors agree for every argument, and therefore when and only when the two dual fractions coincide at all places. As opposed to the equality of two natural numbers (represented by $\mathfrak{St}$), the equality of two real numbers, even when they are stated in the simplest possible form, is, in general, indefinite —since it refers back to an unlimited universality. A *complex* number is an ordered pair of real numbers, and thus an expression of the type r, r; a function of one or two complex numbers is a $^2\mathfrak{fu}$ of the type (r, r : r, r) or (r, r, r, r : r, r) respectively.

In this way all the usual concepts of classical mathematics (*Analysis, Theory of Functions*) can be represented, and all the sentences which have been constructed in this domain can be formulated. The usual axioms of the arithmetic of real numbers need not be set up here in the form of new primitive sentences. These axioms—and hence the theorems derivable from them—are *demonstrable* in Language II.

It will now be shown very briefly how the most important logical *kinds* which are distinguishable with respect to *sequences of natural numbers*, and therefore also with respect to *real numbers*, can be represented by means of *syntactical concepts*. First we must distinguish between a sequence given by means of a mathematical law and one given by a reference to experience. In the representation by means of ${}^1\mathfrak{fu}^1$, this difference is expressed by the difference between $\mathfrak{fu}_\mathrm{I}$ and $\mathfrak{fu}_\mathrm{b}$. Thus the term "sequence of free selections" (*freie Wahlfolge*) of Brouwer and Weyl is represented by the syntactical term '$\mathfrak{fu}_\mathrm{b}$'. The regular sequences can be divided into those that are *calculable* (see Examples 1 *a* and *b*) and those that are *incalculable* (Example 2). Syntactically this difference is characterizable as the difference between definite and indefinite $\mathfrak{fu}_\mathrm{I}$; for the former, by means of a fixed method, the value can be calculated for any position; for the latter, in general, this is not possible. In the case of sequences determined by reference to experience, we can differentiate further into: 1. *Analytically regular* sequences; in the case of these, the reference to experience is not essential, since it is equivalent in meaning to a certain mathematical law (Example 3).—2. *Empirically regular* sequences; although the determination of these cannot be transformed into a law, yet they have the same empirical distribution of values as an analytically regular sequence—whether by chance (Example 4 *a*) or in conformity with a natural law (Example 4 *b*).—3. Irregular or *unordered* sequences; for these there is no mathematical law which, even in a merely empirical way, they could possibly obey.

For an $\mathfrak{fu}_\mathrm{b}$ $\mathfrak{fu}_1$, these three kinds are to be characterized syntactically in the following manner: 1. There is an $\mathfrak{fu}_\mathrm{I}$ $\mathfrak{fu}_2$ such that $\mathfrak{fu}_2$ is synonymous with $\mathfrak{fu}_1$, and therefore such that $\mathfrak{fu}_1 = \mathfrak{fu}_2$ is an analytic sentence.—2. There is an $\mathfrak{fu}_\mathrm{I}$ $\mathfrak{fu}_2$ such that $\mathfrak{fu}_1 = \mathfrak{fu}_2$ is a synthetic but at the same time scientifically acknowledged sentence (that is to say, in Language II it is a consequence of scientifically acknowledged premisses; in a P-language it is P-valid (compare p. 184)).—3. Condition 2 is not fulfilled. [For all three concepts a further classification may be made according to whether the mathematical law in question is calculable or not, that is to say, whether the $\mathfrak{fu}_\mathfrak{l}$ concerned is definite or not.] It is to be noted that, in the definition of the concept of the unordered sequences, the kind of laws which are to be excluded must be stated; or, more exactly, in syntactical terminology, the rules of formation for the definitions of the $\mathfrak{fu}_\mathfrak{l}$ which are to be excluded must be stated, for example by means of reference to a certain language. [E.g., let a sequence $\mathfrak{fu}_1$ be called unordered in relation to Language II if there is no $\mathfrak{fu}_\mathfrak{l}$ $\mathfrak{fu}_2$ definable in II such that $\mathfrak{fu}_1 = \mathfrak{fu}_2$ is valid in a non-contradictory language which contains II (Example 5).] The same holds good for the term "irregular collective" in von Mises's Theory of Probability.

Examples. 1. *Calculable regular sequences:* (a) The recurring dual fraction with the period 'o11'; (b) the dual fraction for π.— 2. *Incalculable regular sequence* 'k_1': let $k_1(n)$ be equal to 1 if a Fermat equation with the exponent n exists; and otherwise let $k_1(n)$ be equal to 0.—3. *Analytically regular sequence* 'k_2': let $k_3(n)$ be equal to m if the nth cast of a certain dice shows an m; our definition is: $k_2(n) = k_3(n) + 2 - k_3(n)$, according to which the $\mathfrak{fu}_\mathfrak{b}$ 'k_2' is synonymous with the $\mathfrak{fu}_\mathfrak{l}$ 'k_4' whose definition is: $k_4(n) = 2$.— 4. *Empirically regular sequences:* (a) Let $k_5(n)$ be the number turned up at the nth throw, where, however, whenever the dice falls, it shows by chance alternately either a 3 or a 4. (Of course, this can never be completely established, but it is conceivable as an assumption.) (b) Let $k_6(n)$ be equal to 1 when a certain compass-needle, used as a roulette pointer, in the position of rest after the nth play points to the South, and equal to 2 when it points to the North. According to natural laws, $k_6 = k_4$ is valid.—5. Sequence 'k_7', unordered in relation to Language II: let $k_7(n)$ be equal to 1 when n is a series-number of an analytic sentence of II, and otherwise equal to 0. Since 'analytic in II' is not definable in II (see p. 219) there is no $\mathfrak{fu}_\mathfrak{l}$ in II which has the same distribution of values as k_7.

§ 40. The Language of Physics

Since, in Language II, not only logical but also descriptive symbols ($\mathfrak{pr}$ and $\mathfrak{fu}$) of the various types may occur, there is a possibility of representing *physical concepts*. A physical magnitude (of a state or condition) is an $\mathfrak{fu}_\mathfrak{b}$; the argument-expression contains four real numerical expressions, namely, the time-space co-ordinates; the value-expression contains one or more real numerical expressions (for instance, in the case of a scalar, one; in the case of an ordinary vector, three). A set of four co-ordinates is an expression of the type r, r, r, r; we will designate this type in a shorter way by 'q'. [*Examples:* 1. "At the point k_1, k_2, k_3, at the time k_4, the temperature is k_5" may be expressed e.g. as follows: 'temp $(k_1, k_2, k_3, k_4) = k_5$', where 'temp' is a ${}^2\mathfrak{fu}^4$ of the type $(q:r)$. 2. "At the space-time point k_1, k_2, k_3, k_4 there is an electrical field with the components k_5, k_6, k_7" may be expressed, say, by 'el $(k_1, k_2, k_3, k_4) = (k_5, k_6, k_7)$', where 'el' is a ${}^2\mathfrak{fu}^4$ of the type $(q:r, r, r)$.]

An empirical statement does not usually refer to one individual space-time point, but to a *finite space-time domain*. A domain of this kind is given by means of a ${}^2\mathfrak{pr}^4$ of the type (q)—namely, by means of a mathematical $(\mathfrak{pr}_l)$ or a physical $(\mathfrak{pr}_b)$ property which belongs to all the space-time points of the domain in question and only to those. A magnitude which is referred, not to individual space-time points but to finite domains (for instance: temperature, density, density of charge, energy), can thus be represented by means of a ${}^3\mathfrak{fu}_b{}^1$ whose argument is a $\mathfrak{pr}$ of the kind stated; in the case of a scalar, the type is $((q):r)$; in the case where there are several components, it is $((q):r, \ldots r)$. A *property of a domain* is represented by means of a ${}^3\mathfrak{pr}_b{}^1$ of the type $((q))$; the argument is again the $\mathfrak{pr}$ which determines the domain. The majority of the concepts of everyday life, as well as those of science, are such properties or relations of domains. [*Examples:* 1. Kinds of things, such as "horse"; "In such and such a place is a horse" means "Such and such a space-time domain has such and such a property."—2. Kinds of substances, such as "iron".—3. Directly perceptible qualities, such as "warm", "soft", "sweet".—4. Terms expressing dispositions, such as "breakable".—5. Conditions and processes of all kinds, such as "storm", "typhus".]

It follows from all these suggestions that *all the sentences of physics can be formulated in a language of the form of II*. To this end it is necessary that suitable $\mathfrak{fu}_b$ and $\mathfrak{pr}_b$ of the types given should be introduced as primitive terms, and that, with their help, the further terms should be defined. (Concerning that form of the physical language in which synthetic physical sentences also—

for example, the most general laws of nature—are laid down as primitive sentences, see § 82.)

According to the thesis of *Physicalism*, which will be stated later (p. 320) but which will not be established in this book, all terms of science, including those of psychology and the social sciences, can be reduced to terms of the physical language. In the last analysis they also express properties (or relations) of space-time domains. [*Examples:* "A is furious" or "A is thinking" means: "The body A (i.e. such and such a space-time domain) is in such and such a state"; "The society of such and such a people is an economy based on a monetary system" means: "In such and such a space-time domain, such and such processes occur."] For anyone who takes the point of view of Physicalism, it follows that our Language II forms a complete syntactical framework for science.

It would be a worth-while task to investigate the syntax of the language of physics and of the whole of science in greater and more exact detail, and to exhibit the most important of its conceptual forms, but we cannot here undertake such a thing.

PART IV

GENERAL SYNTAX

A. OBJECT-LANGUAGE AND SYNTAX-LANGUAGE

We have now constructed the syntax of Languages I and II and have thereby given two examples of *special syntax*. In Part IV we shall undertake an investigation of *general syntax*—that is to say, of that syntax which relates not to any particular individual language but either to all languages in general or to all languages of a certain kind. Before we go on, in Division B, to outline a general syntax applicable to any language whatsoever, we shall first set down, in Division A, some preliminary reflections concerning the nature of syntactical designations and of certain terms which occur in syntax.

§ 41. ON SYNTACTICAL DESIGNATIONS

A *designation* of an object can be either a proper name or a description of that object. The evident necessity of keeping in mind the distinction between a designation and the object designated thereby (for instance, between the word 'Paris' and the city of Paris), although frequently emphasized in logic, is not always observed in practice. If the object designated is such a thing as a town, and the designation itself a word (either spoken or written), the distinction is obvious. And for precisely that reason, in such cases failure to differentiate between the two does not lead to any harmful consequences.

If instead of "'Paris' is bi-syllabic" we write: "Paris is bi-syllabic", the method of writing is incorrect, because we are using the word 'Paris' in two different senses; in other sentences as the designation of the city, and in the sentence in question as the designation of the word 'Paris' itself. [In the second use, the word 'Paris' is autonymous. See p. 156.] Nevertheless, in this instance no confusion will arise, since it is quite clear that the subject here is the word and not the city.

It is another matter when the designated object is itself a linguistic expression, as is the case with syntactical designations. Here a failure to pay attention to the distinction leads very easily to obscurities and errors. In meta-mathematical treatises—the greater part of the word-text of mathematical writings is meta-mathematics, and therefore syntax—the necessary distinction is frequently neglected.

If a sentence (in writing) refers to a thing—my writing-table, for instance—then in this sentence a designation of the thing must occupy the position of the subject; one cannot simply place the thing itself—namely, the writing-table—upon the paper (this could only be done in accordance with a special convention; see below). In the case of a writing-table, and perhaps even of a match, this seems self-evident to everyone, but it is not so self-evident when we are dealing with things which are especially adapted to be put on paper, namely, with written characters. For example, in order to say that the Arabic figure three is a figure, one often writes something of this kind: "3 is a figure." Now here, the thing itself which is under discussion occupies the place of the subject on the paper. The correct mode of writing would be: "A three is . . . " or "'3' is. . . ." *If a sentence is concerned with an expression, then a designation of this expression*—namely, a syntactical designation in the syntax-language—*and not the expression itself, occupies the place of the subject in the sentence.* The syntax-language may be either a word-language or a symbol-language, or, again, a language composed of a mixture of words and symbols (for instance, in our text it consists of a mixture of English words and Gothic symbols). The most important kinds of syntactical designations of expressions are enumerated below:

A. *Designation of an expression* as an individual, spatio-temporally determined thing. (Occurs only in descriptive syntax.)

1. *Name* of an expression. [Occurs very seldom. *Example:* "the Sermon on the Mount" (which can also be interpreted as a description).]

2. *Description* of an expression. [*Example:* "Caesar's remark on crossing the Rubicon (was heard by so-and-so)."]

3. *Designation* of an expression by means of a like expression

in inverted commas. [*Examples:* "the saying 'alea iacta est'"; "the inscription 'nutrimentum spiritus'."]

B. *Designation of an expressional design* (see p. 15).

1. *Name* of an expressional design (e.g. of a symbolic design). [*Examples:* "A three"; "omega"; "the Lord's Prayer"; "Fermat's Theorem" (which can also be interpreted as a description); "nu"; "$\mathfrak{N}$".]

2. *Description* of an expressional design by means of the statement of a spatio-temporal position (indirect description, so-called ostension, see p. 80). [*Examples:* "Caesar's remark made at the Rubicon (consists of three words)"; "ausdr (b, a)" (see p. 80).]

3. *Description* of an expressional design by means of syntactical terms. [*Examples:* "The expression which consists of a three, a plus symbol, and a four"; "$\left(\mathfrak{z}_1 = \mathfrak{z}_1\right) \binom{\mathfrak{z}_1}{\mathfrak{nu}}$"; "$\sim \mathfrak{N}$".]

4. *Designation* of an expressional design by means of an expression of this design in *inverted commas*. [*Examples:* "'3'"; "'ω'"; "'3+4'"; "'alea iacta est' (consists of three words)".]

C. *Designation of a more general form* (that is, a form that can also apply to unequal expressions; see p. 16).

1. *Name* of a form (for instance, of a kind of symbol). [*Examples:* "variable"; "numerical expression"; "equation"; "$\mathfrak{v}$"; "$\mathfrak{pr}$"; "$\mathfrak{z}$".]

2. *Description* of a form. [*Examples:* "An expression consisting of two numerical expressions with a plus symbol between them"; "$\mathfrak{z} = \mathfrak{z}$".]

3. *Description* of a form by means of an expression of this form *in inverted commas* together with a *statement of the modifications permitted*. [*Example:* "An expression of the form '$x = y$', where any two unequal variables may occur in the places of 'x' and 'y'."]

It is frequently overlooked that the designation of a form with the help of an expression in inverted commas leads to obscurities if the modifications permitted are either not given at all or are given inexactly. For instance, we often find: "For sentences of the form '$(x)(p \lor F(x))$' so and so holds", which leaves open such questions as the following: Is it necessary for the ⌈ 'p' to occur in the sentence, or may any ⌐ occur in its place, or any sentence? Must the p '*F*' occur, or may any p take its place, or any pr? Or, again, in the place of '*F*(*x*)' may we have any sentence with the one free variable '*x*', or even with several free variables? This formulation is accordingly obscure and ambiguous (quite apart from the fact that the inverted commas are usually left out altogether, and that very often "for the sentence..." is written instead of "for sentences of the form...").

§ 42. ON THE NECESSITY OF DISTINGUISHING BETWEEN AN EXPRESSION AND ITS DESIGNATION

The importance of *distinguishing clearly between an expression and its syntactical designation* will readily be seen from such examples as the following; if, in the five sentences below, instead of the expressions '*ω*', "*ω*", 'omega', "omega", "'omega'", we were in every case to use the word 'omega', a very serious confusion would ensue:

(1) *ω* is an ordinal type.

(2) '*ω*' is a letter of the alphabet.

(3) Omega is a letter of the alphabet.

(4) 'Omega' is not a letter of the alphabet but a word of five letters.

(5) The fourth sentence is not concerned with omega and therefore not with '*ω*', but with 'omega'; hence in this sentence it is not, as in the third sentence, 'omega', but "omega" which occupies the place of the subject.

Since the name of a given object may be chosen arbitrarily, it is quite possible to take as a name for the thing, the thing itself, or, as a name for a kind of thing, the things of this kind. We can, for instance, adopt the rule that, instead of the word 'match', a match shall always be placed on the paper. But it is more often a linguistic expression than an extra-linguistic object that is used as its own designation. We call an expression which is used in this way *autonymous*. In this case the expression is used in some places as the designation of itself and in others as the designation of something else. In order to obviate this ambiguity of all expressions which also occur autonymously, a rule must be laid down to determine under what conditions the first, and under what the second, interpretation is to be taken. *Example:* We have used the symbols ' ∼ ', ' ∨ ', ' = ', and so forth sometimes as autonymous and sometimes as non-autonymous symbols, but we have at the same time stipulated that they are autonymous only when they occur in an expression containing Gothic symbols (see p. 17). *Counter-example:* Formulations of the following kind are frequently found: "We substitute $a + 3$ for x; if $a + 3$ is a prime number,...." Here the expression '$a + 3$' is used autonymously in the first case and non-autonymously in the second, namely (to put it in the material mode of speech), as the designation of a number. For this, no rule is given. The correct method of writing would be: "We substitute '$a + 3$' for 'x'; if $a + 3$ is a prime number,...." On the employment of autonymous designations in other systems, see §§ 68 and 69.

Sometimes (even by good logicians) an *abbreviation* for an expression is mistaken for a *designation* of the expression. *But the difference is essential.* If it is a question of an expression of the object-language, then the abbreviation also belongs to the object-language, but the designation to the syntax-language. The meaning of an abbreviation is not the original expression itself, but the meaning of the original expression.

Examples: If we write 'Const' as an abbreviation for 'Constantinople', this abbreviation does not mean the long name, but the city. If '2' is introduced as an abbreviation for '$1 + 1$', then '$1 + 1$' is not the meaning of '2', but both expressions have (in the material mode of speech) the same meaning—that is (formally expressed) they are synonymous. An expression may be replaced in a sentence by its abbreviation (and conversely), but not by its designation. The designation of an expression is not its representative, as an abbreviation is. Very often obscurities ensue because a new symbol is introduced in connection with a particular expression without its being made clear whether this symbol is to serve as an abbreviation or as a name for the expression. And sometimes the confusion which results is impossible to eradicate, because the new symbol is used in both senses, now in the word-text as a syntactical designation, and now in the symbolic formulae of the object-language.

Possibly many readers will think that, even though, strictly speaking, it is necessary to distinguish between a designation and a designated expression, yet the ordinary breaches of this rule are harmless. It is true that this is often the case (for instance, in the example given above of '$a + 3$'), but the constant common disregard of this distinction has already caused a great deal of confusion. It is this disregard which is probably partly responsible for the fact that so much uncertainty still exists concerning the nature of all logical investigations as syntactical theories of the forms of language. Perhaps the confusion between designation and designated object is also to blame for the fact that the fundamental difference between the sentential junctions (e.g. implication) and the syntactical relations between sentences (e.g. the consequence-relation) is frequently overlooked (see § 69). Similarly, the obscurity in the interpretation of many formal systems and logical investigations may be traced back to this. We shall come across various examples of such obscurity later.

Frege laid special emphasis on the need for differentiating between an object-symbol and its designation (even in the witty but fundamentally serious satire [*Zahlen*]). In his detailed expositions of his own symbolism and of arithmetic, he always maintained this distinction very strictly. In so doing, Frege presented us with the first example of an exact syntactical form of speech. He does not use any special symbolism as his syntax-language, but simply the word-language. Of the methods mentioned above he uses for the most part A 3, B 4, and C 2—expressions of the symbolism in inverted commas, together with descriptions of forms with the help of the word-language. He says ([*Grundgesetze*], Vol. I, p. 4): "Probably the constant use of inverted commas will seem strange; but by means of these I differentiate between the cases in which I am speaking about the symbol itself and those in which I am speaking about its meaning. However pedantic this may appear, I hold it to be necessary. It is remarkable how an inexact method of speech or of writing, which may have been adopted originally only for the sake of brevity and convenience, with full awareness of its inexactitude, can in the end confuse thought to an inordinate degree, once the consciousness of its inaccuracy has vanished."

The requirement laid down by Frege forty years ago was for a long time forgotten. It is true that, on the whole, as a result of the works of Frege, Peano, Schröder, and particularly of Whitehead and Russell [*Princ. Math.*], an exact method of working with logical formulae has been developed. But the contextual matter of nearly all logical writings since Frege lacks the accuracy of which he gave the model. Two examples may serve to indicate the ambiguities which have arisen in consequence of this.

Example 1. In the text of the majority of text-books and treatises on logistics (Russell's [*Princ. Math.*], Hilbert's [*Logik*], and Carnap's [*Logistik*] amongst them) a sentential variable is used in three or four different senses: (1) As a sentential variable of the object-language (as an $\int$, for instance: 'p'). (2) As an abbreviation (and thus a constant) for a compound sentence of the object-language (as a constant $\int a$, for instance: 'A'). (3) As an autonymous syntactical designation of a sentential variable ('$\int$'). (4) As a syntactical designation of any sentence ('$\mathfrak{S}$'). Thus in many cases it is not possible to arrive at the correct way of writing by merely adding inverted commas. The usual formulation: "If p is false, then for any q, $p \supset q$ is true" cannot be replaced by "If 'p' is false,..."; for 'p' is certainly false (by substitution every sentence is derivable). We must write either: "If 'A' is false, then for any 'B', 'A⊃B' is true", where 'A' and 'B' are abbreviating constants of the object-language (in this case with meanings left undetermined); or: "If $\mathfrak{S}_1$ is false, then for any $\mathfrak{S}_2$ the implication-sentence of $\mathfrak{S}_1$ and $\mathfrak{S}_2$ is true." If suitable conventions are established (as on p. 17) then, instead of "the implication-sentence of $\mathfrak{S}_1$ and $\mathfrak{S}_2$", we may here write more briefly: "$\mathfrak{S}_1 \supset \mathfrak{S}_2$."

Example 2. In a treatise by a distinguished logician, the following sentence occurs: "$\binom{p}{x} a$ is the formula which results from the formula a when the variable x (if it occurs in a) is replaced throughout by the combination of symbols p." Here we are from the beginning completely uncertain as to the interpretation. Which of the symbolic expressions in this statement are used as autonymous designations, and are accordingly to be enclosed in inverted commas if the correct mode of expressing the author's meaning is to be achieved? At first we shall probably be inclined to put 'a', 'x', and 'p' in inverted commas, and, on the other hand, to interpret '$\binom{p}{x}a$' as a syntactical mode of writing, and therefore not to enclose it as a whole in inverted commas, but only its component letters: "$\binom{'p'}{'x'}$'a'." (This would correspond approximately to our own formula: '$\mathfrak{S}_1\left(\begin{smallmatrix}\mathfrak{z}_1\\ \mathfrak{A}_1\end{smallmatrix}\right)$' or, more closely, to: "'p'$\binom{'x'}{'0'}$.") But the occurrence of the phrases "the combination of symbols p" and "if x occurs in a" rules out this interpretation; for 'p' is certainly no combination, and obviously 'x' does not occur in 'a'. Perhaps 'x' only is autonymous, while 'p', 'a', and '$\binom{p}{x}a$' (for which we should then have to write '$\binom{p}{'x'}a$') are not to be taken as autonymous syntactical designations? But opposed to this possibility is the circumstance that in the symbolic formulae of the object-language which is dealt with in the treatise, 'p' and 'a' and even '$\binom{p}{x}a$' occur (for instance, in the axiom '$(x)a\supset\binom{p}{x}a$'). Possibly all the symbolic symbols and expressions—not only in the sentences of the text but also in the symbolic formulae of the system, are intended as non-autonymous syntactical designations? In that case the way of writing that sentence of the text was legitimate; and the axiom referred to would correspond to our syntactical schema PSII 16. But, on the other hand, this is not easy to reconcile with the rest of the text of the treatise as it stands. We do not know to which object-language all the formulae, as syntactical formulae, are to refer. For our context here it is a matter of no importance which of these different interpretations is intended. Our object is only to show what confusions arise when it is not made clear whether an expression belongs to the object-language or is a syntactical designation, and, if the latter, whether it is autonymous or not.

Frege's demand for the maintenance of the distinction between a designation and a designated expression is, as far as I know, strictly fulfilled only in the writings of the Warsaw school (Lukasiewicz, Leśniewski, Tarski, and their pupils) who have consciously taken him as their model. These logicians make use of special syntactical symbols. This method has great advantages, although (as Frege's own example shows) it is not essential for correctness. The clear symbolic separation of object-symbols and syntax-symbols does not merely facilitate correct formulation, but, in the case of the Warsaw logicians, has been further justified by the fruitfulness of their investigations, which have led to a plenitude of important results. The use of special syntactical symbols within the word-text ought, in the majority of cases, to prove by far the most productive method; for it is both elastic and easily comprehensible, as well as sufficiently exact. [This method is applied in the text of the present work: word-language combined with Gothic symbols. The employment of Gothic letters by Hilbert and of heavy print by Church are preliminary steps in this direction.] In special cases, it may appear desirable to symbolize completely the sentences and definitions of syntax and thus to eliminate the word-language altogether. By this means an increased exactness is attained, albeit at the cost both of facility in treatment and of comprehensibility. Completely symbolized syntactical definitions of this kind are used by Leśniewski and Gödel. In his [*Neues System*] Leśniewski takes as object-language the sentential calculus (with junction-variables in operators as well), and in [*Ontologie*] the system of the ϵ-sentences. As syntax-language, he uses the symbolism of Russell, which, however, is only intended to serve as an abbreviation for the word-language. Gödel [*Unentscheidbare*] takes as object-language the arithmetic of the natural numbers in a modified form of the Russellian symbolism; as syntax-language, he uses the symbolism of Hilbert. (We have also applied this more exact method in the formal construction of Part II, where Language I is at the same time both object-language and syntax-language.)

§ 43. On the Admissibility of Indefinite Terms

We have called a defined symbol of Language II *definite* when no unrestricted operator occurs in the chain of its definitions; otherwise, *indefinite* (§ 15). If pr_1 is a definite ^1pr_I then the property which is expressed by means of pr_1 is resoluble; every sentence of the form $pr_1\,(\mathfrak{Arg}_1)$ in which the arguments are definite $\mathfrak{Z}$—in the simplest case, accented expressions—can be decided according to a fixed method. For an indefinite pr_I this does not hold in general.

For certain indefinite pr_I we are sometimes able to find a synonymous definite pr_I and by this means a method of resolution. But this is not possible in the majority of cases.

Examples: We can represent tne concept 'prime number' by an indefinite pr '$Prim_1$' as well as by a synonymous definite pr '$Prim_2$'. For example, we may define as follows (compare D 11, p. 60):

$$'Prim_1(x) \equiv \lfloor \sim(x=0) \cdot \sim(x=1) \cdot (u)\,((u=1)\, \vee \\ (u=x)\, \vee \sim Tlb\,(x,u))]\,';$$

and in the same way for '$Prim_2$', but with the restricted operator '$(u)x$' instead of '(u)'. Then '$Prim_1 = Prim_2$' is demonstrable; and thus the two pr are synonymous. On the other hand, for the indefinite pr 'BewbII' defined in II (where 'BewbII (a)' means, in syntactical interpretation: "The ^{SN}sentence a is demonstrable in II"; see p. 75), there is no synonymous definite pr; this was proved by Church.

The lack of a method of resolution for indefinite terms has induced many logicians to reject these terms altogether, as meaningless (e.g. Poincaré, Brouwer, Wittgenstein, and Kaufmann). Let us consider as examples two indefinite $^1pr_I^1$, 'P_1' and 'P_2' (in II, for example), which, by means of a definite $^1pr_I^2$, 'Q', may be defined in the following manner:

$$P_1(x) \equiv (\exists y)\,(Q\,(x,y)) \qquad (1)$$
$$P_2(x) \equiv (y)\,(Q\,(x,y)) \qquad (2)$$

The logicians referred to argue roughly as follows: the question whether, for instance, '$P_1(5)$' (or '$P_2(5)$') is true or not, is meaningless, inasmuch as we know of no method by which the answer may be sought, and the meaning of a term consists solely in the method of determination of its applicability or non-applicability. To this it may be replied: it is true that we know of no method of searching for the answer, but we do know what form the discovery of the answer would take—that is to say, we know under what conditions we should say that the answer had been found. This would be the case, for example, if we discovered a proof of which the last sentence was '$P_1(5)$'; and the question whether a given series of sentences is a proof of this kind or not is a definite question. Thus there exists the *possibility of the discovery of an answer*, and there appears to be no cogent reason for rejecting the question.

Some logicians take the view that a question of this nature is meaningless to begin with but becomes significant as soon as an answer is discovered. We regard such an approach as particularly inexpedient. It leads to our considering, e.g. '$P_1(5)$?' as a significant question, and '$P_1(6)$?' as a meaningless one, or as meaningless to-day and possibly significant to-morrow. Th.'s procedure is not, however, to be confused with the unquestionably useful and universally applied method by which previously established syntactical rules are altered as soon as certain fresh discoveries have been made (for instance, concerning the mutual dependence of primitive sentences, contradictions, etc.). As opposed to this, in the former method reference to historical events is included amongst the syntactical rules (concerning significance and non-significance).

Sometimes, in the case of the rejection of indefinite pr, a further distinction is made between the occurrence of an existential operator and that of a universal operator. The reason advanced for this differentiation is as follows: while for the proof of '$P_1(5)$' the discovery of a *single* number possessing the property designated by '$Q(5,y)$' is sufficient, for the proof of '$P_2(5)$' it must be shown that *every* number possesses this property. There is, however, no essential difference between these two cases. The discovery of a number which has a particular, definite property, and the discovery of a proof of a given sentence—that is to say, the discovery of a sentence-series which has a particular, definite property—are essentially similar operations; in both cases, it is a question of discovering an element having a given definite property in a denumerable class (that is to say, in an infinite series progressing in accordance with a given law).

§ 44. ON THE ADMISSIBILITY OF IMPREDICATIVE TERMS

Some logicians, while not rejecting all indefinite terms, reject a number of them, namely, the so-called *impredicative terms* (e.g. Russell in his so-called vicious-circle principle. See [*Princ. Math.*] Vol. I, p. 37, and Fraenkel [*Mengenlehre*], pp. 247 ff.). A thing is usually called impredicative (in the material mode of speech) when it is defined (or can only be defined) with the help of a totality to which it itself belongs. This means (translated into the formal mode of speech) that a defined symbol a_1 is called impredicative when an unrestricted operator with a variable to whose range of values a_1 belongs, occurs in its chain of definitions. Example [(3) serves only as an abbreviation]:

$$M(F, x) \equiv \left[\left(F(7) \cdot (y) \left[F(y) \supset F(y^!) \right] \right) \supset F(x) \right] \tag{3}$$
$$P_3(x) \equiv (F) \left[M(F, x) \right] \tag{4}$$

['$P_3(c)$' means: "c possesses all the hereditary properties of 7."] As opposed to 'P_1' and 'P_2' (Examples in § 43), 'P_3' is not only indefinite but impredicative as well, since it is of the same type as 'F'. Now, against the admissibility of such a term, the following objection is usually advanced. Assume that a concrete case is to be decided, such as '$P_3(5)$', i.e. '$(F) \left[M(F, 5) \right]$'. For this purpose it must be determined whether every property has the relation M to 5; it must also be known, it is said, amongst other things, whether this is true for P_3, that is to say, whether '$M(P_3, 5)$' is true. But this, according to (3), is equivalent in meaning to '$\left(P_3(7) \cdot \ldots \right) \supset P_3(5)$'. In order to find out the truth-value of this implication, the values of both members must be established, and hence also that of '$P_3(5)$'. In short, in order to determine whether '$P_3(5)$' is true, a series of other questions must be answered, amongst them whether '$P_3(5)$' is true. This is said to be an obvious circle; therefore '$P_3(5)$' is meaningless and consequently 'P_3' also.

This form of argument seems, however, to be beside the point (Carnap [*Logizismus*]): in order to demonstrate the truth of a universal sentence, it is not necessary to prove the sentences which result from it by the substitution of constants; rather, the truth of the universal sentence is established by a proof of that sentence itself. The demonstration of all individual cases is impossible from the start, because of their infinite number, and if such a test were necessary, all universal sentences and all indefinite pr (not only the impredicative ones) would be irresoluble and therefore (by that argument) meaningless. As opposed to this, in the first place, the construction of the proof is a finite operation; and in the second place, the possibility of the proof is quite independent of whether the defined symbol occurs amongst the constant values of the variable in question. In our example, '$M(P_3, 5)$' can be resolved before we resolve '$P_3(5)$'—for '$\sim M(P_3, 5)$' can easily be proved. For the purposes of abbreviation, we define as follows:

$$\text{'}P_4(x) \equiv (x \geqq 6)\text{'}.$$

Then first

$$\text{'} \sim [(P_4(7) \cdot (y) [P_4(y) \supset P_4(y')]) \supset P_4(5)]\text{'}$$

is demonstrable; and next, from this,

$$\text{'}\sim M(P_4, 5)\text{'}, \quad \text{'}\sim(F) [M(F, 5)]\text{'},$$

and consequently '$\sim P_3(5)$'; and similarly for every 33 from '0' to '6' in place of '5'. Further, '$P_3(8)$' is easily demonstrable, and similarly for every 33 from '7' onwards.

In general, since there are sentences with unrestricted operators which are demonstrable, *there is always the possibility of coming to a decision as to whether or not a certain indefinite or impredicative term is applicable in a particular individual case*, even though we may not always have a method at hand for arriving at this decision. Hence such terms are justified even from the standpoint which makes the admissibility of any term dependent on the possibility of a decision in every individual case. [Incidentally, in my opinion, this condition is too narrow, and its necessity is not convincingly established.]

The proper way of framing the question is not "Are indefinite (or impredicative) symbols admissible?" for, since there are no morals in logic (see § 17), what meaning can 'admissible' have here? The problem can only be expressed in this way: "How shall we construct a particular language? Shall we admit symbols of this kind or not? And what are the consequences of either procedure?" It is therefore a question of choosing a form of language —that is, of the establishment of rules of syntax and of the investigation of the consequences of these. Here, there are two principal points to be considered: first of all, we have to decide whether or not unrestricted operators are to be admitted, and second, whether or not universal predicate-variables are to be admitted for the different types. We will call p_1 *universal* when all the constants of the type of p_1 belong to the range of values of p_1 (that is to say, can be substituted for p_1). In II all p are universal; for instance, for a $^1p^1$ any $^1pr^1$ may be substituted. On the other hand, in [*Princ. Math.*] the type (0), by the branched rule of types, is divided again into sub-types, in such a way that for a particular p only the pr of a particular sub-type may be substituted.—1. If the first point is decided in the negative and unrestricted operators are excluded (as, for instance, in our Language I), then all the indefinite and consequently all the impredicative symbols are excluded. If, however, we admit the unrestricted operators, then the definiens of an indefinite definition (compare Examples (1) to (4)) is in accordance with the rules of syntax; but then it is natural to admit the definiendum as an abbreviation for the definiens.—2. The impredicative definitions of pr of any types whatsoever can be excluded by deciding the second point in the negative, and so not admitting universal variables for these types. [In this way Russell rejects all universal p, and Kaufmann all p in general.] If, however, we admit universal p and, moreover, admit them also in operators, then the definiens of an impredicative definition (compare Example (4)) is in accordance with the rules of syntax. But then, again, it is natural to admit the definiendum as an abbreviation for the definiens. In any case, the material reasons so far brought forward for the rejection either of indefinite or of impredicative terms are not sound. We are at liberty to admit or reject such definitions without giving any reason. But if we wish to justify either procedure, we must first exhibit its formal consequences.

§ 45. INDEFINITE TERMS IN SYNTAX

Our attitude towards the question of indefinite terms conforms to the principle of tolerance; in constructing a language we can either exclude such terms (as we have done in Language I) or admit them (as in Language II). It is a matter to be decided by convention. If we admit indefinite terms, then strict attention must be paid to the distinction between them and the definite terms; especially when it is a question of resolubility. Now this holds equally for the terms of syntax. If we use a definite language in the formalization of a syntax (e.g. Language I in our formal construction), then only definite syntactical terms may be defined. Some important terms of the syntax of transformations are, however, indefinite (in general); as, for instance, 'derivable', 'demonstrable', and *a fortiori* 'analytic', 'contradictory', 'synthetic', 'consequence', 'content', and so on. If we wish to introduce these terms also, we must employ an indefinite syntax-language (such as Language II).

In connection with the use of indefinite syntactical terms in the construction of a particular language, we must above all differentiate the formation and the transformation rules. The task of the formation rules is the construction of the definition of 'sentence'. This is frequently effected by defining a term 'elementary sentence', and determining several operations for the formation of sentences. An expression is then called a sentence when it can be constructed from elementary sentences by means of a finite application of sentence-forming operations. Usually the rules are so qualified that not only the terms 'elementary sentence' and 'sentence-forming operation' but also the term 'sentence' is definite. In this case it can always be decided whether a particular expression is a sentence or not. Although the adoption of an indefinite term 'sentence' is not inadmissible, it would in most cases be inexpedient.

Examples of 'sentence' as an indefinite term: (1) Heyting [*Math.* 1] p. 5; the definition of 'sentence' (there 'expression') is by rules 5.3 and 5.32 dependent upon the indefinite term 'demonstrable' (there 'correct'), and is thus itself indefinite. (2) Dürr [*Leibniz*] p. 87; whether a certain combination of two sentences ('general value' and 'principal value of the remainder') is a sentence or not (there 'significant' or 'meaningless') depends on the truth-values of the two sentences; here therefore the term 'sentence' is not only not logically definite, but is moreover descriptive (i.e. dependent on synthetic sentences).—If, in a language (e.g. in Peano), conditioned definitions are admitted ($\mathfrak{S}_1 \supset (\mathfrak{A}_1 = \mathfrak{A}_2)$, where $\mathfrak{A}_1$ is the definiendum), then the term 'sentence' is in general not logically definite. An indefinite term 'sentence' would perhaps be least open to objection if it referred back to definite terms, 'elementary sentence' and 'sentence-forming operation'. Von Neumann ([*Beweisth.*] p. 7) holds that the definiteness of the term 'sentence' is indispensable; otherwise the system is "incomprehensible and useless".

The principal terms concerning transformations, namely 'derivable' and 'demonstrable', are indefinite in the case of most languages; they are only definite in the case of very simple systems, for instance in that of the sentential calculus. Nevertheless, we can formulate the rules of transformation definitely, if, as is usually done, we do not define those terms directly but proceed from the definition of the definite terms 'directly derivable' (usually formulated by means of rules of inference) and 'primitive sentence'. [Here 'primitive sentence' can be represented as "directly derivable from the null series of premisses"; the definitions can be taken as primitive sentences of a particular form.] 'Derivable' is determined by means of a finite chain of the relation 'directly derivable'; 'demonstrable' is defined as "derivable from the null series of premisses". With the term 'consequence' (which has not been defined in the languages in use hitherto), it is another matter. Here the rules are indefinite even if they first define, not 'consequence', but only 'direct consequence' (as, for instance, those for Language I in § 14).

B. THE SYNTAX OF ANY LANGUAGE

(a) GENERAL CONSIDERATIONS

§ 46. FORMATION RULES

In this section we shall attempt to construct a *syntax for languages in general*, that is to say, a system of definitions of syntactical terms which are so comprehensive as to be applicable to any language whatsoever. [We have, it is true, had chiefly in mind as examples languages similar in their principal features to the usual symbolic languages, and, in many cases, the choice of the definitions has been influenced by this fact. Nevertheless, the terms defined are also applicable to languages of quite different kinds.]

The outline of a general syntax which follows is to be regarded as no more than a first attempt. The definitions framed will certainly need improvement and completion in many respects; and, above all, the connections between the concepts will have to be more closely investigated (that is to say, further syntactical theorems will have to be proved). As yet there have been very few attempts at a general syntactical investigation; the most important are Tarski's [*Methodologie*] and Ajdukiewicz's [*Sprache*].

By a language we mean here in general any sort of calculus, that is to say, a system of formation and transformation rules concerning what are called *expressions*, i.e. finite, ordered series of elements of any kind, namely, what are called *symbols* (compare §§ 1 and 2). In pure syntax, only syntactical properties of expressions, in other words, those that are dependent only upon the kind and order of the symbols of the expression, are dealt with.

As opposed both to the symbolic languages of logistics and to the strictly scientific languages, the common word-languages contain also sentences whose logical character (for example, logical validity or being the logical consequence of another particular sentence, etc.) depends not only upon their syntactical structure but also upon extra-syntactical circumstances. For instance, in the English language, the logical character of the sentences 'yes' and 'no', and of sentences which contain words like 'he', 'this' (in the sense of "the afore-mentioned") and so on, is also dependent upon what sentences have preceded them in the same context (treatise, speech, conversation, etc.). In the case of sentences in which words like 'I', 'you', 'here', 'now', 'to-day', 'yesterday', 'this' (in the sense of "the one pre-sent") and so forth occur, the logical character is not only dependent upon the preceding sentences, but also upon the extra-linguistic situation—namely, upon the spatio-temporal position of the speaker.

In what follows, we shall deal only with languages which contain *no expressions dependent upon extra-syntactical factors*. The logical character of all the sentences of these languages is then invariant in relation to spatio-temporal displacements; two sentences of the same wording will have the same character independently of where, when, or by whom they are spoken. In the case of sentences having extra-syntactical dependence, this invariance can be attained by means of the addition of person-, place-, and time-designations.

In the treatment of Languages I and II we introduced the term 'consequence' only at a late stage. *From the systematic standpoint, however, it is the beginning of all syntax. If for any language the term 'consequence' is established, then everything that is to be said concerning the logical connections within this language is thereby determined.* In the following discussion we assume that the trans-formation rules of any language S, i.e. the definition of the term 'direct consequence in S', are given. [For the sake of brevity in the case of syntactical terms, we usually leave out the specification 'in S' or 'of S'.] We shall, then, show how *the most important syntactical concepts can be defined by means of the term 'direct conse-quence'*. In this process it will become clear that the transforma-tion rules determine, not only concepts, such as 'valid' and 'con-tra-valid', but also *the distinction between logical and descriptive symbols, between variables and constants*, and further, *between logical and extra-logical (physical) transformation rules*, from which the difference between 'valid' and 'analytic' arises; also that the different kinds of operators and the various sentential connections can be characterized, and the existence of an *arithmetic* and an *infinitesimal calculus* in S can be determined.

As *syntactical Gothic symbols*, we use (as previously) '$\mathfrak{a}$' for symbols, '$\mathfrak{A}$' for (finite) expressions, '$\mathfrak{R}$' for (finite or infinite) classes of expressions (for the most part, of sentences). All further Gothic symbols in the general syntax (even those used previously in I and II) are defined in what follows. We say of an expression that it has the form $\mathfrak{A}_1 \begin{bmatrix} \mathfrak{A}_2 \\ \mathfrak{A}_3 \end{bmatrix}$ when it results from $\mathfrak{A}_1$ by the *replacement* at some place in $\mathfrak{A}_1$ of a partial expression $\mathfrak{A}_2$ by $\mathfrak{A}_3$. (On the difference between replacement and substitution, see pp. 36 f.)

We restrict ourselves to finite expressions only because, up to now, there has been no particular reason for dealing with *infinite* expressions. There is no fundamental objection to the introduction of infinite expressions and sentences. The treatment of them in an arithmetized syntax is quite possible. While a finite expression is represented by a series of numbers which can be replaced by a single series-number, an infinite expression would have to be represented by an infinite series of numbers or a real number. Such a series is expressed by means of a (definite or indefinite) functor. According to what was said previously (§ 39) we can speak not only of infinite expressions which are systematically constructed, but also of infinite expressions which are not determined by any mathematical law. An $\mathfrak{fu}_1$ corresponds to the former, an $\mathfrak{fu}_b$ to the latter.

We will assume the *definition of 'direct consequence'* to be stated in the following form: "$\mathfrak{A}_1$ is called a direct consequence of $\mathfrak{R}_1$ in S if: (1) $\mathfrak{A}_1$ and every expression of $\mathfrak{R}_1$ has one of the following forms: ...; and (2) $\mathfrak{A}_1$ and $\mathfrak{R}_1$ fulfil one of the following conditions: ...." The definition thus contains under (1) the formation rules and under (2) the transformation rules of S. Now we call $\mathfrak{A}_2$ a **sentence** ($\mathfrak{S}$) if $\mathfrak{A}_2$ has one of the forms under (1). Those $\mathfrak{a}$ that are $\mathfrak{S}$ are called **sentential symbols** ($\mathfrak{fa}$).

$\mathfrak{A}_1$ and $\mathfrak{A}_2$ (an $\mathfrak{a}$ is also an $\mathfrak{A}$) are said to be syntactically *related* when there exists an $\mathfrak{S}_1$ such that $\mathfrak{A}_1$ occurs in $\mathfrak{S}_1$ and $\mathfrak{S}_1 \begin{bmatrix} \mathfrak{A}_1 \\ \mathfrak{A}_2 \end{bmatrix}$ is a sentence. Two related expressions $\mathfrak{A}_1$ and $\mathfrak{A}_2$ are called **isogenous** if for any $\mathfrak{S}_1$, $\mathfrak{S}_1 \begin{bmatrix} \mathfrak{A}_1 \\ \mathfrak{A}_2 \end{bmatrix}$ and $\mathfrak{S}_1 \begin{bmatrix} \mathfrak{A}_2 \\ \mathfrak{A}_1 \end{bmatrix}$ are sentences. A class $\mathfrak{R}_1$ of expressions is called a **genus** if every two expressions of $\Re_1$ are isogenous, and no expression of $\Re_1$ is isogenous with an expression which does not belong to $\Re_1$. [Relatedness is a similarity (on these and the following terms see Carnap [*Logistik*] p. 48); further, isogeneity is transitive, and therefore an equality; the genera are the abstractive classes with respect to isogeneity; hence different genera have no members in common.] The sub-class of a genus of expressions which contains all the symbols and only the symbols of this genus is called a **symbolic genus**. Every $\mathfrak{A}$ of S belongs to exactly one genus; if the genus of $\mathfrak{A}_1$ is $\{\mathfrak{A}_1\}$, so that $\mathfrak{A}_1$ is not isogenous with any unequal $\mathfrak{A}$, then $\mathfrak{A}_1$ is called **isolated**. Two expressional genera or two symbolic genera are called related when at least one expression of the one is related to one of the other; in this case every expression of the one is related to every expression of the other.

In what follows, definitions of further syntactical formation terms will result from the transformation terms.

Examples: In I and II every $\mathfrak{z}$ is isolated; for $(\mathfrak{z}_1)\,\mathfrak{z}_2(\mathfrak{S}_1)\begin{bmatrix}\mathfrak{z}_2\\\mathfrak{z}_1\end{bmatrix}$ is not a sentence. In Hilbert's symbolism also, every $\mathfrak{z}$ is isolated; here, namely, $(\mathfrak{z}_1)\,(\mathfrak{pr}_1(\mathfrak{z}_1))\begin{bmatrix}\mathfrak{z}_1\\\mathfrak{z}_2\end{bmatrix}$ for unequal $\mathfrak{z}_1$ and $\mathfrak{z}_2$ is not a sentence. In I and II all constant $\mathfrak{z}\mathfrak{z}$ together form a genus. On the other hand, in I and II $\mathfrak{z}_1$ and $\mathfrak{nu}$, for example, are related but not isogenous, since in an operator $\mathfrak{z}_1$ cannot be replaced by $\mathfrak{nu}$.

The $\mathfrak{Pr}$ or $\mathfrak{Fu}$ of any type t in II are to be divided into two related genera: that of the $\mathfrak{p}$ (or $\mathfrak{f}$) of t and that of the remaining $\mathfrak{Pr}$ (or $\mathfrak{Fu}$, respectively). Thus the $\mathfrak{pr}$ (or $\mathfrak{fu}$) of t are to be divided into two related symbolic genera: that of the $\mathfrak{p}$ (or $\mathfrak{f}$) of t and that of the constant $\mathfrak{pr}$ (or $\mathfrak{fu}$, respectively) of t.

§ 47. Transformation Rules; d-Terms

We will now assume that the transformation rules of S which have been given in one way or another are converted into the form previously indicated of a definition of 'direct consequence in S'. It makes no difference in what terminology the rules were originally stated; all that is necessary is that it be clear to what forms of expressions the rules are in general applicable (which gives us the definition of 'sentence') and under what conditions a transformation or inference is permitted (which gives us the definition of 'direct consequence').

For instance, instead of 'direct consequence', we frequently have the terms 'derivable', 'deducible', 'inferable', 'results from', 'may be concluded (inferred, derived...) from', etc.; and, instead of 'direct consequence of the null class', it is customary to find 'primitive sentence', 'axiom', 'true', 'correct', 'demonstrable', 'logically valid', etc. We shall assume that even those rules concerning symbols of S, that are usually designated as definitions, are included in the rules concerning 'direct consequence' (for instance, as primitive sentences or rules of inference of a special kind); the definitions can either be finite in number and stated singly, or unlimited in number and established by means of a general law (as, for example, in I and II).

The second part of the definition of 'direct consequence' consists of a series of rules of the following form: " $\mathfrak{S}_1$ is a direct consequence of the sentence-class $\mathfrak{R}_1$ if (but not only if) $\mathfrak{S}_1$ and $\mathfrak{R}_1$ have such and such syntactical properties." We will extend this series by means of the following rule (which sometimes already belongs to the original series): " $\mathfrak{S}_1$ is always a direct consequence of $\{\mathfrak{S}_1\}$." We call the rules of the whole series *rules of consequence*, or, briefly, **c-rules**. Those in which the properties stipulated for $\mathfrak{S}_1$ and $\mathfrak{R}_1$ are definite we call *rules of derivation*, or, briefly, **d-rules**. $\mathfrak{S}_1$ is called *directly derivable* from $\mathfrak{R}_1$ if $\mathfrak{R}_1$ and $\mathfrak{S}_1$ satisfy one of the d-rules. $\mathfrak{S}_1$ is called a *primitive sentence* if $\mathfrak{S}_1$ is directly derivable from the null class. A finite series of sentences is called a **derivation** with the premiss class $\mathfrak{R}_1$ if every sentence of the series either belongs to $\mathfrak{R}_1$ or is directly derivable from a class $\mathfrak{R}_2$, the sentences of which precede it in the series. A derivation with a null premiss-class is called a **proof**. $\mathfrak{S}_1$ is called **derivable** from (or a d-consequence of) the sentential-class $\mathfrak{R}_1$ if $\mathfrak{S}_1$ is the last sentence of a derivation with the premiss-class $\mathfrak{R}_1$. $\mathfrak{S}_1$ (or $\mathfrak{R}_1$) is called **demonstrable** (or d-valid) if $\mathfrak{S}_1$ (or every sentence of $\mathfrak{R}_1$, respectively) is derivable from the null class and is therefore the last sentence of a proof. $\mathfrak{S}_1$ (or $\mathfrak{R}_1$) is called **refutable** (or d-contravalid) if every sentence of S is derivable from $\{\mathfrak{S}_1\}$ (or $\mathfrak{R}_1$, respectively). $\mathfrak{S}_1$ (or $\mathfrak{R}_1$) is called **resoluble** (or d-determinate) if $\mathfrak{S}_1$ (or $\mathfrak{R}_1$, respectively) is either demonstrable or refutable; otherwise **irresoluble** (or d-indeterminate).

Let $\mathfrak{R}_1$ be the largest class of symbols in S having the following properties. The symbols of $\mathfrak{R}_1$ can be arranged (not necessarily univocally) in a series. If $\mathfrak{a}_1$ belongs to $\mathfrak{R}_1$, then there is by the d-rules a definite direction for construction (in an arithmetized syntax, that means a definite syntactical functor), according to which, for every sentence $\mathfrak{S}_1$ in which $\mathfrak{a}_1$ occurs, a sentence $\mathfrak{S}_2$ can be constructed such that $\mathfrak{S}_2$ does not contain $\mathfrak{a}_1$, but only symbols which either do not belong to $\mathfrak{R}_1$ or which precede $\mathfrak{a}_1$ in that series, and such that $\mathfrak{S}_1$ and $\mathfrak{S}_2$ are derivable from one another. We call such a direction a **definition** of $\mathfrak{a}_1$, and the transformation of $\mathfrak{S}_1$ into $\mathfrak{S}_2$ the **elimination** of $\mathfrak{a}_1$. We call the symbols of $\mathfrak{R}_1$ **defined**, the others **undefined**.

We divide the syntactical terms into **d-terms** and **c-terms**, according to whether their definition refers only to the d-rules (as for instance in the preceding definitions) or to c-rules in general.

§ 48. c-Terms

We shall now define a number of c-terms, beginning with 'consequence', one of the most important syntactical terms. In what follows the $\mathfrak{R}$ are always sentential classes. $\mathfrak{S}_1$ is called a **consequence** of $\mathfrak{R}_1$, if $\mathfrak{S}_1$ belongs to every sentential class $\mathfrak{R}_i$ satisfying the following two conditions: 1. $\mathfrak{R}_1$ is a sub-class of $\mathfrak{R}_i$; 2. Every sentence which is a direct consequence of a sub-class of $\mathfrak{R}_i$ belongs to $\mathfrak{R}_i$.* $\mathfrak{R}_2$ is called a **consequence-class** of $\mathfrak{R}_1$ if every sentence of $\mathfrak{R}_2$ is a consequence of $\mathfrak{R}_1$. If d-rules only are given, then the terms 'derivable' and 'consequence' coincide; and if the term 'direct consequence' already possesses a certain kind of transitivity then it coincides with 'consequence'.

What has previously been said in the case of Language I holds in general for the fundamental difference between '*derivable in S*' and '*consequence in S*' (see pp. 38 f.), and analogously for every pair which consists of a d-term and its correlative c-term; compare the second and third columns in the survey on p. 183.

In almost all known systems, only definite rules of transformation are stated, that is to say, only d-rules. But we have already seen that it is possible to use also *indefinite syntactical terms* (§ 45). We shall therefore admit the possibility of laying down indefinite transformation rules and of introducing the c-terms which are based upon these. In dealing with the syntax of Languages I and

---

* (*Note*, 1935.) The above definition of 'consequence' is a correction of the German original, the need for which was pointed out to me by Dr. Tarski.

II we have come to recognize both the importance and the fertility of c-terms (such as 'consequence', 'analytic', 'content', etc.). One important advantage of the c-terms over the d-terms consists in the fact that with their help the complete division of $\mathfrak{S}_\mathrm{I}$ into analytic and contradictory is possible, whereas the corresponding classification of $\mathfrak{S}_\mathrm{I}$ into demonstrable and refutable is incomplete.

Only d-rules are given in the systems of Russell [*Princ. Math.*], Hilbert [*Logik*], von Neumann [*Beweisth.*], Gödel [*Unentscheidbare*], Tarski [*Widerspruchsfr.*].

Hilbert [*Grundl.* 1931] [*Tertium*] recently stated a rule of transformation which (in our terminology) runs approximately as follows: " If $\mathfrak{S}_1$ contains exactly one free variable $\mathfrak{z}_1$, and if every sentence of the form $\mathfrak{S}_1\left(\dfrac{\mathfrak{z}_1}{\mathfrak{S}\mathfrak{t}}\right)$ is demonstrable, then $(\mathfrak{z}_1)(\mathfrak{S}_1)$ may be laid down as a primitive sentence." Hilbert calls this rule a "new finite rule of inference". What is to be understood by 'finite' is not precisely stated; according to indications given by Bernays [*Philosophie*] p. 343, it means about what we mean by 'definite'. The rule is, however, obviously indefinite. Its formulation was presumably motivated by the incompleteness, indicated above, of all arithmetics which are restricted to d-rules. The rule given, however, which refers only to numerical variables $\mathfrak{z}$, is not sufficient to secure a complete classification.

Herbrand [*Non-contrad.*] p. 5 makes use of Hilbert's rule, but with certain restrictions; $\mathfrak{S}_1$ and the definitions of the $\mathfrak{fu}$ which occur in $\mathfrak{S}_1$ must not contain any operators.

Tarski discusses Hilbert's rule ("Rule of infinite induction" [*Widerspruchsfr.*] p. 111)—he himself had previously (1927) laid down a similar one—and rightly attributes to it an "infinitist character". In his opinion: "it cannot easily be harmonized with the interpretation of the deductive method that has been accepted up to the present"; and this is correct in so far as this rule differs fundamentally from the d-rules which have hitherto been exclusively used. In my opinion, however, there is nothing to prevent the practical application of such a rule.

In Language I, DC 1 refers back to the definite rules PSI 1–11 and RI 1–3; DC 2 is indefinite.

$\mathfrak{R}_1$ is called **valid** if $\mathfrak{R}_1$ is a class of consequences of the null class (and hence of every class). [We do not use the term 'analytic' here because we wish to leave open the possibility that S contains not only logical rules of transformation (as do Languages I and II) but also physical rules such as natural laws (see § 51). In relation to languages like I and II, the terms 'valid' and 'analytic' coincide.] $\Re_1$ is called **contravalid** if every sentence is a consequence of $\Re_1$. $\Re_1$ is called **determinate** if $\Re_1$ is either valid or contravalid; otherwise **indeterminate**. In a word-language it is convenient in many cases to use the same term for properties both of sentences and of classes of sentences. We shall call a sentence $\mathfrak{S}_1$ valid (or contravalid, determinate, or indeterminate) if $\{\mathfrak{S}_1\}$ is valid (or contravalid and so on, respectively). And we shall proceed in the same way with the terms which are to be defined later.

Theorem 48.1. Let $\Re_2$ be a consequence-class of $\Re_1$; if $\Re_1$ is valid, $\Re_2$ is also valid; if $\Re_2$ is contravalid, so also is $\Re_1$.

Theorem 48.2. Let $\mathfrak{S}_2$ be a consequence of $\mathfrak{S}_1$; if $\mathfrak{S}_1$ is valid, $\mathfrak{S}_2$ is also valid; if $\mathfrak{S}_2$ is contravalid, so also is $\mathfrak{S}_1$.

Theorem 48.3. If every sentence of $\Re_1$ is valid, $\Re_1$ is also valid; and conversely.

Theorem 48.4. If at least one sentence of $\Re_1$ is contravalid, then $\Re_1$ is contravalid; the converse is not universally true.

Two or more sentences are called **incompatible** (or d-incompatible) with one another if their class is contravalid (or refutable, respectively); otherwise they are called **compatible** (or d-compatible). Two or more sentential classes are called incompatible (or d-incompatible) with one another if their sum is contravalid (or refutable, respectively); otherwise they are called compatible (or d-compatible).

$\Re_2$ is called **dependent** upon $\Re_1$ if $\Re_2$ is a consequence-class of $\Re_1$, or is incompatible with $\Re_1$; otherwise it is called **independent** of $\Re_1$. $\Re_2$ is called d-dependent upon $\Re_1$ if either every sentence of $\Re_2$ is derivable from $\Re_1$, or $\Re_2$ is d-incompatible with $\Re_1$; otherwise it is called d-independent of $\Re_1$. (The definitions are analogous for $\mathfrak{S}_1$ and $\mathfrak{S}_2$.)

Theorem 48.5. If $\Re_1$ is dependent (or d-dependent) upon the null class, then $\Re_1$ is determinate (or resoluble, respectively); and conversely.

We say that there is (mutual) *independence* within $\Re_1$ if every two sentences of $\Re_1$ are independent of one another. And we say that there is *complete independence* within $\Re_1$ if every proper non-null sub-class of $\Re_1$ is independent of its complementary class in $\Re_1$.

Theorem 48.6. If $\Re_1$ is not contravalid and is not a consequence-class of a proper sub-class, then there is complete independence within $\Re_1$; and conversely.

$\Re_1$ is called **complete** (or d-complete) if every $\Re$ (and consequently every $\mathfrak{S}$ of S) is dependent (or d-dependent, respectively)
upon $\Re_1$; otherwise it is called **incomplete**.

Theorem 48.7. If $\Re_2$ is complete and is a consequence-class of
$\Re_1$, then $\Re_1$ also is complete.

Theorem 48.8. If the sentential null class is complete (or d-
complete) in S, then every $\Re$ in S is complete (or d-complete,
respectively).

The arrows in the table on p. 183 indicate the dependence between the defined d- and c-concepts. Although the d-method is the
fundamental method and the d-terms have the simpler definitions,
yet the c-terms are the more important from the standpoint of
certain general considerations. They are more closely connected
with the material interpretation of language; and this is shown
formally by the fact that simpler relations obtain among them.
In what follows we shall be dealing principally with the c-terms,
and shall only state the corresponding d-terms occasionally (if no
special term is given, one is constructed from the c-term by pre-
fixing a 'd-').

§ 49. Content

By the **content** of $\Re_1$ (or of $\mathfrak{S}_1$; cf. p. 174) in S, we understand
the class of the non-valid sentences which are consequences of $\Re_1$
(or $\mathfrak{S}_1$, respectively). This definition is analogous to the previous
definitions for Language I (p. 42) and Language II (p. 120); it
must here be noted that in Languages I and II 'valid' coincides
with 'analytic'.

Other possibilities of definition. Instead of the class of the non-
valid consequences, one might perhaps designate as 'content' the
class of all consequences. As opposed to this, our definition has the
advantage that by it the analytic sentences in pure L-languages (see
below) such as I and II have the null content. Again, it might be
possible to take as 'content' the class of all indeterminate consequences, or even the class of all non-contravalid consequences. Let
S be a non-descriptive language (such as a mathematical calculus).
Then, in S there are no indeterminate (or synthetic) sentences. In
this case, on the basis of our definition, the analytic sentences are
equipollent, and similarly the contradictory sentences; but there is
not equipollence between the two. On the basis of either of the above
definitions, on the other hand, all sentences would be equipollent,

though they differ essentially from one another in that only analytic sentences are consequences of an analytic sentence, but all sentences are consequences of a contradictory sentence. Ajdukiewicz gives a formal definition of 'sense' which is worthy of note. It differs considerably from our definition of 'content', for, according to it, the term 'equivalence of sense' is very much narrower than our term 'equipollence'.

$\Re_1$ and $\Re_2$ are called **equipollent** when their contents coincide. If the content of $\Re_2$ is a proper sub-class of the content of $\Re_1$, then $\Re_2$ is called *poorer in content* than $\Re_1$, and $\Re_1$ *richer in content* than $\Re_2$. We say that $\Re_1$ has the *null content* if the content of $\Re_1$ is empty, i.e. the null class. We say that $\Re_1$ has the *total content* if the content of $\Re_1$ is the class of all non-valid sentences. Two or more classes are said to have *exclusive contents* if their contents have no member in common. All these terms are also applied to sentences (see p. 174). We say that a mutual *exclusiveness in content* subsists in $\Re_1$ if every two sentences of $\Re_1$ have exclusive contents.

Theorem 49.1. If $\Re_2$ is a consequence-class of $\Re_1$, then the content of $\Re_2$ is contained in that of $\Re_1$; and conversely. *In the transition to a consequence, an increase in the content never occurs.* It is in this that the so-called *tautological character* of the *consequence-relation* consists.

Theorem 49.2. If $\Re_1$ and $\Re_2$ are consequence-classes of one another, then they are *equipollent*; and conversely.

Theorem 49.3. If $\Re_2$ is a consequence-class of $\Re_1$, but $\Re_1$ not a consequence-class of $\Re_2$, then $\Re_1$ is *richer in content* than $\Re_2$; and conversely.

Theorem 49.4. If $\Re_1$ is *valid*, then $\Re_1$ has the *null content*; and conversely.

Theorem 49.5. If $\Re_1$ is *contravalid*, then $\Re_1$ has the *total content*; and conversely.

Theorems 1 to 5 hold likewise for $\mathfrak{S}_1$ and $\mathfrak{S}_2$.

$\Re_1$ is called *perfect* if the content of $\Re_1$ is contained in $\Re_1$. According to this, every content is perfect. The product of two perfect classes is also perfect; but this is in general not true for the sum.

$\mathfrak{A}_1$ is said to be replaceable by $\mathfrak{A}_2$ if $\mathfrak{S}_1$ is always equipollent to $\mathfrak{S}_1 \begin{bmatrix} \mathfrak{A}_1 \\ \mathfrak{A}_2 \end{bmatrix}$. $\mathfrak{A}_1$ and $\mathfrak{A}_2$ are called **synonymous** (with one another) if they are mutually replaceable. Only expressions of the same genus can be synonymous. [If $\mathfrak{A}_1$ is replaceable by $\mathfrak{A}_2$, it is usually also synonymous with $\mathfrak{A}_2$.]

$\mathfrak{A}_1$ is called a *principal expression* if $\mathfrak{A}_1$ is not empty and there exists an expression which is related to, but not synonymous with, $\mathfrak{A}_1$. We count as *principal symbols*, first, every symbol which is a principal expression, and, second, symbols of certain kinds which will be described later on (e.g. $\mathfrak{B}$, $\mathfrak{v}$, $^0\mathfrak{a}$, $\mathfrak{pr}$, $\mathfrak{vf}$, $\mathfrak{z}\mathfrak{z}$); the rest of the symbols are called *subsidiary symbols*. [*Example:* The principal symbols of Language II are the $\mathfrak{fa}$, $\mathfrak{z}\mathfrak{z}$, $\mathfrak{pr}$, $\mathfrak{fu}$, $\mathfrak{verfn}$, and '$\sim$', ' = ', '|', '∃' (by the definitions of general syntax, '$\sim$' is a $\mathfrak{vf}$, ' = ' a $\mathfrak{pr}$, '|' a $\mathfrak{zfu}$; the null expression is related to '∃' but is not synonymous with it). The remaining symbols are subsidiary symbols, namely, brackets, commas, and 'K' (because in II there are no numerical operators other than the K-operators).]

§ 50. LOGICAL AND DESCRIPTIVE EXPRESSIONS; SUB-LANGUAGES

If a material interpretation is given for a language S, then the symbols, expressions, and sentences of S may be divided into logical and descriptive, i.e. those which have a purely logical, or mathematical, meaning and those which designate something extra-logical—such as empirical objects, properties, and so forth. This classification is not only inexact but also non-formal, and thus is not applicable in syntax. But if we reflect that all the connections between logico-mathematical terms are independent of extra-linguistic factors, such as, for instance, empirical observations, and that they must be solely and completely determined by the transformation rules of the language, we find the formally expressible distinguishing peculiarity of logical symbols and expressions to consist in the fact that each sentence constructed solely from them is determinate. This leads to the construction of the following definition. [The definition must refer not only to symbols but to expressions as well; for it is possible for $\mathfrak{a}_1$ in S to be logical in certain contexts and descriptive in others.]

Let $\mathfrak{R}_1$ be the product of all expressional classes $\mathfrak{R}_i$ of S, which fulfil the following four conditions. [In the majority of the usual language-systems, there exists only one class of the kind $\mathfrak{R}_i$; this is then $\mathfrak{R}_1$.] 1. If $\mathfrak{A}_1$ belongs to $\mathfrak{R}_i$, then $\mathfrak{A}_1$ is not empty and there exists a sentence which can be sub-divided into partial expressions in such a way that all belong to $\Re_i$ and one of them is $\mathfrak{A}_1$. 2. Every sentence which can be thus sub-divided into expressions of $\Re_i$ is determinate. 3. The expressions of $\Re_i$ are as small as possible, that is to say, no expression belongs to $\Re_i$ which can be sub-divided into several expressions of $\Re_i$. 4. $\Re_i$ is as comprehensive as possible, that is to say, it is not a proper sub-class of a class which fulfils both (1) and (2). An *expression* is called **logical** ($\mathfrak{A}_1$) if it is capable of being sub-divided into expressions of $\Re_1$; otherwise it is called **descriptive** ($\mathfrak{A}_b$). A *language* is called *logical* if it contains only $\mathfrak{a}_1$; otherwise *descriptive*.

With a language which is used in practice—for instance, that of a particular domain of science—it is usually quite clear whether a certain symbol has a logico-mathematical or an extra-logical, say a physical, meaning. In an unambiguous case of this kind, the formal differentiation just given coincides with the usual one. There are occasions, however, when a mere non-formal consideration leaves it doubtful whether a symbol is of the one kind or the other. In such a case, the formal criterion helps us to a clear decision, which on closer examination will also be found to be materially satisfactory.

Example: Is the metrical fundamental tensor '$g_{\mu\nu}$', by means of which the metrical structure of physical space is determined, a mathematical or a physical term? According to our formal criterion, there are here two cases to be distinguished. Let S_1 and S_2 be physical languages, each of them containing not only mathematics but also the physical laws as rules of transformation (this will be examined more closely in § 51). In S_1 a homogeneous space may be assumed: '$g_{\mu\nu}$' has the same value everywhere, and at every point the measure of curvature is the same in all directions (in the simplest case, 0 —Euclidean structure). In S_2, on the other hand, the Einsteinian non-homogeneous space may be assumed: then '$g_{\mu\nu}$' has various values, depending upon the distribution of matter in space. They are therefore—and this is an essential point for our differentiation—not determined by a general law. '$g_{\mu\nu}$' is thus a *logical symbol* in S_1 and a *descriptive symbol* in S_2. For the sentences which give the values of this tensor for the various space-time points are in S_1 all determinate; and on the other hand, in S_2 at least part of them are indeterminate. At a first glance, it may appear strange that the fundamental tensor should not have the same character in all languages. But on closer examination we must admit that there is here a fundamental difference between S_1 and S_2. The metrical calculations (for example, the calculation of a triangle from suitable determinations) are made in S_1 by means of mathematical rules which, it is true, in some respects (for instance, in the choice of the value of a fundamental constant such as the constant curvature of space) are based on empirical observations (see § 82). But on the other hand, for such calculations in S_2 empirical data are regularly required, namely, data concerning the distribution of the values of the fundamental tensor (or of the density) in the space-time domain in question.

Theorem 50.1. *Every logical sentence is determinate;* every indeterminate sentence is descriptive. With the given form of definition for 'logical' this follows directly. If 'logical expression' is defined in some other way (for instance, by the statement of the logical primitive symbols, as in Languages I and II) then the definitions of the terms 'valid' and 'contravalid' (which in I and II coincide with 'analytic' and 'contradictory') must be so contrived that every $\mathfrak{S}_I$ is determinate.

Theorem 50.2. (*a*) If S is logical, then every $\mathfrak{K}$ in S is determinate; and conversely. (*b*) If S is descriptive, then there is an indeterminate $\mathfrak{K}$ in S; and conversely.

S_2 is called a **sub-language** of S_1 if the following conditions hold: 1. every sentence of S_2 is a sentence of S_1; 2. if $\mathfrak{K}_2$ is a consequence-class of $\mathfrak{K}_1$ in S_2, then it is likewise a consequence-class of $\mathfrak{K}_1$ in S_1. S_2 is called a *conservative sub-language* of S_1 when, in addition: 3. if $\mathfrak{K}_2$ is a consequence-class of $\mathfrak{K}_1$ in S_1, and $\mathfrak{K}_2$ and $\mathfrak{K}_1$ also belong to S_2, then $\mathfrak{K}_2$ is also a consequence-class of $\mathfrak{K}_1$ in S_2. If S_2 is a sub-language of S_1 but not S_1 of S_2, then S_2 is called a *proper sub-language* of S_1. By the *logical sub-language* of S, we understand the conservative sub-language of S which results from S by the elimination of all the descriptive sentences.

Let S_2 be a sub-language of S_3, and $\mathfrak{K}_1$ and $\mathfrak{K}_2$ sentential classes of S_2. The table on p. 225 states under what conditions a syntactical property of $\mathfrak{K}_1$, or a relation between $\mathfrak{K}_1$ and $\mathfrak{K}_2$, which obtains in S_2, obtains also in S_3 (rubric 3); or conversely (rubric 5). Thus, for example, we can see from the table that if $\mathfrak{K}_1$ is valid in S_2, then it is also valid in S_3; if $\mathfrak{K}_1$ is valid in S_3 and S_2 is a conservative sub-language of S_3, then $\mathfrak{K}_1$ is also valid in S_2.

Example: I is a proper conservative sub-language of II. Let I' be the language which results from I if unrestricted operators with 3 are admitted; then I is a proper sub-language of I' although both languages possess the same symbols.

§ 51. LOGICAL AND PHYSICAL RULES

For Languages I and II we have set up only rules of transformation that on a material interpretation can be represented as having a logico-mathematical basis. The same is true of the majority of symbolic languages which have hitherto been formulated. We may, however, also construct a language with *extra-logical rules of transformation*. The first thing which suggests itself is to include amongst the primitive sentences the so-called laws of nature, i.e. universal sentences of physics ('physics' is here to be understood in the widest sense). It is possible to go even further and include not only universal but also concrete sentences—such as empirical observation-sentences. In the most extreme case we may even so extend the transformation rules of S that every sentence which is momentarily acknowledged (whether by a particular individual or by science in general) is valid in S. For the sake of brevity, we shall call all the logico-mathematical transformation rules of S logical or L-*rules*; and all the remainder, physical or P-*rules*. Whether in the construction of a language S we formulate only L-rules or include also P-rules, and, if so, to what extent, is not a logico-philosophical problem, but a matter of convention and hence, at most, a question of expedience. If P-rules are stated, we may frequently be placed in the position of having to alter the language; and if we go so far as to adopt all acknowledged sentences as valid, then we must be continuously expanding it. But there are no fundamental objections to this. If we do not include certain acknowledged sentences as valid in S, this does not mean that they are excluded from S. They can still appear in S as indeterminate premisses for the derivation of other sentences (as for instance all the synthetic sentences of I and II).

Now how is the *difference between* L-*rules and* P-*rules*—which we have here only indicated in an informal way—to be *formally defined*? This difference, when related to primitive sentences, does not coincide with the difference between logical and descriptive sentences. An $\mathfrak{S}_l$ as a primitive sentence is always an L-rule; but an $\mathfrak{S}_b$ as a primitive sentence need not be a P-rule. [*Example:* Let 'Q' be a $\mathfrak{pr}_b$ of Language I. Then, for example,

$$\text{`Q(3)} \supset (\sim Q(3) \supset Q(5))\text{'} \quad (\mathfrak{S}_1)$$

is a descriptive primitive sentence of the kind PSI 1. But $\mathfrak{S}_1$ is obviously true in a purely logical way, and we must arrange the further definitions so that $\mathfrak{S}_1$ is counted amongst the L-rules and is called, not P-valid, but analytic (L-valid). That $\mathfrak{S}_1$ is logically true is shown formally by the fact that every sentence which results from $\mathfrak{S}_1$ when 'Q' is replaced by any other pr is likewise a primitive sentence of the kind PSI 1.] The example makes it clear that we must take the general replaceability of the $\mathfrak{A}_b$ as the definitive characteristic of the L-rules.

Let $\mathfrak{S}_2$ be a consequence of $\mathfrak{R}_1$ in S. Here three cases are to be distinguished: 1. $\mathfrak{R}_1$ and $\mathfrak{S}_2$ are logical. 2. Descriptive expressions occur in $\mathfrak{R}_1$ and in $\mathfrak{S}_2$, but only as undefined symbols; here two further cases are to be distinguished: 2 a. for any $\mathfrak{R}_3$ and $\mathfrak{S}_4$ which are formed from $\mathfrak{R}_1$ (or $\mathfrak{S}_2$) by the replacement of every descriptive symbol of $\mathfrak{R}_1$ (or $\mathfrak{S}_2$ respectively) by an expression of the same genus, and specifically of equal symbols by equal expressions, the following is true: $\mathfrak{S}_4$ is a consequence of $\mathfrak{R}_3$; 2 b. the condition mentioned is not fulfilled for every $\mathfrak{R}_3$ and $\mathfrak{S}_4$. 3. In $\mathfrak{R}_1$ and $\mathfrak{S}_2$ defined descriptive symbols also occur; let $\tilde{\mathfrak{R}}_1$ and $\tilde{\mathfrak{S}}_2$ be constructed from $\mathfrak{R}_1$ (or $\mathfrak{S}_2$ respectively) by the elimination of every defined descriptive symbol (including those which are newly introduced as the result of an elimination); 3 a. the condition given in 2 a for $\mathfrak{R}_1$ and $\mathfrak{S}_2$ is fulfilled for $\tilde{\mathfrak{R}}_1$ and $\tilde{\mathfrak{S}}_2$; 3 b. the said condition is not fulfilled. In cases 1, 2 a, 3 a, we call $\mathfrak{S}_2$ an **L-consequence** of $\mathfrak{R}_1$; in cases 2 b, 3 b, we call $\mathfrak{S}_2$ a **P-consequence** of $\mathfrak{R}_1$. Thus the formal distinction between L- and P-rules is achieved.

If S contains only L-rules (that is to say, if every consequence in S is an L-consequence), we call S an **L-language**; otherwise, a **P-language**. By the L-sub-language of S we shall mean that sublanguage of S which has the same sentences as S but which has as transformation rules only the L-rules of S.

Theorem 51.1. Every logical language is an L-language. The converse is not always true.

The distinction between L- and P-languages must not be confused with that between logical and descriptive languages. The latter is dependent upon the symbolic apparatus (although only, it is true, upon a property of the symbolic apparatus which appears in the transformation rules), the former on the kind of the transformation rules. Languages I and II are, for example, descriptive languages (they contain a_b, as is shown by the occurrence of indeterminate, namely, synthetic sentences), but they are L-languages: every consequence-relation in them is an L-consequence; and only analytic sentences are valid in them. Similarly, the difference between the L-sub-language of S and the logical sub-language of S is to be noted. For instance, if S is a descriptive L-language (like I and II) then the L-sub-language of S is S itself, but the logical sub-language of S is a proper sub-language.

§ 52. L-TERMS; 'ANALYTIC' AND 'CONTRADICTORY'

To the previously defined d- and c-terms we now add **L-terms** (to wit, L-d-terms and L-c-terms). If in the L-sub-language of S, $\mathfrak{R}_1$ has a particular (d- or c-) property, we attribute to it in S the corresponding L-property. For instance, $\mathfrak{S}_1$ is called *L-demonstrable* in S if $\mathfrak{S}_1$ is demonstrable in the L-sub-language of S. $\mathfrak{R}_2$ is called the *L-content* of $\mathfrak{R}_1$ in S if $\mathfrak{R}_2$ is the content of $\mathfrak{R}_1$ in the L-sub-language of S, and so on. Instead of 'L-valid', 'L-contravalid', and 'L-indeterminate', we shall usually say '**analytic**', '**contradictory**', and '**synthetic**'. In the table which follows (p. 183), the correlative terms are placed on the same line. An arrow between two terms shows that one may be inferred from the other. [*Example:* If $\mathfrak{S}_2$ is L-derivable from $\mathfrak{S}_1$ then it is also derivable from $\mathfrak{S}_1$; and if derivable from $\mathfrak{S}_1$, then also a consequence of $\mathfrak{S}_1$. Between an L-d- and an L-c-term, the inference always holds in the same direction as between the correlative d- and c-terms.] Here again the d- and L-d-terms are more fundamental for the method of proof; on the other hand, the c- and L-c-terms are the more important for many applications.

Since I and II are L-languages, in their case every syntactical term coincides with the correlative L-term (for instance, 'demonstrable' with 'L-demonstrable', 'consequence' with 'L-consequence', 'valid' with 'analytic', 'content' with 'L-content', and so on). The L-d- and L-c-terms which were previously defined for I and II agree with those now defined, even where the earlier definition has quite a different form (as for example in the case of 'analytic in II').

Theorem 52.1. (*a*) Every analytic sentence is valid. (*b*) Every valid logical sentence is analytic.—Regarding (*b*): Let $\mathfrak{S}_1$ be a valid

L-d-terms:		*d-terms:*		*c-terms:*		*L-c-terms:*
L-derivable	↑	(d-consequence) derivable	→	consequence	↓	L-consequence
L-demonstrable	↑	(d-valid) demonstrable	→	valid	↓	(L-valid) *analytic*
L-refutable	↑	(d-contravalid) refutable	→	contravalid	↓	(L-contravalid) *contradictory*
L-resoluble	↑	(d-determinate) resoluble	→	determinate	↓	L-determinate
L-irresoluble	↓	(d-indetermin.) irresoluble	↓	indeterminate	↑	(L-indeterminate) *synthetic*
L-d-incompatible	↑	d-incompatible	↑	(c-) incompatible	↓	L-incompatible
L-d-compatible	↓	d-compatible	↓	(c-) compatible	↑	L-compatible
L-d-dependent	↑	d-dependent	↑	dependent	↓	L-dependent
L-d-independent	↓	d-independent	↓	independent	↑	L-independent
L-d-complete	↑	d-complete	↑	complete	↓	L-complete
L-d-incomplete	↓	d-incomplete	↓	incomplete	↑	L-incomplete
				content		L-content
				equipollent	↓	L-equipollent
				perfect	↑	L-perfect
				synonymous	↓	L-synonymous

$\mathfrak{S}_I$. Then $\mathfrak{S}_1$ is a consequence of the null class, and hence an L-consequence of it, and therefore analytic.

Theorem 52.2. (*a*) Every contradictory sentence is contravalid. (*b*) Every contravalid logical sentence is contradictory.—Regarding (*b*): Let $\mathfrak{S}_1$ be a contravalid $\mathfrak{S}_I$. Then every sentence is a consequence of $\mathfrak{S}_1$. Therefore, in the first place, every $\mathfrak{S}_I$, and in the second place, in the case of all $\mathfrak{S}_b$, every $\mathfrak{S}_b$ transformed according to rule 2 *a* or 3 *a* (p. 181), is a consequence of $\mathfrak{S}_1$. Hence every sentence is an L-consequence of $\mathfrak{S}_1$. Therefore, $\mathfrak{S}_1$ is contradictory.

Theorem 52.3. Every logical sentence is L-determinate; *there are no synthetic logical sentences.* This follows from Theorems 50.1, 52.1 *b* and 2 *b*.

Theorem 52.4. If every sentence of $\mathfrak{R}_1$ is analytic, then $\mathfrak{R}_1$ is analytic; and conversely.

Theorem 52.5. If at least one sentence of $\mathfrak{R}_1$ is contradictory then $\mathfrak{R}_1$ is contradictory. If $\mathfrak{R}_1$ is logical, then the converse is also true.

Theorem 52.6. Let $\mathfrak{S}_2$ be a consequence of $\mathfrak{R}_1$. (*a*) If $\mathfrak{R}_1$ is analytic, then $\mathfrak{S}_2$ is also analytic. (*b*) If $\mathfrak{S}_2$ is contradictory, then $\mathfrak{R}_1$ is also contradictory.

Theorem 52.7. If $\mathfrak{S}_1$ is an L-consequence of the sentential null class (and therefore of every class), then $\mathfrak{S}_1$ is analytic; and conversely.

Theorem 52.8. If $\mathfrak{R}_1$ is contradictory, then every sentence is an L-consequence of $\mathfrak{R}_1$; and conversely.

Theorem 52.9. The L-content of $\mathfrak{R}_1$ is the class of the non-analytic sentences that are L-consequences of $\mathfrak{R}_1$.

The ordinary concept of the *equivalence in sense* of two sentences is ambiguous. We represent it by means of two different formal terms, namely, equipollence and L-equipollence. Analogously, we replace the ordinary concept of the *equivalence in meaning* of two expressions by two different terms, synonymity and L-synonymity. (Compare § 75: Examples 6–9.)

The L-*terms* are obtained by restriction to the L-rules of the language. For some of these terms, we will define corresponding **P-terms**. These are characterized by the fact that, for them, the P-rules also are taken into account. In L-languages, they are empty. $\mathfrak{S}_2$ is called a P-*consequence* of $\mathfrak{R}_1$ if $\mathfrak{S}_2$ is a consequence, but not an L-consequence, of $\mathfrak{R}_1$. $\mathfrak{R}_1$ (or $\mathfrak{S}_1$) is **P-valid** if it is valid but not analytic. $\Re_1$ (or $\mathfrak{S}_1$) is **P-contravalid** if it is contravalid but not contradictory. $\Re_1$ and $\Re_2$ are P-*equipollent* if they are equipollent but not L-equipollent. $\mathfrak{A}_1$ and $\mathfrak{A}_2$ are P-*synonymous* if they are synonymous but not L-synonymous. In what follows we shall make very little use of the P-terms.

For a P-language we get the following classification of descriptive sentences (for the $\mathfrak{S}_I$, see p. 210):

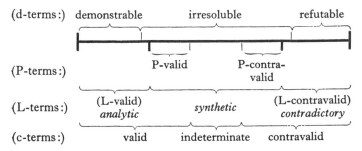

(d-terms:)	demonstrable	irresoluble	refutable
(P-terms:)	P-valid	P-contra-valid	
(L-terms:)	(L-valid) *analytic*	*synthetic*	(L-contravalid) *contradictory*
(c-terms:)	valid	indeterminate	contravalid

For an L-language (such as I and II) the classification of the descriptive sentences is simpler, since the c- and L-c-terms coincide:

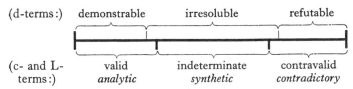

(d-terms:)	demonstrable	irresoluble	refutable
(c- and L-terms:)	valid *analytic*	indeterminate *synthetic*	contravalid *contradictory*

Examples: Assume that S is a P-language with English words used in their ordinary meaning. Let the most important physical laws be stated as primitive sentences of S. Let $\mathfrak{S}_1$ be: 'this body a is of iron'; $\mathfrak{S}_2$: 'a is of metal'; $\mathfrak{S}_3$: 'a cannot float on water'. $\mathfrak{S}_2$ and $\mathfrak{S}_3$ are consequences of $\mathfrak{S}_1$, and, specifically, $\mathfrak{S}_2$ is an L-consequence, but $\mathfrak{S}_3$ is not, and is therefore a P-consequence. Let $\mathfrak{S}_4$ run: 'In this vessel b of volume 5000 c.c. there are 2 grm. of hydrogen under such and such a pressure'; $\mathfrak{S}_5$: 'In b (of volume 5000 c.c.) there are 2 grm. of hydrogen at such and such a temperature.' $\mathfrak{S}_4$ and $\mathfrak{S}_5$ are consequences of one another, and, specifically, P-consequences, since each of these two sentences can be inferred from the other by means of the physical laws. $\mathfrak{S}_4$ and $\mathfrak{S}_5$ are equipollent, but not L-equipollent, and therefore they are P-equipollent. If in the material mode of speech we ask whether $\mathfrak{S}_3$ (like $\mathfrak{S}_2$) is implicit in $\mathfrak{S}_1$ and whether $\mathfrak{S}_4$ and $\mathfrak{S}_5$ mean the same or not, these questions are ambiguous. The answer is dependent upon what is legitimately presupposed in 'being implicit in'. If we assume only logic and mathematics, then the questions are to be answered in the negative; but if we assume the physical laws also, then they must be answered in the affirmative. For instance, in the latter case $\mathfrak{S}_4$ and $\mathfrak{S}_5$ mean the same to us even if we know nothing more about the described volume of gas. The material difference between the two assumptions corresponds to the formal difference between equipollence (in a P-language) and L-equipollence.

The view that the terms 'analytic' and 'contradictory' are purely formal and that analytic sentences have the null content has been expressed by Weyl [*Kontinuum*] pp. 2, 10; he says that a logically contradictory judgment "is recognized as untrue independently of its material content, and solely on the grounds of its logical structure"; "judgments which are true purely because of their formal (logical) structure (and thus possess no material content) we call (logically) self-evident". Later, Wittgenstein made the same view the basis of his whole philosophy. "It is the characteristic mark of logical sentences that one can perceive from the symbol alone that they are true; and this fact contains in itself the whole philosophy of logic" ([*Tractatus*] p. 156). Wittgenstein continues: "And so also it is one of the most important facts that the truth or falsehood of non-logical sentences can *not* be recognized from the sentences alone." This statement, expressive of Wittgenstein's absolutist conception of language, which leaves out the conventional factor in language-construction, is not correct. It is certainly possible to recognize from its form alone that a sentence is analytic; but only if the syntactical rules of the language are given. If these rules are given, however, then the truth or falsity of certain synthetic sentences—namely, the determinate ones—can also be recognized from their form alone. It is a matter of convention whether we formulate only L-rules, or include P-rules as well; and the P-rules can be formulated in just as strictly formal a way as the L-rules.

(b) VARIABLES

§ 53. SYSTEMS OF LEVELS; PREDICATES AND FUNCTORS

By a **system of levels** in S, we understand an ordered series $\mathfrak{R}_1$ of non-empty classes of expressions which fulfil the six conditions given on p. 188. Since the number of the expressions of a language is, at the most, denumerably infinite, the number of the classes of $\mathfrak{R}_1$ is likewise at the most denumerably infinite. These classes we call **levels**; let them be numbered with the finite—and, if necessary, also with the transfinite—ordinal numbers (of the second number-class): level 0 (or the zero level), level 1, 2, ... ω, $\omega + 1$, ... We shall designate the expressions which belong to the classes of $\mathfrak{R}_1$ by '$\mathfrak{Stu}$' [*Stufe*]; and, specifically, those which belong to level α (where 'α' designates an ordinal number) by '$^{\alpha}\mathfrak{Stu}$'. [For the sake of brevity, the phrase "in relation to $\mathfrak{R}_1$" is omitted here and also in the case of the other defined words and the Gothic designations which follow.] We count all the symbols $\mathfrak{Stu}$ as principal symbols.

An ordered series of $m + 1$ expressions $\mathfrak{A}_1, \mathfrak{A}_2, ... \mathfrak{A}_{m+1}$ (which may also be empty) is called an **expressional framework** ($\mathfrak{Ag}$) [*Ausdrucksgerüst*]—more precisely, an m-termed expressional framework ($\mathfrak{Ag}^m$)—for a particular expressional form if there exists at least one expression $\mathfrak{A}_n$ of this form which can occur as a partial expression in a sentence and is composed of the expressions $\mathfrak{A}_1, ... \mathfrak{A}_{m+1}$ of the framework, say $\mathfrak{Ag}_1$, together with m principal expressions $\mathfrak{A}'_1, \mathfrak{A}'_2, ... \mathfrak{A}'_m$, in alternating order. Thus $\mathfrak{A}_n$ has the form $\mathfrak{A}_1\mathfrak{A}'_1\mathfrak{A}_2\mathfrak{A}'_2 ... \mathfrak{A}_m\mathfrak{A}'_m\mathfrak{A}_{m+1}$. The expressions $\mathfrak{A}'_1, ... \mathfrak{A}'_m$ are called the first, ... mth **argument** of $\mathfrak{Ag}_1$ in $\mathfrak{A}_n$; the series which they form (in the correct serial order) is called the m-termed **argument-series** ($\mathfrak{Arg}$ or, more precisely, $\mathfrak{Arg}^m$) of $\mathfrak{Ag}_1$ in $\mathfrak{A}_n$. $\mathfrak{A}_n$ is also designated by '$\mathfrak{Ag}_1(\mathfrak{A}'_1, ... \mathfrak{A}'_m)$'; or, if $\mathfrak{Arg}_1$ is the series of those arguments, by '$\mathfrak{Ag}_1(\mathfrak{Arg}_1)$'. $\mathfrak{A}_n$ is called a **full expression** of $\mathfrak{Ag}_1$. We say that $\mathfrak{Ag}_1^m$ and $\mathfrak{Ag}_2^m$ have the *same course of values* if every two full expressions of $\mathfrak{Ag}_1$ and $\mathfrak{Ag}_2$ containing the same $\mathfrak{Arg}$ are synonymous.

The $\mathfrak{Ag}^m$ for the form $\mathfrak{S}$ are called m-termed **sentential frameworks** ($\mathfrak{Sg}$; $\mathfrak{Sg}^m$) [*Satzgerüst*]. This is the most important kind of $\mathfrak{Ag}$. A full expression of $\mathfrak{Sg}_1$ is an $\mathfrak{S}$; it is called a **full sentence** of $\mathfrak{Sg}_1$. $\mathfrak{Sg}_1^m$ is called *coextensive* with $\mathfrak{Sg}_2^m$ if every two full sentences of $\mathfrak{Sg}_1$ and $\mathfrak{Sg}_2$ containing the same $\mathfrak{Arg}$ are equipollent.

Theorem 53.1. If $\mathfrak{Sg}_1$ and $\mathfrak{Sg}_2$ have the same course of values, then they are coextensive; the converse is not always true (compare, however, Theorem 65.4 b).

Let $\mathfrak{Ag}_1^m$ be composed of $^{\alpha}\mathfrak{Stu}_1$ with or without subsidiary symbols; let $\mathfrak{A}_n$ be the full expression $\mathfrak{Ag}_1(\mathfrak{Arg}_1)$; let here every argument, as well as $\mathfrak{A}_n$ itself, be either an $\mathfrak{S}$ or a $^{\beta}\mathfrak{Stu}$ with $\beta < \alpha$. Then $\mathfrak{A}_n$ is also called a full expression of $\mathfrak{Stu}_1$; $\mathfrak{Arg}_1$ is also called an argument-series of $\mathfrak{Stu}_1$ in $\mathfrak{A}_n$; $\mathfrak{Stu}_1$ is called (in $\mathfrak{A}_n$) m-termed ($\mathfrak{Stu}^m$); we then designate $\mathfrak{A}_n$ also by '$\mathfrak{Stu}_1(\mathfrak{Arg}_1)$'. If in this case $\mathfrak{A}\mathfrak{g}_1$ is an $\mathfrak{S}\mathfrak{g}$, and therefore $\mathfrak{A}_n$ an $\mathfrak{S}$, then $\mathfrak{S}\mathfrak{tu}_1$ is called a **predicate-expression** ($\mathfrak{Pr}, \mathfrak{Pr}^m, {}^\alpha\mathfrak{Pr}$); a symbol $\mathfrak{Pr}$ is called a **predicate** ($\mathfrak{pr}, \mathfrak{pr}^m, {}^\alpha\mathfrak{pr}$). On the other hand, if $\mathfrak{A}_n$ is an $\mathfrak{S}\mathfrak{tu}$, then $\mathfrak{S}\mathfrak{tu}_1$ is called a **functor-expression** ($\mathfrak{Fu}, \mathfrak{Fu}^m, {}^\alpha\mathfrak{Fu}$); a symbol $\mathfrak{Fu}$ is called a **functor** ($\mathfrak{fu}, \mathfrak{fu}^m, {}^\alpha\mathfrak{fu}$). $\mathfrak{Pr}_1$ and $\mathfrak{Pr}_2$, which are isogenous and thus of the same level, are called *coextensive* if the corresponding $\mathfrak{S}\mathfrak{g}$ are coextensive. We say that $\mathfrak{Fu}_1$ and $\mathfrak{Fu}_2$, which are isogenous and thus of the same level, have the *same course of values* if the corresponding $\mathfrak{A}\mathfrak{g}$ have the same course of values. The $^0\mathfrak{S}\mathfrak{tu}$ are called *individual expressions* and, as symbols, individual symbols.

Theorem 53.2. (a) If $\mathfrak{Pr}_1$ and $\mathfrak{Pr}_2$ are synonymous, they are also coextensive. (b) If $\mathfrak{Fu}_1$ and $\mathfrak{Fu}_2$ are synonymous, they have the same course of values. The converse of either is not always true. (Compare, however, Theorem 66.1.)

$\mathfrak{Pr}_1$ and $\mathfrak{Pr}_2$ are synonymous only if *every* sentence $\mathfrak{S}_1$ is equipollent to $\mathfrak{S}_1 \begin{bmatrix} \mathfrak{Pr}_1 \\ \mathfrak{Pr}_2 \end{bmatrix}$. On the other hand, they are coextensive if merely for every full sentence $\mathfrak{S}_1$ the same condition is fulfilled. It is possible for 'P' and 'Q' to be coextensive but, for a particular $^2\mathfrak{pr}$ 'M', the sentences 'M(P)' and 'M(Q)' not to be equipollent, so that 'P' and 'Q' are not synonymous. (In this case, 'M(P)' is intensional in relation to 'P'. See § 66.)

Conditions: (1) An $\mathfrak{S}\mathfrak{tu}$ is not an $\mathfrak{S}$. (2) If $\mathfrak{A}_1$ is isogenous with an $^\alpha\mathfrak{S}\mathfrak{tu}$, then $\mathfrak{A}_1$ also is an $^\alpha\mathfrak{S}\mathfrak{tu}$. (3) Every $^\alpha\mathfrak{S}\mathfrak{tu}$ where $\alpha > 0$ is either a $\mathfrak{Pr}$ or an $\mathfrak{Fu}$. (4) For every $^0\mathfrak{S}\mathfrak{tu}_1$, there exists a $^1\mathfrak{Pr}$ with a full sentence of which $\mathfrak{S}\mathfrak{tu}_1$ is an argument. (5) Let $\mathfrak{S}\mathfrak{tu}_1$ be an $^\alpha\mathfrak{S}\mathfrak{tu}$ where α is greater than 1, and which is therefore either a $\mathfrak{Pr}$ or an $\mathfrak{Fu}$. (a) There exists a greatest ordinal number less than α, say β (so that $\alpha = \beta + 1$); then for that $\mathfrak{Pr}$ or $\mathfrak{Fu}$ $\mathfrak{S}\mathfrak{tu}_1$ there exists a full expression $\mathfrak{A}_1$ such that one of the arguments or $\mathfrak{A}_1$ itself is a $^\beta\mathfrak{S}\mathfrak{tu}$. (b) There is no greatest ordinal number less than α (for instance, where $\alpha = \omega$); then for every β which is less than α there is a γ such that $\beta < \gamma < \alpha$, and a full expression $\mathfrak{A}_1$ for $\mathfrak{S}\mathfrak{tu}_1$ such that one of the arguments or $\mathfrak{A}_1$ itself is a $^\gamma\mathfrak{S}\mathfrak{tu}$. (6) $\mathfrak{R}_1$ is as great in extent as possible, that is to say, the class $\mathfrak{S}\mathfrak{tu}$ in relation to $\mathfrak{R}_1$ is not a proper sub-class of the class $\mathfrak{S}\mathfrak{tu}$ in relation to a series $\mathfrak{R}_2$ which likewise fulfils conditions (1) to (5).—$\mathfrak{A}_1$ is called a *suitable argument* in general (or for the ith argument-place) for

$\mathfrak{Sg}_1$, $\mathfrak{Pr}_1$, or $\mathfrak{Fu}_1$ (later also for $\mathfrak{Sfu}_1$ or $\mathfrak{Afu}_1$), if there exists either a full expression or a full sentence in which $\mathfrak{A}_1$ occurs at some argument-place (or at the ith place, respectively).

Examples: In Language II (as in all the usual languages with higher functional calculus) there is exactly one system of levels. To this the $\mathfrak{Z}$ belong as $^0\mathfrak{Stu}$, and also the $\mathfrak{Pr}$ and $\mathfrak{Fu}$. The terms '$\mathfrak{Pr}$' and '$\mathfrak{Fu}$' which are defined here in general syntax are, however, wider than those previously applied in Language II. According to the new terms, the *verhn* are $^1\mathrm{pr}^2$; '$\sim$' is a $^1\mathrm{pr}^1$; '$|$' is a $^1\mathrm{fu}^1$. Further, '$=$' is a pr^2; let it be pr_1; it is an $^\omega\mathrm{pr}$ since for every integer $n\,(>0)$ there exists a full sentence $\mathrm{pr}_1(^n\mathrm{pr}, \,^n\mathrm{pr})$ (e.g. '$\mathrm{P}=\mathrm{Q}$'). If we were to specify that the symbol 'c' for the different types (Def. 37.10) should not be furnished with the corresponding type index, but that it should be used for all types of $\mathfrak{Pr}$ irrespectively, then 'c' would also be an $^\omega\mathrm{pr}^2$. Under like conditions 'v' in '$\mathrm{F\,v\,G}$' (Def. 37.5) would be an $^\omega\mathrm{fu}^2$.

In [*Princ. Math.*] Russell has used the symbol 'c' and many others with arguments of any (finite) level whatever, so that, according to our definition, they belong to the level ω. Russell does not, however, attribute a transfinite level to these, but interprets their mode of use as "systematic ambiguity". Hilbert [*Unendliche*], p. 184, and Gödel [*Unentscheidbare*], p. 191, were the first to point out the possibility of introducing *transfinite levels*.

§ 54. SUBSTITUTION; VARIABLES AND CONSTANTS

What is a variable? It has long been recognized that the old answers "a varying magnitude" or "a varying concept" are inadequate. A concept, a magnitude, a number, a property—none of these can vary (although a thing can, of course, have different properties at different times). A variable is, rather, a *symbol* with a certain property. But what property? The answer: "a symbol with a varying meaning" is equally inadequate. For a variation in the meaning of a symbol is not possible within one language; it constitutes the transition from one language to another. More correct is another answer which is frequently given: "A symbol with a determined meaning is a constant, and one with an undetermined meaning is a variable." But even this is not quite correct. For it is possible to use constants which have undetermined meanings; these differ essentially from the variables in that they do not permit of substitution.

Examples: In a name-language, in addition to names with determined meanings, such as 'Prague', names with undetermined

meanings, such as 'a' and 'b', may also be used. If 'Q' is a constant
$\mathfrak{pr}$ (whether of determined or undetermined meaning makes no difference), then from 'Q(x)' the sentences 'Q(Prague)', 'Q(a)',
'Q(b)' and so on are derivable, but they are not derivable from
'Q(a)'. This shows that while 'x' is a variable, 'a', in spite of having
an undetermined meaning, is a constant. In material interpretation:
'a' designates a certain thing; it is merely not stated for the moment
(but may, however, be stated later) what thing it designates. In the
examples to be found in this book, constants with undetermined
meanings have frequently been used; for example, 'a', 'b' on pp. 12 f.,
'P' and 'Q' in many places, such as pp. 25 and 47. The difference
between the variable 'p' and the constant of undetermined meaning
'A' is brought out especially clearly in the examples on p. 158.

*Variables and constants are distinguished from one another by their
syntactical character;* variables are the symbols of S for which,
according to the rules of transformation of S, under certain conditions, *substitution is permissible.* This rough distinction is true
for all the ordinary symbolic languages. The exact definition of
'variable', however, cannot be so simple, inasmuch as it must take
into account the various possible kinds of substitution, and especially the three principal kinds—substitution for free variables,
for bound variables, and for constants.

W. V. Quine (in a verbal communication) has shown that it is
possible to use an *operator-constant* instead of an operator-variable.
Instead of '$(x)(x=x)$' we can, for example, write '$(0)(0=0)$'.
Incidentally, we can extend this method so that a language (even a
language which includes both arithmetic and infinitesimal calculus)
contains *no variables* at all. For instance, in Language II we may,
to begin with, construct a Language II' in which no free variables
appear in sentences. Here PSII 16 and 17 have to be replaced by
rules of substitution: $(\mathfrak{v}_1)(\mathfrak{S}_1)$ may be transformed into $\mathfrak{S}_1\left(\dfrac{\mathfrak{v}_1}{\mathfrak{A}_1}\right)$,
and $(\mathfrak{p}_1)(\mathfrak{S}_1)$ into $\mathfrak{S}_1\left(\dfrac{\mathfrak{p}_1(\mathfrak{Arg}_1)}{\mathfrak{S}_2}\right)$. RII 2 drops out; but several new
rules must be formulated. II'' is then constructed from II' by writing
instead of a bound $\mathfrak{v}_1$, in the operator and in the places of substitution
in the operand, some expression or other from the range of values of
$\mathfrak{v}_1$. [In II'', as opposed to the usual languages, related symbols are
always isogenous.] In the symbolic languages hitherto in use,
substitution for constants does not occur. Languages of the kind
indicated, with no variables (but having constants as variable-expressions) must be differentiated from languages *without substitution*
(that is to say, with no variable-expressions whatever). See the
example of I$_k$ on p. 194.
Examples of the three principal kinds of substitution: in I and II

'$2=2$' is derivable from '$x=x$'; in II from '$(x)(x=x)$'; and in II″ from '$(3)(3=3)$'.

We say that substitution occurs in S when there are expressions in S—we call them **variable-expressions** ($\mathfrak{B}$)—to which what now follows is applicable, and which, in particular, fulfil the condition given below, p. 193. [This condition can at that point be formulated more simply with the help of the terms which will by then have been defined.] [To facilitate the comprehension of what we are about to say, it should be noted that in the ordinary symbolic languages, all $\mathfrak{B}$ are symbols, and, specifically, variables.] To every $\mathfrak{B}$, say $\mathfrak{B}_1$, there is correlated a class (which may also be empty) of expressions which we call **operators** ($\mathfrak{O}\mathrm{p}$), or, more precisely, operators with $\mathfrak{B}_1$ ($\mathfrak{O}\mathrm{p}_{\mathfrak{B}_1}$). Let $\mathfrak{O}\mathrm{p}_1$ be an $\mathfrak{O}\mathrm{p}_{\mathfrak{B}_1}$; then there is correlated to $\mathfrak{O}\mathrm{p}_1$ a class of principal expressions which we call **substitution-values** of $\mathfrak{B}_1$ *in relation to* $\mathfrak{O}\mathrm{p}_1$; this class contains at least one expression which is not synonymous with $\mathfrak{B}_1$. Further, to $\mathfrak{B}_1$ itself is correlated a class of principal expressions which we call *substitution-values for free* $\mathfrak{B}_1$; this class, when it is not empty, contains at least two expressions which are not synonymous with one another. Let $\mathfrak{R}_1$ be that class to which belong all substitution-values for free $\mathfrak{B}_1$ and all substitution-values for $\mathfrak{B}_1$ in relation to some $\mathfrak{O}\mathrm{p}_{\mathfrak{B}_1}$, together with all expressions which are isogenous with one of the above. We call the expressions of $\mathfrak{R}_1$ the **values** of $\mathfrak{B}_1$. $\mathfrak{O}\mathrm{p}_{1\mathfrak{B}_1}$ is called *unlimited* if every value of $\mathfrak{B}_1$ is also a substitution-value of $\mathfrak{B}_1$ in relation to $\mathfrak{O}\mathrm{p}_1$; otherwise, *limited*.

Let $\mathfrak{A}_1$ be a full expression of $\mathfrak{A}\mathrm{g}_1^m$, and specifically either an $\mathfrak{S}$ or an $\mathfrak{S}\mathfrak{tu}$; and let $\mathfrak{A}_2$ be constructed from $\mathfrak{A}_1$ by replacing every argument $\mathfrak{A}_i$ ($i=1$ to m) by a $\mathfrak{B}_i$ to the values of which $\mathfrak{A}_i$ belongs, $\mathfrak{A}_2$ being so qualified that it can occur as a partial expression in a sentence. $\mathfrak{A}_2$ is then called an m-termed **expressional function** ($\mathfrak{A}\mathfrak{fu}$, $\mathfrak{A}\mathfrak{fu}^m$); $\mathfrak{B}_i$ is called the ith argument in $\mathfrak{A}_2$. An $\mathfrak{A}\mathfrak{fu}^m$ is called *improper* when $m=0$; proper when $m>0$. If $\mathfrak{A}_1$ is here an $\mathfrak{S}$, then $\mathfrak{A}_2$ is called an m-termed **sentential function** ($\mathfrak{S}\mathfrak{fu}$, $\mathfrak{S}\mathfrak{fu}^m$). The $\mathfrak{S}\mathfrak{fu}$ constitute the most important kind of $\mathfrak{A}\mathfrak{fu}$.

The difference between sentential framework, sentential function, and predicate-expression should be carefully noted, since, owing to the fact that the term 'sentential function' is used in all three meanings, this difference is often disregarded. *Examples* of $\mathfrak{S}\mathrm{g}$ in II (here we separate the expressions of the expressional series by dashes):

'P$(3, -)$ ∨ Q$(-)$', 'Q$(-)$' [but also '(A) — (B)' (with the argument ' ∨ ') and '$(-x)($P$(x))$' (to which '∃' and the null expression are the suitable arguments)]; examples of $\mathfrak{Sfu}$: 'P$(3, x)$ ∨ Q(x)', 'Q(x)'; examples of $\mathfrak{Pr}$: 'Q' [but also 'sm(P, Q)'—see p. 86]. The differences between the remaining $\mathfrak{Ag}$, the remaining $\mathfrak{Afu}$, and the $\mathfrak{Fu}$ are analogous. The only reason why we must also deal with the $\mathfrak{Ag}$ and the $\mathfrak{Sg}$ in addition to the $\mathfrak{Afu}$ and the $\mathfrak{Sfu}$ is that it cannot be generally assumed that there are in every language variable-expressions for the arguments concerned.

The $\mathfrak{Sfu}^0$ are $\mathfrak{S}$. In I and II, all the $\mathfrak{Sfu}$ are $\mathfrak{S}$, and, specifically, the proper $\mathfrak{Sfu}$ are open $\mathfrak{S}$, and the improper $\mathfrak{Sfu}$ are closed $\mathfrak{S}$. In the majority of the usual symbolic languages, all the $\mathfrak{Sfu}$ are $\mathfrak{S}$; in many of them, however, the rules which govern this point are not clear.

Let $\mathfrak{Op}_1$ occur at a certain place in $\mathfrak{S}_1$; then, to this $\mathfrak{Op}_1$ is correlated by means of definite rules of formation (which, like all rules of formation, are contained in the rules of transformation; see above), a partial expression $\mathfrak{Afu}_1$ of $\mathfrak{S}_1$ consisting of $\mathfrak{Op}_1$, an $\mathfrak{Sfu}_1$, and sometimes subsidiary symbols as well; $\mathfrak{Sfu}_1$ is called the **operand** of $\mathfrak{Op}_1$ (at this place) in $\mathfrak{S}_1$. [Usually, $\mathfrak{Sfu}_1$ here comes after $\mathfrak{Op}_1$; and sometimes the beginning, the end, or both, of the operand $\mathfrak{Sfu}_1$ is indicated by means of special subsidiary symbols (for example, by brackets in I and II and by dot-symbols in Russell) as well as by $\mathfrak{Op}_1$.] We designate $\mathfrak{Afu}_1$ also by '$\mathfrak{Op}_1 (\mathfrak{Sfu}_1)$'. If $\mathfrak{Sfu}_1$ can be an operand belonging to $\mathfrak{Op}_1$—that is to say, if there exists an $\mathfrak{Afu}$ of the form $\mathfrak{Op}_1 (\mathfrak{Sfu}_1)$—we call $\mathfrak{Sfu}_1$ **operable** in relation to $\mathfrak{Op}_1$. $\mathfrak{B}_1$ is called **bound** in $\mathfrak{A}_2$ at a particular place if this particular place belongs to a partial expression of $\mathfrak{A}_2$ which has the form $\mathfrak{Op}_{1\mathfrak{B}_1} (\mathfrak{Sfu})$; and, specifically, it is called limitedly (or unlimitedly) bound if $\mathfrak{Op}_1$ is limited (or unlimited, respectively). If $\mathfrak{B}_1$ occurs in $\mathfrak{A}_2$ at a place at which $\mathfrak{B}_1$ is not bound, then $\mathfrak{B}_1$ is called **free** at this place in $\mathfrak{A}_2$. The places at which $\mathfrak{B}_1$ occurs freely in $\mathfrak{A}_2$ are called *substitution-places* for $\mathfrak{B}_1$ in $\mathfrak{A}_2$. We designate by '$\mathfrak{Afu}_1 \begin{pmatrix} \mathfrak{B}_1 \\ \mathfrak{A}_1 \end{pmatrix}$' the expression which results from $\mathfrak{Afu}_1$ on replacing $\mathfrak{B}_1$ by $\mathfrak{A}_1$ at all substitution-places in $\mathfrak{Afu}_1$; here $\mathfrak{A}_1$ must be a value of $\mathfrak{B}_1$, and there must be no $\mathfrak{B}_2$ which occurs freely in $\mathfrak{A}_1$ and is bound in $\mathfrak{Afu}_1$ at one of the substitution-places for $\mathfrak{B}_1$. [If $\mathfrak{A}_1$ does not fulfil these conditions, or if $\mathfrak{B}_1$ does not occur freely in $\mathfrak{Afu}_1$, then '$\mathfrak{Afu}_1 \begin{pmatrix} \mathfrak{B}_1 \\ \mathfrak{A}_1 \end{pmatrix}$'

designates $\mathfrak{Afu}_1$ itself.] We call $\mathfrak{Afu}_1\left(\begin{smallmatrix}\mathfrak{B}_1\\\mathfrak{A}_1\end{smallmatrix}\right)$ a **variant** of $\mathfrak{Afu}_1$ (in $\mathfrak{B}_1$). A sentence of the form $\mathfrak{Sfu}_1\left(\begin{smallmatrix}\mathfrak{B}_1\\\mathfrak{A}_1\end{smallmatrix}\right)$ is called a *variant* of $\mathfrak{Sfu}_1$ *in relation to* $\mathfrak{Op}_{1\mathfrak{B}_1}$ if $\mathfrak{Sfu}_1$ is operable in relation to $\mathfrak{Op}_1$ and $\mathfrak{A}_1$ a substitution-value of $\mathfrak{B}_1$ in relation to $\mathfrak{Op}_1$.

We distinguish between two different kinds of operators: sentential operators and descriptional operators. If $\mathfrak{Op}_1\left(\mathfrak{Sfu}_1\right)$ is an $\mathfrak{Sfu}$, say $\mathfrak{Sfu}_2$, then $\mathfrak{Op}_1$ is called a sentential operator in $\mathfrak{Sfu}_2$; and if every expression of the form $\mathfrak{Op}_1\left(\mathfrak{Sfu}\right)$ is an $\mathfrak{Sfu}$, then $\mathfrak{Op}_1$ is called a **sentential operator**. Assume that $\mathfrak{Op}_1\left(\mathfrak{Sfu}_1\right)$ is not an $\mathfrak{Sfu}$, and is hence another $\mathfrak{Afu}$, say $\mathfrak{Afu}_2$; then $\mathfrak{Afu}_2$ is called a *descriptional function*, or, if it is closed, a **description**. A description is, accordingly, always an $\mathfrak{Stu}$. $\mathfrak{Op}_1$ is then called a descriptional operator in $\mathfrak{Afu}_2$; and if every expression of the form $\mathfrak{Op}_1\left(\mathfrak{Sfu}\right)$ is a descriptional function, $\mathfrak{Op}_1$ is called a **descriptional operator**.

Let $\mathfrak{S}_1$ be $\mathfrak{Op}_{1\mathfrak{B}_1}\left(\mathfrak{Sfu}_1\right)$; $\mathfrak{Op}_1$ is accordingly a sentential operator in $\mathfrak{S}_1$. If, here, $\mathfrak{B}_1$ occurs freely in $\mathfrak{Sfu}_1$, and if every variant of $\mathfrak{Sfu}_1$ in relation to $\mathfrak{Op}_1$ is a consequence of $\mathfrak{S}_1$, then $\mathfrak{Op}_1$ is called a universal operator in $\mathfrak{S}_1$. If $\mathfrak{Op}_{1\mathfrak{B}_1}$ is a universal operator in every sentence of the form $\mathfrak{Op}_1\left(\mathfrak{Sfu}_2\right)$, where $\mathfrak{Sfu}_2$ is any $\mathfrak{Sfu}$ in which $\mathfrak{B}_1$ occurs freely, then $\mathfrak{Op}_1$ is called a **universal operator**.

Let $\mathfrak{B}_1$ occur freely in $\mathfrak{S}_1$; then, if every variant $\mathfrak{S}_1\left(\begin{smallmatrix}\mathfrak{B}_1\\\mathfrak{A}_2\end{smallmatrix}\right)$, where $\mathfrak{A}_2$ is any substitution-value whatsoever of free $\mathfrak{B}_1$, is a consequence of $\mathfrak{S}_1$, we say that in $\mathfrak{S}_1$ there exists substitution for free $\mathfrak{B}_1$. If in every sentence in which $\mathfrak{B}_1$ occurs freely, substitution for free $\mathfrak{B}_1$ exists, then we say that there exists (in S) substitution for free $\mathfrak{B}_1$.

For the foregoing definitions, beginning with '$\mathfrak{B}$', it is required that the following condition be fulfilled: namely, for every $\mathfrak{B}_1$ there is at least one $\mathfrak{S}_1$ such that either there exists *substitution for free* $\mathfrak{B}_1$ in $\mathfrak{S}_1$, or $\mathfrak{S}_1$ has the form $\mathfrak{Op}_{1\mathfrak{B}_1}\left(\mathfrak{Sfu}_1\right)$, where $\mathfrak{B}_1$ occurs freely in $\mathfrak{Sfu}_1$ and $\mathfrak{Op}_1$ is a *universal operator* in $\mathfrak{S}_1$.

$\mathfrak{A}_1$ is called a *substitution-value* of $\mathfrak{B}_1$ if at least one of the following conditions is fulfilled: (1) There is in S substitution for free $\mathfrak{B}_1$, and $\mathfrak{A}_1$ is a substitution-value for free $\mathfrak{B}_1$; (2) There exists in S a universal operator $\mathfrak{Op}_{1\mathfrak{B}_1}$ and $\mathfrak{A}_1$ is a substitution-value in relation to $\mathfrak{Op}_1$.

If $\mathfrak{B}_1$ occurs freely in $\mathfrak{S}_1$, but if at the same time there exists no substitution for free $\mathfrak{B}_1$ in $\mathfrak{S}_1$, then we say that $\mathfrak{B}_1$ is *constant* in $\mathfrak{S}_1$ (in the usual languages this does not occur). If $\mathfrak{B}_1$ is constant in every sentence in which it occurs freely, and if at least one such sentence exists, then we call $\mathfrak{B}_1$ *constant*. If $\mathfrak{a}_1$ is a $\mathfrak{B}$ and constant (either in $\mathfrak{S}_1$ or generally), then we call $\mathfrak{a}_1$ (either in $\mathfrak{S}_1$ or generally) a *variable-constant*; if $\mathfrak{a}_1$ is a $\mathfrak{B}$ and constant in no sentence, then $\mathfrak{a}_1$ is called a **variable** ($\mathfrak{v}$). All symbols which are $\mathfrak{B}$, and hence all $\mathfrak{v}$ also, are counted amongst the principal symbols. If $\mathfrak{a}_1$ is not a $\mathfrak{v}$ (and hence either not a $\mathfrak{B}$ at all or a $\mathfrak{B}$ which is constant in at least one sentence), $\mathfrak{a}_1$ is called a **constant** ($\mathfrak{f}$). If $\mathfrak{f}_1$ is an $^{\alpha}\mathfrak{Stu}$, then $\mathfrak{f}_1$ is called a constant of the level α ($^{\alpha}\mathfrak{f}$).

$\mathfrak{S}_1$ is called **open** if there exists a $\mathfrak{B}_1$ such that it occurs freely in $\mathfrak{S}_1$ and there is substitution for free $\mathfrak{B}_1$ in $\mathfrak{S}_1$; otherwise, $\mathfrak{S}_1$ is called **closed**. An $\mathfrak{A}_1$ which is not an $\mathfrak{S}$ is called *open* if there exists a $\mathfrak{B}_1$ and an $\mathfrak{S}_1$ such that $\mathfrak{A}_1$ is a partial expression of $\mathfrak{S}_1$, $\mathfrak{B}_1$ occurs at a place in $\mathfrak{A}_1$ at which it is free in $\mathfrak{S}_1$, and there is in $\mathfrak{S}_1$ substitution for free $\mathfrak{B}_1$; otherwise, $\mathfrak{A}_1$ is called *closed*. If no substitution for free $\mathfrak{B}$ exists in S, then all $\mathfrak{A}$ are closed; S is then called a *closed language-system*.

Example of a closed language-system: II', p. 190.

A language-system without variable-expressions can easily be constructed; obviously such a system is also a closed system. An example is afforded by Language I_k, which is constructed in the following way as a proper conservative sub-language of I. Symbols of I_k are the $\mathfrak{f}$ of I. The $\mathfrak{Z}$ (and $\mathfrak{S}$) of I_k are the $\mathfrak{Z}$ (and $\mathfrak{S}$, respectively) without $\mathfrak{v}$ of I. As schemata of primitive sentences, PSI 1–3 remain unchanged, PSI 4–6 and 11 drop out, PSI 7–10 are replaced by the following: 7. $\mathfrak{Z}_1 = \mathfrak{Z}_1$. 8. $(\mathfrak{Z}_1 = \mathfrak{Z}_2) \supset \left(\mathfrak{S}_1 \supset \mathfrak{S}_1 \left[\begin{matrix} \mathfrak{Z}_1 \\ \mathfrak{Z}_2 \end{matrix} \right] \right)$. 9. $\sim (\mathfrak{nu} = \mathfrak{Z}_1')$. 10. $(\mathfrak{Z}_1{}' = \mathfrak{Z}_2{}') \supset (\mathfrak{Z}_1 = \mathfrak{Z}_2)$. Of the rules, RI 2 and 3 remain unchanged; RI 1 and 4 drop out. The definitions are not formulated as sentences, but as syntactical rules concerned with synonymity. All the definitions in I can be correspondingly transferred to I_k. For instance, in place of D 3 (p. 59) the rule is given: "If $\mathfrak{fu}_1$ is 'prod', then for any $\mathfrak{Z}_2$, $\mathfrak{fu}_1(\mathfrak{nu}, \mathfrak{Z}_2)$ is synonymous with $\mathfrak{nu}$, and for any $\mathfrak{Z}_1$ and $\mathfrak{Z}_2$, $\mathfrak{fu}_1(\mathfrak{Z}_1{}', \mathfrak{Z}_2)$ is synonymous with $\mathfrak{fu}_2[\mathfrak{fu}_1(\mathfrak{Z}_1, \mathfrak{Z}_2), \mathfrak{Z}_2]$, where $\mathfrak{fu}_2$ is 'sum'." To a syntactical sentence concerning an open sentence of I, there corresponds a syntactical sentence concerning sentences of I_k of a particular form. For instance, the sentence: "Every sentence of the form $\mathfrak{fu}_1(\mathfrak{Z}_1, \mathfrak{Z}_2)$ $= \mathfrak{fu}_1(\mathfrak{Z}_2, \mathfrak{Z}_1)$, where $\mathfrak{fu}_1$ is 'prod', is demonstrable in I_k" corresponds to the sentence: "'prod $(x, y) = $ prod (y, x)' is demonstrable in I." In this way, arithmetic can be formulated in I_k. It must nevertheless be noted that here $\mathfrak{B}$ are only given up in I_k itself; for the syntax-language, on the other hand, $\mathfrak{B}$ are necessary in order to formulate the primitive sentences and rules as general stipulations.

If $\mathfrak{S}_1$ is closed and contains no $\mathfrak{S}\mathfrak{f}\mathfrak{u}$ (and hence no $\mathfrak{S}$) as proper parts, then we call $\mathfrak{S}_1$ an *elementary sentence*. In an elementary sentence, neither $\mathfrak{v}$, $\mathfrak{Dp}$, nor $\mathfrak{Bf}$ (§ 57) occur.

If $\mathfrak{v}_1$ is an $\mathfrak{ja}$, the $\mathfrak{v}_1$ is called a *sentential variable* (f). If all substitution-values of $\mathfrak{v}_1$ (in $\mathfrak{S}_1$ or in general) are $\mathfrak{Pr}$, then $\mathfrak{v}_1$ is called a *predicate-variable* (p) (in $\mathfrak{S}_1$ or in general, respectively); if all substitution-values are $\mathfrak{Pr}^m$, then $\mathfrak{v}_1$ is called a $\mathfrak{p}^m$. The same applies to the $\mathfrak{Fu}$: *functor-variable* (f, $\mathfrak{f}^m$). Let all the substitution-values of $\mathfrak{B}_1$ (in $\mathfrak{S}_1$ or in general) be $^\alpha\mathfrak{S}\mathfrak{tu}$. Then $\mathfrak{B}_1$ is called (in $\mathfrak{S}_1$ or in general) an $^\alpha\mathfrak{B}$ (correspondingly $^\alpha\mathfrak{v}$, $^\alpha\mathfrak{p}$, $^\alpha\mathfrak{f}$). A $^0\mathfrak{v}$ is called an *individual variable*, a $^0\mathfrak{f}$ an *individual constant*. Let all the substitution-values of $\mathfrak{B}_1$ (in $\mathfrak{S}_1$ or in general) be $\mathfrak{S}\mathfrak{tu}$, but of various levels; then $\mathfrak{B}_1$ is called (in $\mathfrak{S}_1$ or in general, respectively) an $^{(\alpha)}\mathfrak{B}$ if for every $\beta < \alpha$ there exists a γ such that $\beta \leqq \gamma < \alpha$, so that at least one of the substitution-values (in $\mathfrak{S}_1$ or in general) belongs to the level γ, but none to the level α or to a higher one. [According to this, for example, in the $\mathfrak{S}\mathfrak{f}\mathfrak{u}$, $\mathfrak{Pr}_1(\mathfrak{p}_1)$, $\mathfrak{p}_1$ is an $^{(\omega)}\mathfrak{p}$ if and only if $\mathfrak{Pr}_1$ is an $^\omega\mathfrak{Pr}$.] $^\alpha\mathfrak{B}_1$ is not necessarily an $\mathfrak{S}\mathfrak{tu}$; $^\alpha\mathfrak{B}_1$ is an $\mathfrak{S}\mathfrak{tu}$ (in $\mathfrak{S}_1$ or in general) and, more precisely, an $^\alpha\mathfrak{S}\mathfrak{tu}$ if and only if $\mathfrak{B}_1$ occurs freely (in $\mathfrak{S}_1$ or in at least one $\mathfrak{S}$ respectively). An $^{(\alpha)}\mathfrak{B}$ is not an $\mathfrak{S}\mathfrak{tu}$.

Examples: 1. *Languages I and II.* All $\mathfrak{B}$ are $\mathfrak{v}$. $^0\mathfrak{v}$ are the $\mathfrak{z}$. Substitution-values for free 'x' are the $\mathfrak{z}$; substitution-values for 'x' in relation to '$(\exists x)\mathfrak{z}(P(x))$' are the $\mathfrak{z}$ which are synonymous with '0', '1', or '2'. Every $\mathfrak{p}$ (or $\mathfrak{f}$) is an $\mathfrak{S}\mathfrak{tu}$ of a certain level; values and substitution-values are all $\mathfrak{Pr}$ (or $\mathfrak{Fu}$, respectively) of the same type. $\mathfrak{S}\mathfrak{f}\mathfrak{u}$ are the $\mathfrak{S}$. Every $\mathfrak{S}$ is operable in relation to every operator. Substitution for free $\mathfrak{v}$: 'P(3)' is a consequence of 'P(x)'; for bound $\mathfrak{v}$: 'P(3)' is a consequence of '(x)$\mathfrak{z}(P(x))$'. Sentential operators are the universal and existential operators; descriptional operators are the K-operators.—2. In Russell's language, there are descriptions which are $^0\mathfrak{S}\mathfrak{tu}$, and also descriptions which are $\mathfrak{Pr}$. For instance, '$\hat{x}(P(x))$' is a class-expression and thus a $^1\mathfrak{Pr}^1$; it is a description with the descriptional operator '$\hat{x}$'. Correspondingly, '$\hat{x}\hat{y}$' is a descriptional operator for a $^1\mathfrak{Pr}^2$.

§ 55. Universal and Existential Operators

We shall first discuss the subject in the material mode of speech. Let a domain contain m objects, and a certain property be attributed to each one of these objects by means of the sentences $\mathfrak{S}_1, \mathfrak{S}_2, \ldots \mathfrak{S}_m$ respectively. Now if $\mathfrak{S}_n$ means at least as much as the sentences $\mathfrak{S}_1$ to $\mathfrak{S}_m$ taken together, we may call $\mathfrak{S}_n$ a corresponding universal sentence in the wider sense; and specifically, if $\mathfrak{S}_n$ does not mean more than all the individual sentences put together—that is to say, if it means exactly what they do—a proper universal sentence. If the universal sentence is constructed with a universal operator, then the closed variants of the operand are the corresponding individual sentences. We therefore define as follows: a universal operator $\mathfrak{O}\mathfrak{p}_1$ (restricted or unrestricted) is called a *proper universal operator* if every closed sentence of the form $\mathfrak{O}\mathfrak{p}_1(\mathfrak{S}\mathfrak{fu}_1)$, for any $\mathfrak{S}\mathfrak{fu}_1$ whatsoever, is a consequence of (and hence equipollent to) the class of the closed variants of $\mathfrak{S}\mathfrak{fu}_1$ in relation to $\mathfrak{O}\mathfrak{p}_1$; otherwise it is called an *improper universal operator* (namely, if there exists a closed sentence $\mathfrak{O}\mathfrak{p}_1(\mathfrak{S}\mathfrak{fu}_2)$ which is not a consequence of the class of the closed variants of $\mathfrak{S}\mathfrak{fu}_2$ in relation to $\mathfrak{O}\mathfrak{p}_1$).

An *existential sentence* follows from every one of the individual corresponding sentences. Materially expressed, its meaning is contained in the meaning of each of the individual corresponding sentences and therefore also in the common meaning. If the sentence means no less than this common meaning, but precisely the same, then it may be called a proper existential sentence. Hence we define in the following manner.

Let $\mathfrak{S}_1$ be $\mathfrak{O}\mathfrak{p}_1\mathfrak{V}_1(\mathfrak{S}\mathfrak{fu}_1)$; $\mathfrak{O}\mathfrak{p}_1$ is accordingly a sentential operator in $\mathfrak{S}_1$; if here $\mathfrak{V}_1$ occurs freely in $\mathfrak{S}\mathfrak{fu}_1$ and if $\mathfrak{S}_1$ is a consequence of every variant of $\mathfrak{S}\mathfrak{fu}_1$ in relation to $\mathfrak{O}\mathfrak{p}_1$, then $\mathfrak{O}\mathfrak{p}_1$ is called an existential operator in $\mathfrak{S}_1$. If $\mathfrak{O}\mathfrak{p}_1\mathfrak{V}_1$ is an existential operator in every sentence of the form $\mathfrak{O}\mathfrak{p}_1(\mathfrak{S}\mathfrak{fu}_2)$, where $\mathfrak{S}\mathfrak{fu}_2$ is any $\mathfrak{S}\mathfrak{fu}$ in which $\mathfrak{V}_1$ occurs freely, then $\mathfrak{O}\mathfrak{p}_1$ is called an **existential operator**. [This definition is analogous to that of 'universal operator' on p. 193.] Let $\mathfrak{O}\mathfrak{p}_1$ be an existential operator. If the content of each closed sentence of the form $\mathfrak{O}\mathfrak{p}_1(\mathfrak{S}\mathfrak{fu}_1)$ coincides with the product of the contents of the closed variants of $\mathfrak{S}\mathfrak{fu}_1$ in relation to $\mathfrak{O}\mathfrak{p}_1$, then $\mathfrak{O}\mathfrak{p}_1$ is called a *proper* existential operator; otherwise it is called an *improper* one (namely, if there exists a closed sentence $\mathfrak{Dp}_1 (\mathfrak{Sfu}_2)$ whose content is a proper sub-class of the product of the contents of the closed variants of $\mathfrak{Sfu}_2$ in relation to $\mathfrak{Dp}_1$).

Examples: Universal operators occur in the languages of Frege, Russell, Hilbert, Behmann, Gödel, and Tarski (see § 33); they have in the majority of cases the form (ɴ). Existential operators also occur in each of these languages; in those of Russell, Hilbert, and Behmann, some are simple (for example, formed either with 'Ⅎ' or with 'E'), but in all such languages there are operators composed of two negation-symbols and a universal operator which are not usually called existential operators. (In II, for instance, ' $\sim((x)(\sim$' is also an existential operator.) In the languages mentioned, the simple universal and existential operators are unlimited; but it is also possible to construct limited operators [such as '$(x)((x<3)\supset$' and '$(\Exists x)((x<3)\cdot$'.]. In Languages I and II there are also limited operators which are simple, that is to say, which contain no partial sentence.

In Languages I and II the universal operators with ₃ are *proper* universal operators. For not only is every sentence—and hence every closed sentence—of the form $\mathfrak{pr}_1(\mathfrak{Z})$ a consequence of $(\mathfrak{Z}_1)(\mathfrak{pr}_1(\mathfrak{Z}_1))$, but, conversely, this universal sentence is also a consequence of the class of those closed sentences (by DC 2, p. 38) and therefore equipollent to it. *In the other languages* which we have mentioned, on the contrary, the same thing is not true for the universal operators with ^{0}ɴ or with ₃ (unless Hilbert's new rule is laid down; see p. 173); hence these operators are *improper*.

The universal and existential *operators of higher levels*—that is to say, with $\mathfrak{p}$ (or $\mathfrak{f}$)—are apparently *improper* in the majority of languages. In the case of the earlier languages, this follows from the same cause as before, namely, from the lack of indefinite rules of transformation. But in the case of Language II, it is true for a different reason. For the sake of simplicity, we will restrict ourselves to the logical sub-language II$_\mathrm{I}$ of II. Let the $^2\mathfrak{pr}_\mathrm{I}, \mathfrak{pr}_2$, of II$_\mathrm{I}$ designate (in material speech) a property which belongs to all the number properties which are definable in II$_\mathrm{I}$ but, on the other hand, not to all the number properties which are indefinable in II$_\mathrm{I}$ (see p. 106). Then $(\mathfrak{p}_1)(\mathfrak{pr}_2(\mathfrak{p}_1))$ is contradictory; the class of all closed variants of the operand is, however, analytic; and hence this contradictory sentence cannot be a consequence of it. Further, on the same hypothesis $(\Exists \mathfrak{p}_1)(\sim \mathfrak{pr}_2(\mathfrak{p}_1))$ is analytic; here all closed variants of the operand are contradictory; the content of the existential sentence is null and the product of the contents of the variants is the total content; therefore the former is a proper sub-class of the latter.

Let $\mathfrak{B}_1$ occur at a certain place in $\mathfrak{S}_1$, and let it be either free or bound by $\mathfrak{Dp}_1$. Let $\mathfrak{R}_1$ in the first case be the class of substitution-values of a free $\mathfrak{B}_1$; and in the second case the class of substitution-values of $\mathfrak{B}_1$ in relation to $\mathfrak{O}p_1$. Let $\mathfrak{R}_1$ be subdivided into the largest sub-classes (non-empty) of expressions synonymous with each other. We call the number of these sub-classes the *variability-number* of $\mathfrak{B}_1$ at the place in question in $\mathfrak{S}_1$; in the case of a finite (or infinite) number we speak of *finite* or *infinite variability* respectively. We say that $\mathfrak{B}_1$ at a certain place in $\mathfrak{S}_1$ has *infinite universality* if $\mathfrak{B}_1$ has infinite variability at that place, and is there either free or bound by a universal operator.

Examples: 'x' has in '$(\exists x)\,5(P(x))$' the variability-number 6; in '$P(x)$' and in '$(x)(P(x))$' it has both infinite variability and infinite universality. In a sentential calculus of the usual form, with only free ʃ, and no constants ʃɑ, every sentence is either analytic or contradictory. Thus every ʃ there has the variability number 2. The same is true even when we introduce universal and existential operators; the ʃ are then unrestrictedly bound but have only finite variability.

We call $\mathfrak{R}_1$ a greatest definite expressional class if the following conditions are fulfilled: (1) For every $\mathfrak{A}_1$ of $\mathfrak{R}_1$ there is a sentence which is capable of being sub-divided into expressions of $\mathfrak{R}_1$ of which $\mathfrak{A}_1$ is one; (2) If $\mathfrak{S}_1$ is determinate and capable of being sub-divided into expressions of $\mathfrak{R}_1$, and if $\mathfrak{S}_1$ contains no expression with infinite variability, then $\mathfrak{S}_1$ is resoluble; (3) $\mathfrak{R}_1$ is not a proper sub-class of an expressional class which likewise fulfils conditions (1) and (2). We call the product $\mathfrak{R}_2$ of all greatest definite classes of expressions of S the definite expression-class of S. $\mathfrak{S}_1$ is called *definite* if it is capable of being sub-divided into expressions of $\mathfrak{R}_2$ and contains no expression having infinite variability; otherwise, *indefinite*. [The terms 'definite' and 'indefinite' hereby defined are themselves indefinite. Before, in the syntax of I and II, we defined the terms 'definite' and 'indefinite' as definite terms; such definitions cannot be formulated generally, but only specifically, for particular languages—that is, if they are to express approximately the meaning which is intended (cf. § 43). The terms 'definite' and 'indefinite' as defined here will not be used in what follows. If in general syntax the word 'definite' or 'indefinite' occurs in relation to the syntax-language (as, for instance, on p. 171), we may look upon Language II (or some kindred language) as the syntax-language and take the earlier definition of 'definite' (§ 15).]

§ 56. Range

(Compare the addition at the end of § 57)

We have called $\Re_1$ *complete* if every sentence is dependent upon $\Re_1$. A complete $\Re$ leaves, as it were, no question open; every sentence is either affirmed or denied (though not, generally, by a definite method). If $\Re_1$ is contravalid, then $\Re_1$ is complete in a trivial sense: every sentence is at the same time affirmed and denied. We will call $\Re_1$ a *premiss-class* if $\Re_1$ is complete but not contravalid, and if there exists no complete class which is a proper sub-class of $\Re_1$.

Theorem 56.1. (*a*) If S is inconsistent (§ 59), then there are no premiss-classes in S. (*b*) If S is consistent and logical, then the empty sentential class is the only premiss-class. (*c*) If S is descriptive (and therefore consistent), then every premiss-class is both non-empty and indeterminate, and every one of its sentences is indeterminate.

Theorem 56.2. Two non-equipollent premiss-classes are always incompatible with one another.

In material interpretation, every non-empty premiss-class represents one of the possible states of the object-domain with which S is concerned. $\Re_1$ is called a premiss-class of $\Re_2$—in the sense of a correlate of 'consequence-class'—if $\Re_1$ is a premiss-class and $\Re_2$ a consequence-class of $\Re_1$. That $\Re_1$ is a premiss-class of $\mathfrak{S}_1$ means, in material interpretation, that $\Re_1$ is one of the possible cases in which $\mathfrak{S}_1$ is true. By a **range** we understand a class $\mathfrak{M}_1$ of premiss-classes such that each class which is equipollent to a premiss-class belonging to $\mathfrak{M}_1$, belongs also to $\mathfrak{M}_1$. By the range of $\Re_1$ we understand the class of premiss-classes of $\Re_1$. That $\mathfrak{M}_1$ is the range of $\mathfrak{S}_1$ means, in material interpretation, that $\mathfrak{M}_1$ is the class of all possible cases in which $\mathfrak{S}_1$ is true; in other words, it is the domain of possibilities left open by $\mathfrak{S}_1$.

Herein lies the reason for the choice of the term 'range' ('*Spielraum*'); in adopting it we have followed Wittgenstein [*Tractatus*], 4.463, p. 98: "The truth-conditions determine the range which is left to the facts by the proposition." Wittgenstein, however, does not give a syntactical definition.

By the *total range* we understand the class of all premiss-classes. The terms 'range' and 'content' to some extent exhibit a duality, as is shown, for example, by the following theorems (3 to 6) which are analogous to theorems 49.1, 2, 4 and 5.[*]

Theorem 56.3. If $\Re_2$ is a consequence-class of $\Re_1$, the range of $\Re_1$ is contained in that of $\Re_2$.

Theorem 56.4. If $\Re_1$ and $\Re_2$ are consequence-classes of one another, they have the same range.

Theorem 56.5. If $\Re_1$ is *valid*, the range of $\Re_1$ is the *total range*.

Theorem 56.6. If $\Re_1$ is *contravalid*, the range of $\Re_1$ is null. Theorems 3 to 6 hold correspondingly for $\mathfrak{S}_1$ and $\mathfrak{S}_2$.

Theorem 56.7. (*a*) The range of $\Re_1 + \Re_2$ is the product of the ranges of $\Re_1$ and $\Re_2$. (*b*) The range of $\Re_1$ is the product of the ranges of the individual sentences of $\Re_1$.

By the **supplementary range** of $\Re_1$, we understand the class of premiss-classes which are not premiss-classes of $\Re_1$. The supplementary range of $\Re_1$ is always also a range; but it is not always the range of a $\Re$. If the supplementary range of $\Re_1$ is the range of $\Re_2$, then we call $\Re_2$ a *contra-class* to $\Re_1$. Correspondingly, $\mathfrak{S}_2$ is called a *contra-sentence* to $\mathfrak{S}_1$ if $\{\mathfrak{S}_2\}$ is a contra-class to $\{\mathfrak{S}_1\}$. If $\mathfrak{S}_2$ is a contra-sentence to $\mathfrak{S}_1$, then $\mathfrak{S}_1$ is likewise a contra-sentence to $\mathfrak{S}_2$. If $\mathfrak{S}_2$ is a contra-sentence to $\mathfrak{S}_1$, then, in material interpretation, $\mathfrak{S}_2$ is true in all the possible cases in which $\mathfrak{S}_1$ is false—and only in these; thus, $\mathfrak{S}_2$ means the *opposite* of $\mathfrak{S}_1$. If, in S, there is no *negation*, then, as a substitute for $\sim \mathfrak{S}_1$, we can take a contra-sentence to $\mathfrak{S}_1$, or a contra-class to $\{\mathfrak{S}_1\}$. In case neither exists, then there is no substitute for $\sim \mathfrak{S}_1$, but there is a substitute for the range of $\sim \mathfrak{S}_1$, namely, the supplementary range of $\mathfrak{S}_1$, there being always exactly one such range.—The terms 'range' and 'supplementary range' will make it possible for us to characterize the individual sentential junctions.

§ 57. SENTENTIAL JUNCTIONS

If there is a full sentence $\mathfrak{S}_1$ of $\mathfrak{S}\mathfrak{g}_1^n$, in which all n arguments are $\mathfrak{S}$, then $\mathfrak{S}\mathfrak{g}_1^n$ is called an n-termed sentential junction in $\mathfrak{S}_1$.

---

[*] (*Note*, 1935.) It is, however, to be noted that the converses of Theorems 3–6 do not generally hold; this fact has been pointed out to me by Dr. Tarski. To ascertain the exact situation a further detailed investigation is required. In particular, it would be worth while to search for a different definition of 'range' which secures duality in a higher degree.

If $\mathfrak{S}\mathfrak{g}_1^n$, with n arbitrary sentences as arguments, constitutes a full sentence, then $\mathfrak{S}\mathfrak{g}_1^n$ is called an *n-termed* **sentential junction** ($\mathfrak{Vf}$, $\mathfrak{Vf}^n$). If $\mathfrak{S}\mathfrak{g}_1^n$ is composed of $\mathfrak{Pr}_1^n$ and possibly subsidiary symbols as well, $\mathfrak{Pr}_1^n$ is called an *n*-termed sentential predicate-expression; if $\mathfrak{a}_1$ is a sentential predicate-expression, $\mathfrak{a}_1$ is called a sentential predicate, or a **junction-symbol** ($\mathfrak{vf}$, $\mathfrak{vf}^n$). A $\mathfrak{vf}^n$ is, accordingly, a ${}^1\mathrm{pr}^n$ to which sentences are suitable as arguments.

In order to prepare for the definitions of particular kinds of junction, we will proceed in a way that is dependent upon the method of the value-tables (see § 5), but without assuming that S contains a negation. Let us consider a value-table for, say, three members, $\mathfrak{S}_1$, $\mathfrak{S}_2$, and $\mathfrak{S}_3$. The second row runs: 'TTF'; and to the case designated by this row corresponds the sentence $\mathfrak{S}_1 \bullet \mathfrak{S}_2 \bullet \sim \mathfrak{S}_3$. Let $\mathfrak{S}_4$ be any junction sentence $\mathfrak{Vf}_1^3(\mathfrak{S}_1, \mathfrak{S}_2, \mathfrak{S}_3)$. For this the column in the value-table may be stated; in the second row it is occupied either by 'T' or by 'F'. 'T' would mean that $\mathfrak{S}_4$ was true in the second case, and that, accordingly, $\mathfrak{S}_4$ was a consequence of $\mathfrak{S}_1 \bullet \mathfrak{S}_2 \bullet \sim \mathfrak{S}_3$; 'F' would mean that $\mathfrak{S}_4$ was false in the second case, and that therefore $\sim \mathfrak{S}_4$ was a consequence of $\mathfrak{S}_1 \bullet \mathfrak{S}_2 \bullet \sim \mathfrak{S}_3$. We want now to express these relations without making use of negation, and this is possible with the help of the ranges. We will (in this section only) designate the range of $\mathfrak{S}_1$ by '$[\mathfrak{S}_1]$' and the supplementary range of $\mathfrak{S}_1$ by '$-[\mathfrak{S}_1]$'. $\mathfrak{S}_1 \bullet \mathfrak{S}_2$ has the same content, and thus the same range, as $\{\mathfrak{S}_1, \mathfrak{S}_2\}$. Hence, according to Theorem 56.7b, $[\mathfrak{S}_1 \bullet \mathfrak{S}_2]$ is the product of $[\mathfrak{S}_1]$ and $[\mathfrak{S}_2]$. We replace the range of $\sim \mathfrak{S}_3$ by $-[\mathfrak{S}_3]$; hence we replace $[\mathfrak{S}_1 \bullet \mathfrak{S}_2 \bullet \sim \mathfrak{S}_3]$ by the product of the classes $[\mathfrak{S}_1]$, $[\mathfrak{S}_2]$, $-[\mathfrak{S}_3]$. That $\mathfrak{S}_4$ (or $\sim \mathfrak{S}_4$) is a consequence of this conjunction is (according to Theorem 56.3) expressed by the fact that $[\mathfrak{S}_1 \bullet \mathfrak{S}_2 \bullet \sim \mathfrak{S}_3]$ is contained in $[\mathfrak{S}_4]$ (or in $-[\mathfrak{S}_4]$, respectively). On the basis of the foregoing conclusions we can now state the following definitions.

Let $\mathfrak{S}_1$, $\mathfrak{S}_2$, ... $\mathfrak{S}_n$ be n closed sentences. We construct (according to the rows of the value-tables) the $m\,(=2^n)$ possible series $\mathfrak{R}_1$, $\mathfrak{R}_2$, ... $\mathfrak{R}_m$ of n ranges each, where the ith ($i = 1$ to n) range is either $[\mathfrak{S}_i]$ or $-[\mathfrak{S}_i]$. The suffixes of the $\mathfrak{R}$ may be determined according to a sort of lexicographical arrangement of the ranges: if $\mathfrak{R}_k$ and $\mathfrak{R}_l$ agree in the first $i-1$ serial terms (ranges), while the ith term of $\mathfrak{R}_k$ is $[\mathfrak{S}_i]$ and of $\mathfrak{R}_l$ is $-[\mathfrak{S}_i]$, then $\mathfrak{R}_k$ must precede

$\mathfrak{R}_l$, that is to say, k must be less than l. We will now construct a series of m ranges, $\mathfrak{M}_1$ to $\mathfrak{M}_m$ (which likewise correspond to the rows of the table, namely, to the conjunctions), in such a way that, for every k ($k = 1$ to m), $\mathfrak{M}_k$ is the product of the ranges of the series $\mathfrak{R}_k$. If, for a certain $\mathfrak{Bf}_1^n$ and a certain k ($1 \leqq k \leqq m$) and n arbitrary closed sentences $\mathfrak{S}_1, \ldots \mathfrak{S}_n$, the class $\mathfrak{M}_k$, constructed for $\mathfrak{S}_1, \ldots \mathfrak{S}_n$ in the way already described, is always a sub-class of $[\mathfrak{Bf}_1(\mathfrak{S}_1, \ldots \mathfrak{S}_n)]$, we say that the kth characteristic letter for $\mathfrak{Bf}_1$ is 'T'. If, on the other hand, for any closed $\mathfrak{S}_1, \ldots \mathfrak{S}_n$, $\mathfrak{M}_k$ is always a sub-class of $-[\mathfrak{Bf}_1(\mathfrak{S}_1, \ldots \mathfrak{S}_n)]$, we say that the kth characteristic letter for $\mathfrak{Bf}_1$ is 'F'. If neither of the two conditions is fulfilled, then $\mathfrak{Bf}_1$ does not possess any kth characteristic letter. If $\mathfrak{Bf}_1$ possesses a characteristic letter for every k ($k = 1$ to m), we call the series of these m letters the **characteristic** of $\mathfrak{Bf}_1$.—Let $\mathfrak{S}_1, \ldots \mathfrak{S}_n$ be n closed sentences of any kind; $\mathfrak{M}_1, \ldots \mathfrak{M}_m$ the ranges which are constructed from these in the manner stated. Then every premiss-class of S belongs to exactly one of these classes $\mathfrak{M}$. For any $\mathfrak{Bf}_1^n$ which possesses a characteristic, $[\mathfrak{Bf}_1(\mathfrak{S}_1, \ldots \mathfrak{S}_n)]$ is the sum of those $\mathfrak{M}_k$ for which the kth characteristic letter is 'T'.—For the $\mathfrak{Bf}^n$ there are 2^{2^n} possible characteristics.

With the help of the characteristic we are now in a position to define the various special kinds of junctions; we will restrict ourselves here to the most important of these. We call a $\mathfrak{Bf}^1$ with the characteristic 'FT' a *proper* **negation**, and a $\mathfrak{Bf}^2$ with the characteristic 'TTTF' (or 'TFFF', 'TFTT', 'TFFT', 'FTTF') a proper **disjunction** (or **conjunction, implication, equivalence, exclusive disjunction**, respectively).

If for every $\mathfrak{S}_1$, $\mathfrak{Bf}_1^1(\mathfrak{S}_1)$ is incompatible with $\mathfrak{S}_1$, then $\mathfrak{Bf}_1$ is called a *negation*. $\mathfrak{Bf}_2^2$ is called a *disjunction* if for any $\mathfrak{S}_1$ and $\mathfrak{S}_2$ whatsoever, $\mathfrak{Bf}_2(\mathfrak{S}_1, \mathfrak{S}_2)$ is always a consequence of $\mathfrak{S}_1$ and a consequence of $\mathfrak{S}_2$. $\mathfrak{Bf}_3^2$ is called a *conjunction* if, for any $\mathfrak{S}_1$ and $\mathfrak{S}_2$, $\mathfrak{S}_1$ and $\mathfrak{S}_2$ are always consequences of $\mathfrak{Bf}_3(\mathfrak{S}_1, \mathfrak{S}_2)$. $\mathfrak{Bf}_4^2$ is called an *implication* if, for any $\mathfrak{S}_1$ and $\mathfrak{S}_2$, $\mathfrak{S}_2$ is always a consequence of $\{\mathfrak{S}_1, \mathfrak{Bf}_4(\mathfrak{S}_1, \mathfrak{S}_2)\}$. If a junction of these kinds is not a proper one, we call it *improper*. If for one of the junctions mentioned there exists a junction-symbol, we call it a symbol of negation (proper or improper) or a symbol of disjunction, etc., respectively.

Theorem 57.1. If $\mathfrak{Vf}_1$ is a negation, then for any $\mathfrak{S}_1$ every sentence is a consequence of $\{\mathfrak{S}_1, \mathfrak{Vf}_1(\mathfrak{S}_1)\}$.—The class here mentioned is contravalid.

Theorem 57.2. If $\mathfrak{Vf}_1$ is a proper negation, $\mathfrak{Vf}_2$ a proper disjunction, and $\mathfrak{Vf}_3$ a proper conjunction, then for any $\mathfrak{S}_1$ the following is true: (a) If $\mathfrak{S}_1$ is closed, $\mathfrak{Vf}_1(\mathfrak{S}_1)$ is a contra-sentence to $\mathfrak{S}_1$; (b)*; (c) $\mathfrak{Vf}_2\big(\mathfrak{Vf}_1(\mathfrak{S}_1), \mathfrak{S}_1\big)$ is valid; (d) $\mathfrak{Vf}_3\big(\mathfrak{Vf}_1(\mathfrak{S}_1), \mathfrak{S}_1\big)$ is contravalid. According to (c) and (d), the *principles* of traditional logic such as those *of excluded middle* and *of contradiction* are valid in every language S for the proper junctions, if such occur in S.

Theorem 57.3. If $\mathfrak{Vf}_1$ has a characteristic, and if $\mathfrak{Vf}_2$ is co-extensive with $\mathfrak{Vf}_1$, then $\mathfrak{Vf}_2$ has the same characteristic.

Examples: The junctions which are designated as 'negation' are, in the majority of systems (for instance, in those of Frege, Russell, and Hilbert, and in our own Languages I and II), *negations* in the sense here defined. In I, ' $\sim \text{Prim}(x)$ ' is not a contra-sentence to ' $\text{Prim}(x)$ '; both sentences are contradictory, and their range is thus null. In spite of this, ' $\sim \sim \text{Prim}(x)$ ' is equipollent and equal in range to ' $\text{Prim}(x)$ '. If ' Q ' is an undefined $\mathfrak{pr}_\mathfrak{d}$, then in II there exists a contra-sentence to ' $Q(x)$ ', namely ' $\sim(x)(Q(x))$ '. In I, on the other hand, there is neither a contra-sentence nor a contra-class to ' $Q(x)$ '; but there is a supplementary range.

In the systems of Russell and of Hilbert and in our own Languages I and II, ' $\vee$ ' is a *symbol of proper disjunction*. In Hilbert's system, the junction which consists of three null expressions is also a proper disjunction ($\mathfrak{S}_1 \mathfrak{S}_2$ is equipollent to $\mathfrak{S}_1 \vee \mathfrak{S}_2$). In the English language the connectives 'either...or' ($\mathfrak{A}_3$ is empty)—as also 'aut... aut' in the Latin language—constitute a proper exclusive disjunction. Hilbert's symbol ' & ' and the ' . ' of I and II and Russell's system (and in the latter also the many-point-symbols) are *symbols of proper conjunction*. In Russell and in I and II, ' $\supset$ ' is a *symbol of proper implication*, as is also Hilbert's ' $\rightarrow$ '.

In the systems of Russell and Hilbert and Languages I and II, all $\mathfrak{vf}$ have a characteristic; but in those of Heyting and Lewis $\mathfrak{vf}$ without a characteristic also occur. For instance, Heyting's symbol of negation (we will here write it thus ' — ') is a *symbol of improper negation*, without a characteristic. $\mathfrak{S}_1$ and — $\mathfrak{S}_1$ are certainly always incompatible with one another; but — $\mathfrak{S}_1$ is not always a contra-sentence to $\mathfrak{S}_1$. $\mathfrak{S}_1$ and — $\mathfrak{S}_1$ possess the common consequence $\mathfrak{S}_1 \vee - \mathfrak{S}_1$, which is in most cases not valid but indeterminate. — — $\mathfrak{S}_1$ is not generally equipollent to $\mathfrak{S}_1$. In Lewis's system, the symbol of strict implication is a *symbol of improper implication*,

---

* Omitted in this edition.

without a characteristic (see § 69). (Concerning the *intensionality* of the $\mathfrak{v}\mathfrak{f}$ which have no characteristic, see § 65.)

Let $\mathfrak{Op}_1\mathfrak{V}_1$ be a *universal operator*, and $\mathfrak{Op}_2\mathfrak{V}_1$ an *existential operator*; let the substitution-values of $\mathfrak{V}_1$ be the same in relation to $\mathfrak{Op}_2$ as they are in relation to $\mathfrak{Op}_1$; and let $\mathfrak{Vf}_1$ be a *negation*. We call $\mathfrak{Op}_1$, $\mathfrak{Op}_2$, and $\mathfrak{Vf}_1$ *associated*, if for every $\mathfrak{Sfu}_1$ which is operable in relation to $\mathfrak{Op}_1$ and $\mathfrak{Op}_2$, $\mathfrak{Vf}_1\left(\mathfrak{Op}_1\left(\mathfrak{Sfu}_1\right)\right)$ is equipollent to $\mathfrak{Op}_2\left(\mathfrak{Vf}_1\left(\mathfrak{Sfu}_1\right)\right)$. If both the operators as well as the negation are proper, then they are also associated.

Example: In II, $(\mathfrak{p}_1)$ and $(\exists\,\mathfrak{p}_1)$ are certainly improper; but these operators and ' $\sim$ ' are associated, since $\sim(\mathfrak{p}_1)\left(\mathfrak{Sfu}_1\right)$ is always equipollent to $(\exists\,\mathfrak{p}_1)\left(\sim\mathfrak{Sfu}_1\right)$.

(*Addition*, 1935.) Since the concept of 'range' as defined above does not always fulfil the requirement of duality (see footnote, p. 200), the definitions of the sentential junctions based upon this concept are not always in accordance with the usual meanings of the junctions as laid down by the truth-value-tables. Dr. Tarski has found simpler definitions of the sentential junctions which do not make use of the term '*range*'. It is possible to proceed, for instance, as follows. We say that the relationship of negation subsists between $\mathfrak{R}_1$ and $\mathfrak{R}_2$ if $\mathfrak{R}_1$ and $\mathfrak{R}_2$ are incompatible and have exclusive contents. $\mathfrak{R}_3$ stands in the relationship of disjunction to $\mathfrak{R}_1$ and $\mathfrak{R}_2$ if the content of $\mathfrak{R}_3$ is the product of the contents of $\mathfrak{R}_1$ and $\mathfrak{R}_2$ (compare Theorem 34g.8). $\mathfrak{R}_3$ stands in the relationship of conjunction to $\mathfrak{R}_1$ and $\mathfrak{R}_2$ if $\mathfrak{R}_3$ is equipollent to $\mathfrak{R}_1+\mathfrak{R}_2$. $\mathfrak{R}_3$ stands in the relationship of implication to $\mathfrak{R}_1$ and $\mathfrak{R}_2$ if the following two conditions are fulfilled: 1. $\mathfrak{R}_2$ is a consequence-class of $\mathfrak{R}_1+\mathfrak{R}_3$; 2. if $\mathfrak{R}_4$ is smaller in content than $\mathfrak{R}_3$, then $\mathfrak{R}_2$ is not a consequence-class of $\mathfrak{R}_1+\mathfrak{R}_4$ (compare § 65, paragraph 1). $\mathfrak{R}_3$ stands in the relationship of equivalence to $\mathfrak{R}_1$ and $\mathfrak{R}_2$ if $\mathfrak{R}_3$ stands in the relationship of implication both to $\mathfrak{R}_1$ and $\mathfrak{R}_2$, and to $\mathfrak{R}_2$ and $\mathfrak{R}_1$.—We then call $\mathfrak{Vf}_1^1$ a proper negation if, for every closed $\mathfrak{S}_1$, $\mathfrak{Vf}_1^1\left(\mathfrak{S}_1\right)$ stands in the relationship of negation to $\mathfrak{S}_1$. We call $\mathfrak{Vf}_2^2$ a proper disjunction if, for closed $\mathfrak{S}_1$ and $\mathfrak{S}_2$, $\mathfrak{Vf}_2^2\left(\mathfrak{S}_1,\mathfrak{S}_2\right)$ always stands in the relationship of disjunction to $\mathfrak{S}_1$ and $\mathfrak{S}_2$. The remaining junctions are to be similarly defined.

NOTE (1955). I have given a more exact and more detailed analysis, both syntactical and semantical, of the sentential connections in my book *Formalization of Logic* (1943).

(c) ARITHMETIC; NON-CONTRADICTORINESS; THE ANTINOMIES

§ 58. ARITHMETIC

Let $\mathfrak{A}_0$ be an $^{\alpha}\mathfrak{Stu}$, $\mathfrak{Fu}_1$ an $^{\alpha+1}\mathfrak{Fu}^1$, and $\mathfrak{R}_1$ the infinite series o expressions constructed in the following manner: the first term is $\mathfrak{A}_0$, and for every n the $(n+1)$th term is the full expression of $\mathfrak{Fu}_1$ with the nth term as argument. $\mathfrak{R}_1$ has accordingly the form $\mathfrak{A}_0$; $\mathfrak{Fu}_1(\mathfrak{A}_0)$; $\mathfrak{Fu}_1(\mathfrak{Fu}_1(\mathfrak{A}_0))$; ... $\mathfrak{A}_n$; $\mathfrak{Fu}_1(\mathfrak{A}_n)$; .... If every two different expressions of $\mathfrak{R}_1$ are isogenous (hence each one an $^{\alpha}\mathfrak{Stu}$) but not synonymous, we call $\mathfrak{R}_1$ a *numerical expression-series* or $\mathfrak{z}$-series. The expressions of $\mathfrak{R}_1$ and those synonymous with them are called **numerical expressions** ($\mathfrak{z}$) of $\mathfrak{R}_1$. Those $\mathfrak{z}$ which are synonymous with $\mathfrak{A}_0$ are called zero-expressions, or 0-$\mathfrak{z}$, of $\mathfrak{R}_1$; those which are synonymous with $\mathfrak{Fu}_1(\mathfrak{A}_0)$ are called 1-$\mathfrak{z}$ of $\mathfrak{R}_1$, etc. A $\mathfrak{z}$ which is synonymous with $\mathfrak{Fu}_1(\mathfrak{z}_1)$ is called a *successor-expression* of $\mathfrak{z}_1$. [These and the following terms are always related to a particular $\mathfrak{z}$-series $\mathfrak{R}_1$; for the sake of brevity, the phrase "of $\mathfrak{R}_1$" or "in relation to $\mathfrak{R}_1$" will usually be omitted.]

If $\mathfrak{a}_1$ is a $\mathfrak{z}$, it is called a **numeral** ($\mathfrak{zz}$). If $\mathfrak{a}_1$ is a 0-$\mathfrak{z}$, it is called a *zero-symbol* ($\mathfrak{nu}$). $\mathfrak{B}_1$ is called a numerical $\mathfrak{B}$ if the $\mathfrak{z}$ belong to the substitution-values of $\mathfrak{B}_1$. If $\mathfrak{v}_1$ is a numerical $\mathfrak{B}$, then $\mathfrak{v}_1$ is called a *numerical variable* ($\mathfrak{z}$).

If, for $\mathfrak{Sg}_1^n$ (or $\mathfrak{Pr}_1^n$), there exists a full sentence with only $\mathfrak{z}$ as arguments, then $\mathfrak{Sg}_1$ (or $\mathfrak{Pr}_1$) is called a numerical $\mathfrak{Sg}$ (or $\mathfrak{Pr}$). If for $\mathfrak{Fu}_1^n$ there exists a full expression such that this expression itself and all the arguments are $\mathfrak{z}$, then $\mathfrak{Fu}_1$ is called a numerical $\mathfrak{Fu}$. If $\mathfrak{pr}_1$ (or $\mathfrak{fu}_1$) is a numerical $\mathfrak{Pr}$ or $\mathfrak{Fu}$, then $\mathfrak{pr}_1$ (or $\mathfrak{fu}_1$) is called a **numerical predicate** ($\mathfrak{zpr}$) (or a **numerical functor** ($\mathfrak{zfu}$), respectively).

$\mathfrak{Sg}_1^3$ (or $\mathfrak{Pr}_1^3$) is called a *sum-$\mathfrak{Sg}$* (or -$\mathfrak{Pr}$, respectively) for the kth place ($k=1$, 2, or 3) if for any m and n whatsoever, the following is true: if $\mathfrak{z}_1$ is an m-$\mathfrak{z}$, and $\mathfrak{z}_2$ an n-$\mathfrak{z}$, then the full sentence of $\mathfrak{Sg}_1$ (or of $\mathfrak{Pr}_1$, respectively) in which $\mathfrak{z}_3$ is the kth argument and $\mathfrak{z}_1$ and $\mathfrak{z}_2$ the two other arguments, is valid when and only when $\mathfrak{z}_3$ is an $(m+n)$-$\mathfrak{z}$. $\mathfrak{Fu}_1^2$ is called a *sum-$\mathfrak{Fu}$* provided that $\mathfrak{Fu}_1$ is a numerical $\mathfrak{Fu}$ and the following is true for any m and n: if $\mathfrak{z}_1$ is an m-$\mathfrak{z}$ and $\mathfrak{z}_2$ an n-$\mathfrak{z}$, then $\mathfrak{Fu}_1(\mathfrak{z}_1, \mathfrak{z}_2)$ is an $(m+n)$-$\mathfrak{z}$.

'*Product*-$\mathfrak{S}$g', '-$\mathfrak{Pr}$', '-$\mathfrak{Fu}$' are analogously defined, where $\mathfrak{Z}_3$, or $\mathfrak{Fu}_1(\mathfrak{Z}_1, \mathfrak{Z}_2)$ respectively, is an $(m \bullet n)$-$\mathfrak{Z}$. If $\mathfrak{Z}\mathfrak{pr}_1$ is a sum-$\mathfrak{Pr}$ (or product-$\mathfrak{Pr}$), $\mathfrak{Z}\mathfrak{pr}_1$ is called a *sum-predicate* (or *product-predicate*, respectively). If $\mathfrak{Z}\mathfrak{fu}_1$ is a sum-$\mathfrak{Fu}$ (or product-$\mathfrak{Fu}$), $\mathfrak{Z}\mathfrak{fu}_1$ is called a *sum-functor* (or *product-functor*, respectively). It will readily be seen that in a similar way all the other arithmetical terms which occur in the arithmetic contained in S can be syntactically characterized; that is to say, those kinds of $\mathfrak{S}$g, $\mathfrak{Pr}$, or $\mathfrak{Fu}$ to which a particular arithmetical meaning belongs can be defined. We shall content ourselves here with the foregoing examples.

We say that S contains an **arithmetic** if, in S, there is at least one $\mathfrak{Z}$-series $\mathfrak{R}_1$, one sum-$\mathfrak{S}$g, and one product-$\mathfrak{S}$g, in relation to $\mathfrak{R}_1$. Let S contain an arithmetic in relation to $\mathfrak{R}_1$. If an $\mathfrak{S}_1$ and a $\mathfrak{B}_1$ exist such that for every $\mathfrak{Z}$ of $\mathfrak{R}_1$ there is a synonymous substitution-value of $\mathfrak{B}_1$ in $\mathfrak{S}_1$ and that $\mathfrak{B}_1$ in $\mathfrak{S}_1$ has infinite universality, then we say that S contains a *general arithmetic* (in relation to $\mathfrak{R}_1$).

$\mathfrak{Z}_1$ and $\mathfrak{Z}_2$ are called *corresponding* $\mathfrak{Z}$ in $\mathfrak{R}_1$ and $\mathfrak{R}_2$ if an n exists such that $\mathfrak{Z}_1$ is an n-$\mathfrak{Z}$ of $\mathfrak{R}_1$, and $\mathfrak{Z}_2$ is an n-$\mathfrak{Z}$ of $\mathfrak{R}_2$. Here $\mathfrak{R}_1$ and $\mathfrak{R}_2$ may belong to different levels, and even to different languages. We say that two numerical $\mathfrak{S}$g^n (or two numerical $\mathfrak{Pr}^n$) (in one or two languages) have a *corresponding extent* if every two full sentences of them with corresponding $\mathfrak{Z}$ as arguments are either both valid or both contravalid.

If S contains an arithmetic, then it certainly contains expressions which can be interpreted as designations of **real numbers**, namely the numerical $\mathfrak{S}$g^1; and further, it may contain numerical $\mathfrak{Pr}^1$ and numerical $\mathfrak{Fu}^1$ of which the full expressions are $\mathfrak{Z}$ (see § 39). We will call $\mathfrak{B}_1$ a $\mathfrak{B}$ for real numbers if there are infinitely many numerical $\mathfrak{Pr}^1$ (or numerical $\mathfrak{Fu}^1$ of the kind mentioned) which belong to the substitution-values of $\mathfrak{B}_1$. If $\mathfrak{B}_1$ is a $\mathfrak{B}$ for real numbers and if $\mathfrak{B}_1$ in $\mathfrak{S}_1$ has infinite universality, then we call $\mathfrak{S}_1$ a *universal sentence concerning real numbers*. The arithmetical equality between two real numbers that are represented by two $\mathfrak{S}$g^1 (or two $\mathfrak{Pr}^1$) in relation to the same $\mathfrak{Z}$-series $\mathfrak{R}_1$ finds its syntactical expression in the coextensiveness of the two $\mathfrak{S}$g (or $\mathfrak{Pr}$, respectively), or in the case of $\mathfrak{Fu}$ in the equality of the course of values. If, however, it is a question of different $\mathfrak{R}_1$ and $\mathfrak{R}_2$ which may also belong to different languages, the arithmetical equality will be represented by correspondence in extent. In this way, real numbers of various languages can be compared with one another; an expression can be characterized as being the expression of a particular real number (for example: 'π-expression in relation to $\Re_1$'). We can easily see how it may be syntactically determined whether a *differential and integral calculus* and a *theory of functions* of more or less wide extent is contained in S. We shall not go any further into this question here.

Examples: 1. *Language I.* The following series are examples of 3-series. $\Re_1$: '0', '0I', '0II', ...; $\Re_2$: '0', '0II', '0IIII', ...; $\Re_3$: '3', '3I', ...; $\Re_4$: '0', 'nf(0)', 'nf(nf(0))', ...; $\Re_5$: '3', 'fak(3)', 'fak(fak(3))', ... The ſu of I are 3ſu in relation to each of these series; and moreover 'I' is also a 3ſu in relation to each of these series, and specifically it is the series-forming 3ſu in $\Re_1$. 'sum' is a sum-ſu, 'prod' a product-ſu. Language I contains a general arithmetic inasmuch as there are sentences with free 3 in it. Real numbers can be represented in Language I by means of pr¹ or ſu¹; there is, however, no $\mathfrak{B}$ for real numbers and no $\mathfrak{Pr}$ for real-number arguments.

2. *Language II* (see § 39). Here also, the aforesaid series $\Re_1, ... \Re_5$ are 3-series; but there are also others of quite different kinds. The ²pr can be used as pr of real numbers. Since there are ¹p, ²p, and ²ſ having infinite universality, there are consequently universal sentences concerning real numbers and functions of real numbers, etc.

§ 59. The Non-Contradictoriness and Completeness of a Language

S is called **contradictory** (or d-inconsistent) if every sentence of S is demonstrable; otherwise, **non-contradictory** (or d-consistent). [It is to be noted that the term 'contradictory' when applied to sentences (German: *kontradiktorisch*) is an L-c-term (see § 52), but when applied to languages (German: *widerspruchsvoll*) is a d-term and not an L-term.] The following c-terms correspond to these d-terms. S is called **inconsistent** if every sentence of S is valid; otherwise, **consistent**. If the L-sub-language of S is contradictory (or non-contradictory, inconsistent or consistent), then S is called L-contradictory (or L-non-contradictory, etc., respectively). The relations between the defined d-, c-, and L-terms are indicated by the arrows shown in the table on p. 210.

Theorem 59.1. If S is contradictory (or inconsistent), then every

$\Re$ and every $\mathfrak{S}$ is, at the same time, both demonstrable and re-futable (or valid and contravalid, respectively); there are no irresoluble (or indeterminate) $\Re$ or $\mathfrak{S}$.

Theorem 59.2. If, in S, there is a $\Re$ or an $\mathfrak{S}$ which is either non-demonstrable (or non-valid) or non-refutable (or non-contravalid, respectively), then S is non-contradictory (or con-sistent, respectively). By Theorem 1.

Theorem 59.3. If, in S, there is a $\Re$ or an $\mathfrak{S}$ which is at the same time both demonstrable and refutable (or valid and contravalid), then S is contradictory (or inconsistent, respectively); and con-versely.

Theorem 59.4. If S contains the ordinary sentential calculus (with the negation '$\sim$') then in S every sentence is derivable from $\mathfrak{S}_1$ and $\sim \mathfrak{S}_1$. In I and II this is arrived at with the help of PSI 1 and PSII 1, respectively.

Theorem 59.5. If S contains the ordinary sentential calculus, then S is contradictory when and only when an $\mathfrak{S}_1$ exists such that $\mathfrak{S}_1$ and $\sim \mathfrak{S}_1$ are demonstrable in S. By Theorem 4.

Theorem 59.6. If S contains a negation $\mathfrak{Bf}_1$, then S is incon-sistent when and only when an $\mathfrak{S}_1$ exists such that $\mathfrak{S}_1$ and $\mathfrak{Bf}_1(\mathfrak{S}_1)$ are valid in S. By Theorem 57.1.

The definitions of 'contradictory' and 'non-contradictory' correspond (as Theorem 5 shows) to the ordinary use of language without, however, negation being assumed. (See Tarski [*Methodologie*] I, p. 27 f., and Post [*Introduction*].)

A non-contradictory language may nevertheless be inconsistent. For although it contains no d-contradiction, it may still contain a c-contradiction, that is to say, a contradiction which depends upon the c-rules only. This is the reason for introducing the narrower term 'consistent', which applies only to languages that contain no contradictions of any sort.

Theorem 59.7. If S is inconsistent or contradictory, then it is true that: (*a*) every two sentences of S are equipollent; (*b*) every two expressions of S which are isogenous are synonymous.

Theorem 59.8. If S is inconsistent or contradictory, then S con-tains no $\mathfrak{Z}$-series and therefore no arithmetic.—By Theorem 7*b*; different terms of a $\mathfrak{Z}$-series are not synonymous.

Example of a non-contradictory but inconsistent language. Let $\mathfrak{S}\mathfrak{f}\mathfrak{u}_1$ be '$[(x>0) \cdot (y>0) \cdot (z>0) \cdot (u>2)] \supset (x^u+y^u \neq z^u)$'. Let $\mathfrak{S}_1$ be

$()(\mathfrak{S}\mathfrak{f}\mathfrak{u}_1)$, in other words, Fermat's theorem. Let every closed logical variant of $\mathfrak{S}\mathfrak{f}\mathfrak{u}_1$ be demonstrable in S (hence, for every individual set of four positive integers Fermat's property can be demonstrated). Let $\mathfrak{S}_1$ itself be analytic but non-demonstrable; i.e. let S contain an indefinite rule analogous to DC 2 (p. 38) by which $\mathfrak{S}_1$ is a direct consequence of the class of those variants. Further, let the sentence $\sim \mathfrak{S}_1$ (although possibly contradictory in classical mathematics) be demonstrable in S (for instance, laid down as a primitive sentence, other sentences such as are d-incompatible with it being cancelled). Then S is inconsistent (and moreover L-inconsistent). At the same time, however, S may be non-contradictory, since $\mathfrak{S}_1$ and $\sim \mathfrak{S}_1$ are not both demonstrable. There is indeed no d-contradiction here but there is a c-contradiction—namely, that between the class of those variants and $\sim \mathfrak{S}_1$. This c-contradiction is evident in the ordinary material interpretation: the demonstrable sentence $\sim \mathfrak{S}_1$ means that not all sets of four positive integers have Fermat's property, while for every such set a demonstrable variant occurs, which means that this quadruple has Fermat's property. But the c-contradiction, the inconsistency, is also purely formal without any reference to material interpretation: the class which consists of those variants and $\sim \mathfrak{S}_1$ contains only demonstrable sentences but is nevertheless contradictory, that is to say, every sentence is a consequence of it; hence every sentence of S is at the same time both analytic and contradictory.

For such languages as have no other $\mathfrak{v}$ than the $\mathfrak{z}$, our term 'consistent' corresponds to Gödel's term, [*Unentscheidbare*] p. 187, 'ω-non-contradictory'; see also Tarski [*Widerspruchsfr.*].

The language S is called **complete** (or d-complete) if the sentential null-class (and hence, according to Theorem 48.8, every $\mathfrak{R}$) is complete (or d-complete, respectively); otherwise, *incomplete* (or d-incomplete). The language S is called **determinate** (or **resoluble**) if every $\mathfrak{R}$ (and hence every $\mathfrak{S}$ also) is determinate (or resoluble, respectively) in S; otherwise, *indeterminate* (or irresoluble). The corresponding L-terms ('L-complete' and so on) are only attributed to the language S when the original term ('complete', etc.) is attributable to the L-sub-language of S.

Theorem 59.9. If S is complete, then it is determinate; and conversely. By Theorem 48.5.

Theorem 59.10. If S is complete, then it is logical; and conversely. By Theorem 50.2 a.

Theorem 59.11. If S is complete, then it is L-complete; and conversely. By Theorems 10 and 51.1.

Theorem 59.12. (a) The terms 'complete language', 'L-complete language', 'determinate language', 'logical language' coincide. (b) The terms 'incomplete language', 'L-incomplete language', 'indeterminate language', 'descriptive language' coincide.

Theorem 59.13. If S is d-complete, then it is resoluble; and conversely. By Theorem 48.5.

For the d-terms, no valid theorems analogous to Theorems 11 and 12 exist.

Theorem 59.14. (a) If S is contradictory, then S is both d-complete and complete. (b) If S is inconsistent, then S is complete. By Theorem 1.

How the properties of languages here defined are transferred from one language to another can be seen from the table on p. 225 (B). The relation of the terms to one another is indicated by the arrows in the table below (as on p. 183).

Properties of languages

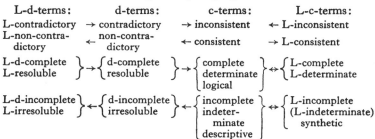

L-d-terms:	d-terms:	c-terms:	L-c-terms:
L-contradictory	→ contradictory	→ inconsistent	← L-inconsistent
L-non-contra-dictory	← non-contra-dictory	← consistent	→ L-consistent
L-d-complete L-resoluble	} → { d-complete resoluble	} → { complete determinate logical	} ↔ { L-complete L-determinate
L-d-incomplete L-irresoluble	} ← { d-incomplete irresoluble	} ← { incomplete indeter- minate descriptive	} ↔ { L-incomplete (L-indeterminate) synthetic

We shall see that every consistent language which contains a general arithmetic is irresoluble. Only poorer languages are resoluble, for example, the sentential calculus. A richer language, though not resoluble, can yet be determinate and complete, provided that sufficient indefinite rules of transformation are laid down. This is the case, for instance, with the logical sub-languages of I and II. For such an *irresoluble but complete* language, the following classification of sentences holds; it is at the same time the classification of the logical sentences of any irresoluble language whatsoever (for the classification of the descriptive sentences, see p. 185):

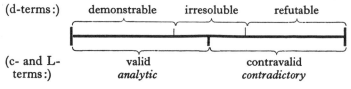

(d-terms:)	demonstrable	irresoluble	refutable
(c- and L- terms:)	valid *analytic*		contravalid *contradictory*

§ 60a. The Antinomies

In investigating the non-contradictoriness of a language, the first thing to be asked is whether the familiar so-called antinomies or paradoxes which appeared in earlier systems of logic and of the Theory of Aggregates have definitely been eliminated. This point is an especially critical one when we are concerned with a language which is rich enough to formulate, to any extent, its own syntax, whether in an arithmetized form or with the help of special syntactical designations. The syntactical sentences may sometimes speak about themselves, and the question arises whether this reflexiveness may not possibly lead to contradictions. This question is significant because it is not concerned with calculi of a specially constructed kind but with all systems whatsoever which contain arithmetic. We shall now investigate this question and in doing so we shall avail ourselves of the results obtained by Gödel.

We shall follow Ramsey's example in dividing the antinomies into two kinds, and we shall see that those of the second kind are the ones which come into consideration for our inquiry. These will therefore be examined more closely. In the examples we propose to use partly the word-language and partly a symbolism similar to that which was used in Language II; for the syntactical designations we shall employ in some cases Gothic symbols, and in others inclusion in inverted commas. Let us consider, to begin with, the following two antinomies.

1. **Russell's antinomy** [*Princ. Math.* I]; [*Math. Phil.*]. We define as follows: a property is called *impredicable* when it does not apply to itself. Expressed in symbols: "$\mathrm{Impr}\,(F) \equiv \sim F(F)$". If in this case we substitute 'Impr' itself for 'F', we get the contradictory sentence: "$\mathrm{Impr}\,(\mathrm{Impr}) \equiv \sim \mathrm{Impr}\,(\mathrm{Impr})$".

2. **Grelling's antinomy.** Definition: in a language which contains its own syntax, a syntactical predicate (for example, an adjective) is called *heterological* if the sentence which ascribes the property expressed by the predicate to the predicate itself is false. If, for instance, 'Q' is a syntactical predicate, then "$\mathrm{Het}\,('Q') \equiv \sim Q\,('Q')$" is true. (The fundamental difference between this antinomy and the foregoing, which is disregarded in many presentations, is to be noted, namely, that here the property Q is attributed, not to the property Q but to the predicate, i.e. the

symbol ' Q '.) *Example:* the adjective 'monosyllabic' is heterological because 'monosyllabic' is not monosyllabic but penta-syllabic. Now, if instead of the predicate ' Q ', we take the predicate 'Het' itself which has just been defined, we get, from the definition as stated, the contradictory sentence "Het('Het') ≡ ∼ Het('Het')".

In order to avoid antinomies in his language, Russell set up a complicated rule of types, which, particularly in the theory of real numbers, gave rise to certain difficulties, to overcome which he found it necessary to state a special axiom, the so-called Axiom of Reducibility. Ramsey ([*Foundations*] Treatise I, 1925) has shown that the same object may be attained by a far simpler method. He discovered, namely, that it is possible to differentiate between two kinds of antinomies which may be designated as logical (in the narrower sense) and syntactical (the latter are also called linguistic, epistemological, or semantic). Example (1) belongs to the first category and (2) to the second. Following Peano, Ramsey pointed out that the antinomies of the second kind do not appear directly in the symbolic system of logic, but only in the accompanying text; for they are concerned with the expressions. From this fact he drew the practical conclusion that in the construction of a symbolic system it is not necessary to take note of these syntactical antinomies. Now since the antinomies of the first kind are already eliminated by the so-called simple rule of types, this is sufficient; the branched rule of types and the axiom of reducibility which it necessitates are superfluous.

On the basis of the *simple rule of types* (as in II for instance) the type of a predicate is determined by the type of the appertaining arguments alone. On the basis of Russell's branched rule of types, the form of the chain of definitions of a predicate is also a factor in determining its type (for instance, whether it is definite or not). But the simple rule of types is sufficient to determine that a predicate always belongs to a type other than that of the appertaining arguments (namely, that it always belongs to a type of a higher level). Thus, here, a sentence cannot have the form '$F(F)$'. And hence a definition of the form given for 'impredicable' is obviously impossible. In the same way, the other well-known antinomies of the first kind are obviated by means of the simple rule of types.

The problem of the *syntactical antinomies*, however, obviously reappears when it is a question of a language S in which the syntax of S itself can be formulated, and therefore in the case of every language which contains arithmetic. There is a prevalent fear that with a syntax of this sort, which refers to itself, either contradictions similar to the syntactical antinomies will be unavoidable, or in order to avoid them, special restrictions, something like the "branched" rule of types, will be necessary. A closer investigation will show, however, that this fear is not justified.

The above-mentioned view is held, for instance, by Chwistek. He had already, before Ramsey, had the idea of stating only the simple rule of types, and thus rendering the axiom of reducibility unnecessary. Later, however, he came to the conclusion that with the rejection of the branched rule of types the syntactical antinomies—that of Richard, for example—would appear (see Chwistek [*Nom. Grundl.*]). In my opinion, however, the indispensability of the branched rule of types in Chwistek's system is due only to the fact that he uses the autonymous mode of speech for his syntax (the so-called Semantics) (see § 68).

Apart from Grelling's, the most important example of a syntactical antinomy is the one which was already famous in antiquity, the *antinomy of the liar* (for the history of this see Rüstow). Someone says: "I am lying", or more exactly: "I am lying in this sentence", in other words: "This sentence is false." If the sentence is true, then it is false; and if it is false, then it is true.

Another antinomy which belongs to the category of the syntactical antinomies is Richard's (see [*Princ. Math.*] I, 61, and Fraenkel [*Mengenlehre*] p. 214 ff.). In its original version it is concerned with the decimals definable in a particular word-language. It can be easily transferred to $\mathfrak{z}\mathfrak{pr}^1$ in the following manner. Let S be a language whose syntax is formulated in S. In S there are at most a denumerable number of $\mathfrak{z}\mathfrak{pr}$ which are definable. Therefore we can correlate univocally a natural number with every such $\mathfrak{z}\mathfrak{pr}^1$ (for instance, by a lexicographical arrangement of the definition-sentences or, in an arithmetized syntax, simply by the term-number of the $\mathfrak{z}\mathfrak{pr}^1$). Let 'c' be a numerical expression; we will call the number c a Richardian number if c is the number of a $\mathfrak{z}\mathfrak{pr}^1$, say 'P', which does not appertain to the number c, so that 'P(c)' is false (contradictory). Accordingly, the adjective 'Richardian' is a defined $\mathfrak{z}\mathfrak{pr}^1$, and thus has correlated with it a certain number, say b. Now b must be either Richardian or not. If b is Richardian, then, according to the definition, the property having the number b does not appertain to b; therefore, in this case, in contradiction to our assumption, b is not Richardian. Hence b must be non-Richardian. b must leave the definition of 'Richardian' unfulfilled, and therefore must possess the property having the number b; that is to say, b must be Richardian. This is a contradiction.

It is characteristic of the syntactical antinomies mentioned that they operate with the concepts 'true' and 'false'. For this reason we will examine these concepts more closely before considering the syntactical antinomies any further.

§ 60b. The Concepts 'True' and 'False'

The concepts 'true' and 'false' are usually regarded as the principal concepts of logic. In the ordinary word-languages, they are used in such a way that the sentences '$\mathfrak{S}_1$ is true' and '$\mathfrak{S}_1$ is false' belong to the same language as $\mathfrak{S}_1$. *This customary usage of the terms 'true' and 'false' leads, however, to a contradiction.* This will be shown in connection with the antinomy of the liar. In order to guard ourselves against false inferences, we will proceed in a strictly formal manner. Let the syntax of S formulated in S contain three syntactical adjectives, '$\mathfrak{N}$', '$\mathfrak{W}$', '$\mathfrak{F}$', concerning which we will make only the following assumptions (V 1–3). In these, we shall write the sentence: "$\mathfrak{A}_1$ has the property $\mathfrak{N}$" in an abbreviated form, thus: '$\mathfrak{N}(\mathfrak{A}_1)$'. If '$\mathfrak{N}(\mathfrak{A}_1)$' is interpreted as "$\mathfrak{A}_1$ is a non-sentence", '$\mathfrak{W}(\mathfrak{A}_1)$' as: "The expression $\mathfrak{A}_1$ is a sentence, and, specifically, a true sentence", and '$\mathfrak{F}(\mathfrak{A}_1)$' as: "$\mathfrak{A}_1$ is a sentence, and, specifically, a false sentence", then our assumptions V 1–3 are in agreement with the ordinary use of language.

V 1. Every expression of S has exactly one of the three properties $\mathfrak{N}$, $\mathfrak{W}$, $\mathfrak{F}$.

V 2a. Let 'A' be any expression whatsoever of S (not: "designation of an expression"); if $\mathfrak{W}('A')$, then A. [For instance: if "this tree is high" is true, then this tree is high.]

V 2b. If A, then $\mathfrak{W}('A')$.

V 3. For any $\mathfrak{A}_1$, the expressions '$\mathfrak{N}(\mathfrak{A}_1)$', '$\mathfrak{W}(\mathfrak{A}_1)$', '$\mathfrak{F}(\mathfrak{A}_1)$' do not possess the property $\mathfrak{N}$ (hence, they do possess either $\mathfrak{W}$ or $\mathfrak{F}$, according to V 1).

From V 1 and 2b it follows that:

If $\mathfrak{F}('A')$, then not $\mathfrak{W}('A')$, and therefore not A.   (4)

From V 1 and 2*a* it follows that:

If not A, then not $\mathfrak{W}$('A'), and therefore $\mathfrak{F}$('A'), or $\mathfrak{N}$('A'). (5)

Now in analogy with the assertion of the liar, it is easy to show that the investigation of an expression $\mathfrak{A}_2$ with the text '$\mathfrak{F}(\mathfrak{A}_2)$' leads to a contradiction. The fact that an expression is here designated by a symbol (namely: '$\mathfrak{A}_2$'), which itself occurs in itself, easily has a confusing effect. But we can also establish the contradiction without this direct reflexive relation; it is not, as is so often believed, the reflexiveness which constitutes the error upon which the contradiction depends; the error lies rather in the unrestricted use of the terms 'true' and 'false'. Let us examine the two expressions '$\mathfrak{F}(\mathfrak{A}_1)$' and '$\mathfrak{W}(\mathfrak{A}_2)$'. Obviously these are expressions, at worst non-sentences. We are entirely at liberty as to which expressions we choose to designate by '$\mathfrak{A}_1$' and '$\mathfrak{A}_2$'; let us agree that:

(*a*) $\mathfrak{A}_1$ shall be the expression '$\mathfrak{W}(\mathfrak{A}_2)$'; (*b*) $\mathfrak{A}_2$ shall be the expression

$$\text{'}\mathfrak{F}(\mathfrak{A}_1)\text{'.} \tag{6}$$

(Here, as can be seen, no designation of an expression occurs in the expression itself.)

According to V 3:

$$\text{Either } \mathfrak{W}(\text{'}\mathfrak{F}(\mathfrak{A}_1)\text{'}) \text{ or } \mathfrak{F}(\text{'}\mathfrak{F}(\mathfrak{A}_1)\text{'}). \tag{7}$$

We first make the assumption: $\mathfrak{W}(\text{'}\mathfrak{F}(\mathfrak{A}_1)\text{'})$. From this, in accordance with V 2*a*, it would follow that: $\mathfrak{F}(\mathfrak{A}_1)$. This, according to (6*a*) is $\mathfrak{F}(\text{'}\mathfrak{W}(\mathfrak{A}_2)\text{'})$; from which, according to (4), would follow: not $\mathfrak{W}(\mathfrak{A}_2)$. This is, by (6*b*): not $\mathfrak{W}(\text{'}\mathfrak{F}(\mathfrak{A}_1)\text{'})$. Our assumption leads to its own opposite and is therefore refuted.

Thence, according to (7), it is true that:

$$\mathfrak{F}(\text{'}\mathfrak{F}(\mathfrak{A}_1)\text{'}). \tag{8}$$

From this, by (4), follows:

$$\text{not } \mathfrak{F}(\mathfrak{A}_1). \tag{9}$$

This, according to (6*a*) is:

$$\text{not } \mathfrak{F}(\text{'}\mathfrak{W}(\mathfrak{A}_2)\text{'}). \tag{10}$$

By V 3:

$$\mathfrak{W}(\text{'}\mathfrak{W}(\mathfrak{A}_2)\text{'}) \text{ or } \mathfrak{F}(\text{'}\mathfrak{W}(\mathfrak{A}_2)\text{'}). \tag{11}$$

From (10) and (11):

$$\mathfrak{W}(\text{'}\mathfrak{W}(\mathfrak{A}_2)\text{'}). \tag{12}$$

Thence, in accordance with V 2 a:

$$\mathfrak{W}(\mathfrak{A}_2). \tag{13}$$

From (8) and (6 b):

$$\mathfrak{F}(\mathfrak{A}_2). \tag{14}$$

Therefore, in accordance with V 1:

$$\text{not } \mathfrak{W}(\mathfrak{A}_2). \tag{15}$$

(13) and (15) constitute a contradiction.

This contradiction only arises when the predicates 'true' and 'false' referring to sentences in a language S are used in S itself. On the other hand, it is possible to proceed without incurring any contradiction by employing the predicates 'true (in S_1)' and 'false (in S_1)' in a syntax of S_1 which is not formulated in S_1 itself but in another language S_2. S_2 can, for instance, be obtained from S_1 by the addition of those two predicates as new primitive symbols and the erection of suitable primitive sentences relating to them, in the following way: 1. Every sentence of S_1 is either true or false. 2. No sentence of S_1 is at the same time both true and false. 3. If, in S_1, $\mathfrak{S}_2$ is a consequence of $\mathfrak{R}_1$, and if all sentences of $\mathfrak{R}_1$ are true, then $\mathfrak{S}_2$ is likewise true. A theory of this kind formulated in the manner of a syntax would nevertheless not be a genuine syntax. *For truth and falsehood are not proper syntactical properties;* whether a sentence is true or false cannot generally be seen by its design, that is to say, by the kinds and serial order of its symbols. [This fact has usually been overlooked by logicians, because, for the most part, they have been dealing not with descriptive but only with logical languages, and in relation to these, certainly, 'true' and 'false' coincide with 'analytic' and 'contradictory', respectively, and are thus syntactical terms.]

Even though 'true' and 'false' do not in general occur in a proper syntax (that is to say, in a syntax which is limited to the design-properties of sentences), yet the majority of ordinary sentences which make use of these words can be translated either into the object-language or into the syntax-language. If $\mathfrak{S}_1$ is 'A', then '$\mathfrak{S}_1$ is true' can, for example, be translated by 'A'. In logical investigation, 'true' (and 'false') appears in two different modes of use. If the truth of the sentence in question follows from the rules of transformation of the language in question, then 'true' can be translated by 'valid' (or, more specifically, by 'analytic', 'demonstrable') and, correspondingly, 'false' by 'contravalid' (or 'contradictory', 'refutable'). 'True' may also refer to indeterminate sentences, but in logical investigations this only happens in the conditional form, as, for example: 'If $\mathfrak{S}_1$ is true, then $\mathfrak{S}_2$ is true (or false, respectively).' A sentence of this kind can be translated into the syntactical sentence: '$\mathfrak{S}_2$ is a consequence of $\mathfrak{S}_1$ (or is incompatible with $\mathfrak{S}_1$, respectively).'

§ 60c. THE SYNTACTICAL ANTINOMIES

We will now return to the question whether, in the formulation of the syntax of S in S, contradictions of the kind known as *syntactical antinomies* may not arise if, in the ordinary phrasing of these antinomies, 'true' and 'false' are replaced by syntactical terms in the manner indicated above.

Let S be a non-contradictory language (and, further, a consistent one), which contains arithmetic, and hence an arithmetized syntax of S itself also. Then a certain method exists whereby it is possible to construct, for any and every syntactical property formulable in S, a sentence of S, $\mathfrak{S}_1$, such that $\mathfrak{S}_1$ attributes this property—whether rightly or wrongly—to itself. This has already been shown in the case of Language II (see § 35). Now, by means of a construction of this kind, we will try to restate the antinomy of the liar. It consists of a sentence which asserts its own falsehood.

First, let us replace 'false' in this antinomy by '*non-demonstrable*'. If we construct a sentence of S, $\mathfrak{S}_1$, which asserts of itself that it is non-demonstrable in S, then we have in $\mathfrak{S}_1$ an analogue to the sentence $\mathfrak{G}$ of Language II which has already been discussed (and to the sentence $\mathfrak{G}_I$ of Language I). Here no contradiction arises. If $\mathfrak{S}_1$ is true (analytic), then $\mathfrak{S}_1$ is not false (contradictory), but is only non-demonstrable in S. This is actually the case (see Theorem 36.2). The properties 'analytic' and 'non-demonstrable' are not incompatible.

Now let us replace 'false' by 'refutable' in the sentence of the liar. Assume that a sentence, $\mathfrak{S}_2$, is constructed in S which asserts that $\mathfrak{S}_2$ is itself refutable (in S). $\mathfrak{S}_2$ is then an analogue to the assertion of the liar. We will now observe whether the contradiction arises in the ordinary way. First let us assume that $\mathfrak{S}_2$ is actually refutable. Then $\mathfrak{S}_2$ will be true, and therefore analytic. On the other hand, however, every refutable sentence is contradictory, and hence not analytic. Therefore the assumption is a false one and $\mathfrak{S}_2$ is non-refutable. From this no contradiction follows. $\mathfrak{S}_2$ is actually non-refutable; since $\mathfrak{S}_2$ means the opposite of this, $\mathfrak{S}_2$ is false, and is therefore contradictory. But the properties 'non-refutable' and 'contradictory' are quite consistent with one another (see the diagram on p. 210); for instance '$\sim()$ $(\mathfrak{G})$' possesses both.

The impossibility of reconstructing the antinomy of the liar with the help of the terms 'non-demonstrable' or 'refutable' is due to the fact that not all analytic sentences are also demonstrable, and similarly not all contradictory sentences are also refutable. But what would happen if we were to use in place of 'true' and 'false' the syntactical terms 'analytic' and 'contradictory'? Like 'true' and 'false', these two terms constitute a complete classification of the logical sentences. It is easy to show that we can construct contradictions if we assume that 'analytic (in S)' and 'contradictory (in S)' are defined in a syntax which is itself formulated in S. We could then, of course, construct a logical sentence $\mathfrak{S}_3$ which, in material interpretation, would mean that $\mathfrak{S}_3$ was contradictory. $\mathfrak{S}_3$ would correspond exactly to the assertion of the liar. Since it would be a logical sentence, $\mathfrak{S}_3$ would be either analytic or contradictory. Now, if $\mathfrak{S}_3$ were contradictory, $\mathfrak{S}_3$ would be true, therefore analytic, therefore not contradictory. Hence, $\mathfrak{S}_3$ would have to be non-contradictory. But then $\mathfrak{S}_3$ would be false, and therefore contradictory—which would be a contradiction.

On the same assumptions it would be possible also to construct Grelling's antinomy. Let us state the procedure for Language II. Assuming that a predicate 'An' is definable in II in such a way that 'An(x)' means: "The ^{SN}sentence x is analytic (in II)." 'Heterological' could then be defined as follows: 'Het$(x) \equiv$ $\sim$ An $(\text{subst } [x, 3, \text{str}(x)])$'. Let 'Het$(x)$' have the series-number b. Then it is easy to show that, for the sentence 'Het(b)', either assumption—that it is analytical or that it is contradictory—leads to a contradiction.

We have seen that if 'analytic in S' is definable in S, then S contains a contradiction; therefore we arrive at the following result:

Theorem 60c.1. If S is consistent, or, at least, non-contra-dictory, then '*analytic (in* S)' *is indefinable in* S. The same thing holds for the remaining c-terms which were defined earlier (in so far as they do not coincide with d-terms), for instance, 'valid', 'consequence', 'equipollent', etc. But it is not true for every c-term which does not coincide with a d-term.

If a syntax of a language S_1 is to contain the term 'analytic (in S_1)' then it must, consequently, be formulated in a language S_2 which is richer in modes of expression than S_1. On the other hand, the d-term 'demonstrable (in S_1)' can, under certain circumstances, be defined in S_1; whether that is possible or not depends upon the wealth of modes of expression which is available in S_1. With Languages I and II the situation on this point is as follows: 'analytic in I' is not definable in I, but it is definable in II; 'analytic in II' is not definable in II, but is only definable in a still richer language. 'Demonstrable in I', because it is indefinite, is not definable in I; but 'demonstrable in II' can be defined in II, namely, by means of '$(\exists r)$ [BewSatzII (r, x)]'.

The foregoing reflections follow the general lines of Gödel's treatise. They show also why it is impossible to prove the non-contradictoriness of S in S. Closely related to Theorem 1 is the following theorem (a generalization of Theorem 36.7; see Gödel [*Unentscheidbare*], p. 196; Gödel intends to give a proof of this generalized theorem in a continuation of that treatise).

Theorem 60c.2. If S is consistent, or at least non-contradictory, then *no proof of the non-contradictoriness or consistency of* S *can be formulated in a syntax which uses only the means of expression which are available in* S.

The investigation of Richard's antinomy (p. 213) leads to a similar conclusion. Assume that in S there is an $\mathfrak{Ag}$ by means of which a univocal enumeration of all the $\mathfrak{zpr^1}$ which are definable in S might be constructed. This could be effected, for example, by means of an $\mathfrak{fu_1}$ such that every full expression $\mathfrak{fu_1}(\mathfrak{zpr^1})$ was a $\mathfrak{z}$. We will use the symbolism of II and write $\mathfrak{fu_1}$ 'num'.

The univocality of the numbering is assumed:

$$(\operatorname{num}(F) = \operatorname{num}(G)) \supset (x)\,(F(x) \equiv G(x)). \qquad (1)$$

With the help of 'num', 'Ri' ("Richardian") could now be defined:

$$\operatorname{Ri}(x) \equiv (F)\,[(\operatorname{num}(F) = x) \supset \sim F(x)]. \qquad (2)$$

Since 'Ri' is a 3pr^1, it has a certain particular number designated by 'num (Ri)'. We assume first that the number of 'Ri' is itself Richardian: 'Ri[num (Ri)]'. Then if we substitute in (2) 'num (Ri)' for 'x', and 'Ri' for 'F', '$\sim$ Ri[num (Ri)]' easily follows. Since our assumption leads to its opposite, it follows that it is refuted; and therefore it is proved that

$$\sim \text{Ri [num (Ri)]}. \tag{3}$$

From (1):

$$\big(\text{num}\,(F) = \text{num (Ri)}\big) \supset \big(\sim F\,[\text{num (Ri)}] \equiv \sim \text{Ri [num (Ri)]}\big). \tag{4}$$

From (3), (4):

$$\big(\text{num}\,(F) = \text{num (Ri)}\big) \supset \sim F\,[\text{num (Ri)}]. \tag{5}$$

From (2):

$$(F)\,\big[\,\big(\text{num}\,(F) = \text{num (Ri)}\big) \supset \sim F\,[\text{num (Ri)}]\,\big] \supset \text{Ri [num (Ri)]}. \tag{6}$$

From (5), (6):

$$\text{Ri [num (Ri)]}. \tag{7}$$

The proved sentences (3) and (7) contradict one another; S is therefore contradictory. Thence follows:

Theorem 60c.3. If S is consistent, or at least non-contradictory, then it is not possible to construct in S either an $\mathfrak{Ag}$ or an $\mathfrak{Fu}$ by means of which a univocal enumeration of the 3pr^1 of S could be constructed.—Although the aggregate of the 3pr^1 which are definable in S is a denumerable aggregate, in accordance with this Theorem an enumeration of them cannot be effected with the means available in S itself. [The condition in this Theorem is only added for the purpose of facilitating understanding; if S is inconsistent, then in S no univocal enumeration of a number of objects is possible at all, since no (non-synonymous) $\mathfrak{Z}$ are available.]

§ 60*d*. EVERY ARITHMETIC IS DEFECTIVE

Let S_1 contain an arithmetic (in relation to a certain $\mathfrak{Z}$-series), and let the real numbers be represented in S_1 by $\mathfrak{Zfu}^1$. Let S_1 be a conservative sub-language of S_2, and let the arithmetized syntax of S_1 be formulated in S_2. We will show that with the help of the arithmetico-syntactical terms of S_2, as referred to S_1, a $\mathfrak{Zfu}^1$ can be defined in S_2 for which there is no $3fu^1$ in S_1 having the same course of values; this is true for every language S_1, however rich it may be, if we take a sufficiently rich language as S_2. We define the $3fu^1$ 'k' in S_2 in the following way: 1. If x is not a term-number of a $3fu^1$ of S_1, then $k(x) = 0$; 2. If x is a term-number of a $3fu^1$ of S_1, let us say 'h', then $k(x) = h(x) + 1$. Then every $3fu^1$ of S_1 deviates from 'k' for a certain argument (namely, for its own term-number); and therefore in S_1 there is no $3fu^1$ having the same course of values as 'k'. In other words: a real number can be given which is not equal to any real number definable in S_1 (see p. 206).

Theorem 60d.1. For every language S *a real number which cannot be defined in S can be given.*

The above definition of 'k' corresponds to the so-called *diagonal method* of the Theory of Aggregates. Theorem 1 corresponds to the well-known theorem of the Theory of Aggregates which states that the aggregate of the real numbers is a non-denumerable aggregate. (On the concept of the non-denumerable aggregates see, however, § 71*d*.) On the other hand, the above line of thought also corresponds to Richard's antinomy.

We will now summarize briefly the results of this investigation of the syntactical antinomies. Let the syntax of a language S be formulated in S. The reconstruction of the syntactical antinomies by means of terms which are defined in S (for instance, in Language II, 'non-demonstrable in II' or 'refutable in II') does not lead to contradictions; but it opens the way to the proof that certain sentences are non-demonstrable or irresoluble in S. With the help of other terms (for instance, 'analytic', 'contradictory', 'consequence', 'correlated number', 'term-number') the reconstruction of the syntactical antinomies is possible. This leads to the proof that these terms (of which the definitions have up to now only been formulated in words and not within a formalized system) cannot be defined in S, if S is consistent, or at least non-contradictory. Since terms and sentences of pure syntax are nothing other than syntactically interpreted terms and sentences of arithmetic, the investigation of the syntactical antinomies leads to the conclusion that *every arithmetic* which is to any extent formulated in any language *is necessarily defective in two respects.*

Theorem 60d.2. *For every arithmetical system* it is possible to state: (*a*) *indefinable arithmetical terms* and (*b*) *irresoluble arith-*

metical sentences (Gödel [*Unentscheidbare*]). In connection with
(*a*) see Theorems 60 *c*.1, 3, 60 *d*.1. In connection with (*b*) see
Theorem 60 *c*.2; further irresoluble sentences analogous to $\mathfrak{G}$ in
II and $\mathfrak{G}_I$ in I (see § 36) can be constructed.

This defectiveness is not to be understood as if there were, for
instance, arithmetical terms which could not be formally (i.e. in a
calculus) defined at all, or arithmetical sentences which could not
be resolved at all. For every term which is stated in any unambiguous way in a word-language, there exists a formal definition in an appropriate language. Every arithmetical sentence $\mathfrak{S}_1$
which is, for instance, irresoluble in the language S_1 is yet determinate in S_1; in the first place there exists a richer syntax-
language S_2, within which the proof either that $\mathfrak{S}_1$ is analytic or
that $\mathfrak{S}_1$ is contradictory can be stated; and secondly, there exists
an object-language S_3 of which S_1 is a proper sub-language, such
that $\mathfrak{S}_1$ is resoluble in S_3. But there exists neither a language in
which all arithmetical terms can be defined nor one in which all
arithmetical sentences are resoluble. [This is the kernel of truth
in the assertion made by Brouwer [*Sprache*], and, following him,
by Heyting [*Logik*], p. 3, that mathematics cannot be completely
formalized.] In other words, *everything mathematical can be
formalized, but mathematics cannot be exhausted by one system*; it
requires an infinite series of ever richer languages.

(*d*) TRANSLATION AND INTERPRETATION

§ 61. TRANSLATION FROM ONE LANGUAGE
INTO ANOTHER

We call $\mathfrak{Q}_1$ a *syntactical correlation* between the syntactical ob-
jects ($\mathfrak{A}$ or $\mathfrak{K}$) of one kind and those of another when $\mathfrak{Q}_1$ is a many-
one relation by means of which exactly one object of the second
kind is correlated to every object of the first, and every object of
the second kind to at least one of the first. The $\mathfrak{A}$ (or $\mathfrak{K}$) which is
correlated to $\mathfrak{A}_1$ (or $\mathfrak{K}_1$, respectively) by means of $\mathfrak{Q}_1$ is called the
$\mathfrak{Q}_1$-*correlate* of $\mathfrak{A}_1$ (or of $\mathfrak{K}_1$), and is designated by '$\mathfrak{Q}_1[\mathfrak{A}_1]$' (or
'$\mathfrak{Q}_1[\mathfrak{K}_1]$'). Herein the following condition is assumed: if $\mathfrak{A}_n$ has
no direct $\mathfrak{Q}_1$-correlate but can be subdivided into the expressions
$\mathfrak{A}_1, \mathfrak{A}_2, \dots \mathfrak{A}_m$, which have such correlates, then $\mathfrak{Q}_1[\mathfrak{A}_n]$ is equal

to the expression composed of $\mathfrak{Q}_1[\mathfrak{A}_1], \mathfrak{Q}_1[\mathfrak{A}_2], \ldots \mathfrak{Q}_1[\mathfrak{A}_m]$. The class which contains all and only the $\mathfrak{Q}_1$-correlates of the sentences of $\mathfrak{R}_1$ is designated by '$\mathfrak{Q}_1[\mathfrak{R}_1]$'. According to this, the correlates of sentences are also determined by means of a correlation between expressions, and the correlates of sentential classes by means of a correlation between sentences. [In a formalized syntax, $\mathfrak{Q}_1$ can, for instance, be either an $\mathfrak{Sg}^2$, a $\mathfrak{Pr}^2$, an $\mathfrak{Ag}^1$, or an $\mathfrak{Fu}^1$.] We say that a certain syntactical relation is transformed into a certain other one by means of $\mathfrak{Q}_1$ if, when the first relation subsists between any two objects, the second subsists between the $\mathfrak{Q}_1$-correlates of these objects.

A syntactical correlation, $\mathfrak{Q}_1$, between all sentential classes (or all sentences, or the expressions of an expressional class $\mathfrak{R}_1$, or all symbols) of S_1 and those of S_2, is called a **transformance** of S_1 into S_2 in respect of classes (or of sentences, or expressions, or symbols, respectively) provided that, by means of $\mathfrak{Q}_1$, the consequence relation in S_1 is transformed into the consequence relation in S_2. For $\mathfrak{R}_1$ it is assumed that no expression of $\mathfrak{R}_1$, but every sentence of S_1 which does not belong to $\mathfrak{R}_1$, is univocally analyzable into several expressions of $\mathfrak{R}_1$. $\mathfrak{Q}_1$ is called a *transformance* of S_1 into S_2 if $\mathfrak{Q}_1$ is a transformance of S_1 into S_2 of one of the kinds mentioned. '*L-transformance* in respect of classes (sentences, and so on)' is analogously defined, the requirement in this case being the maintenance of the relation 'L-consequence'.

Theorem 61.1. If $\mathfrak{Q}_1$ is a transformance of S_1 into S_2, then $\mathfrak{Q}_1$ is also an L-transformance of S_1 into S_2.

Theorem 61.2. If $\mathfrak{Q}_1$ is a transformance of S_1 into S_2 in respect of sentences, then by $\mathfrak{Q}_1$ the consequence relation between sentences in S_1 is transformed into the consequence relation between sentences in S_2. The converse is not universally true.

A transformance of S_1 into S_2 is called **reversible** when its converse (that is, the relation subsisting in the reverse direction) is a transformance of S_2 into S_1; otherwise *irreversible*.

Theorem 61.3. Let $\mathfrak{Q}_1$ be a transformance of S_1 into S_2; if $\mathfrak{Q}_1$ is reversible, then $\mathfrak{Q}_1$ is a one-one relation. The converse is not universally true.

Example of an *irreversible* transformance in respect of sentences: the transformance given by Lewis [*Logic*], p. 178, of his system of strict implication (without the existential postulate) into the ordinary sentential calculus. In this case, the correlate of the three sentences of the first system, 'A', 'M(A)', and ' $\sim$M($\sim$A)' (writing 'M' instead of the symbol of possibility) is the same sentence, 'A'. The transformance is thus not a one-one relation and is therefore irreversible.

If there exists a transformance (in respect of classes, etc.) of S_1 in S_2, then S_1 is called *transformable* (in respect of classes, etc.) in S_2. If S_1 is reversibly transformable in S_2 in respect of symbols, then S_1 and S_2 are called **isomorphic**.

Theorem 61.4. If in S_2 there is a valid sentence $\mathfrak{S}_1$ and a contravalid sentence $\mathfrak{S}_2$, then any language S_1 is transformable into S_2 in respect of sentences.—It is possible, for example, to take $\mathfrak{S}_2$ as the correlate of every contravalid sentence of S_1, and $\mathfrak{S}_1$ as the correlate of every other sentence. This Theorem shows the comprehensiveness of the concept of transformability; the concept of reversible transformability is a much more restricted one, and that of isomorphism more restricted still.

Theorem 61.5. Let S_1 and S_2 be isomorphic with respect to the correlation $\mathfrak{Q}_1$. If $\mathfrak{a}_1$ is a $\mathfrak{vf}^n$ in S_1 with a characteristic, then $\mathfrak{Q}_1[\mathfrak{a}_1]$ is a $\mathfrak{vf}^n$ in S_2 with the same characteristic. If, for instance, $\mathfrak{a}_1$ is a symbol of proper negation (or of disjunction, and so on), then $\mathfrak{Q}_1[\mathfrak{a}_1]$ is likewise a symbol of proper negation, etc.

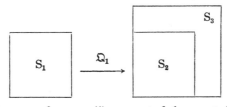

Let $\mathfrak{Q}_1$ be a transformance (in respect of classes, etc.) of S_1 into S_2; and let S_2 be a sub-language of S_3 (see diagram). Then $\mathfrak{Q}_1$ is called a **translation** (in respect of classes, etc.) of S_1 into S_3; and S_1 is called *translatable* (in respect of classes, etc.) into S_3. The following table gives for a number of syntactical properties and relations of $\mathfrak{R}$ or $\mathfrak{S}$ (column 1 A), and for a number of properties of languages (column 1 B), the conditions (sufficient but not necessary) under which they are transferred from one to another of the three languages between which the given relation holds: in the direction of the transformance, that is, from $\mathfrak{R}_1$ to $\mathfrak{Q}_1[\mathfrak{R}_1]$ (column 2); and conversely (6); from the sub-language to the total language

The *property* or *relation* occurring in column (1) *is transferred* under the following conditions:

(1)	(2) from S_1 to S_2 (in the direction of the transformance)	(3) from S_2 to S_3 (from the sub-language)	(4) from S_1 to S_3 (in the direction of the translation)	(5) from S_3 to S_2 (to the sub-language)	(6) from S_2 to S_1 (counter to the transformance)	(7) from S_3 to S_1 (counter to the translation)
A. Properties and relations of sentential classes (or sentences).						
Consequence; equipollent; valid	gen. [L]	gen. [—]	gen. [—]	c [c]	R [R, L]	R, c [R, L, c]
Contravalid; determinate; incompatible; dependent	gen. [L]	r [—]	r [—]	c [c]	R [R, L]	R, c [R, L, c]
Indeterminate; compatible; independent	R [R, L]	c [c]	R, c [R, L, c]	r [—]	gen. [L]	r [—]
Complete	gen. [L]	—[—]	—[—]	c [c]	R [R, L]	R, c [R, L, c]
Incomplete	R [R, L]	c [c]	R, c [R, L, c]	—[—]	gen. [L]	—[—]
B. Properties of languages.						
Inconsistent...	gen. [L]	r [—]	r [—]	c [c]	R [R, L]	R, c [R, L, c]
Consistent	R [R, L]	c [c]	R, c [R, L, c]	r [—]	gen. [L]	r [—]
Complete (L-complete; determinate; L-determinate; logical)	gen.	—	—	c	R	R, c
Incomplete (L-incomplete; indeterminate; L-indeterminate; descriptive)	R	c	R, c	—	gen.	—

(3); and conversely (5); in the direction of the translation (4); and conversely (7).

Abbreviations for the conditions:

gen.: generally, i.e. in all cases;

L: where $\mathfrak{Q}_1$ is an L-*transformance*;

R: where $\mathfrak{Q}_1$ is a *reversible* transformance;

c: where S_2 is a *conservative* sub-language of S_3 (see p. 179);

r: where S_2 is a *sufficiently rich* sub-language of S_3, namely, a language containing either a $\mathfrak{R}$ which is contravalid in S_3, or all the sentences of S_3.

The conditions given in the table in *square brackets* refer to the L-term which corresponds to the term occurring in column (1).

Examples: If $\mathfrak{R}_1$ is valid in S_1, then it is also valid in S_3. If $\mathfrak{R}_1$ is analytic in S_2, then it is also analytic in S_1, provided that $\mathfrak{Q}_1$ is a reversible L-transformance. If S_3 is inconsistent, then S_2 is also inconsistent, provided that S_2 is a conservative sub-language of S_3.

Since every transformance is at the same time a translation (namely, into an improper sub-language), the following theorems and definitions can also be referred to transformances.

Theorem 61.6. If S_1 is translatable into S_2 in respect of symbols, then it is also translatable in respect of expressions; if in respect of expressions, then also in respect of sentences, and conversely; if in respect of sentences, then also in respect of classes.

Let $\mathfrak{Q}_1$ and $\mathfrak{Q}_2$ be translations of S_1 in S_2. We say that $\mathfrak{Q}_1$ and $\mathfrak{Q}_2$ *coincide in content* if, for every $\mathfrak{R}_1$ in S_1, $\mathfrak{Q}_1[\mathfrak{R}_1]$ and $\mathfrak{Q}_2[\mathfrak{R}_1]$ are equipollent in S_2.

Let S_1 and S_2 be sub-languages of S_3; and let $\mathfrak{Q}_1$ be a translation of S_1 into S_2. If in this case, $\mathfrak{R}_1$ and $\mathfrak{Q}_1[\mathfrak{R}_1]$ are always equipollent in S_3, we call $\mathfrak{Q}_1$ an **equipollent** translation in respect of S_3. Analogously, 'L-equipollent translation' is defined by reference to 'L-equipollent classes'. Further, if $\mathfrak{Q}_1$ is a translation in respect of symbols or expressions such that $\mathfrak{A}_1$ and $\mathfrak{Q}_1[\mathfrak{A}_1]$ are always synonymous in S_3, we call $\mathfrak{Q}_1$ a **synonymous** translation in respect of S_3. A synonymous translation is also an equipollent translation.

Theorem 61.7. If S_1 is a conservative sub-language of S_2 then the equality of symbols represents a synonymous translation of S_1 in S_2 in respect of S_2.

Examples: Let I' be the sub-language of I constructed by means of eliminating the variables. Then I' is synonymously translatable into I by means of the equality of symbols. Again, I is translatable into I' in respect of classes, although I′ is a proper sub-language öf I. If, for instance, $\mathfrak{S}_1$ is an open sentence of I with exactly one free variable, $\mathfrak{z}_1$, then the class of all sentences of the form $\mathfrak{S}_1\left(\dfrac{\mathfrak{z}_1}{\mathfrak{S}t}\right)$ may be taken as the correlate of $\{\mathfrak{S}_1\}$. This translation is equipollent in respect of I. There is no equipollent translation of I into I′ in respect of sentences; this example therefore demonstrates the importance of the concept of *translation in respect of classes*.

Let S_1 be the *intuitionist sentential calculus* of Heyting [*Logik*]; and let S_3 be the ordinary sentential calculus (that of Language II, for instance). The ordinary translation, $\mathfrak{Q}_1$, of S_1 into S_3 (that is to say, the translation in which the symbol of negation is the $\mathfrak{Q}_1$-correlate of the symbol of negation, the symbol of disjunction the $\mathfrak{Q}_1$-correlate of the symbol of disjunction, and so on) is a transformance of S_1 into a proper sub-language, S_2, of S_3. This transformance is one in respect of symbols (if, in S_1 and S_3, we insert all the brackets as in Language II). S_2 is a *proper* sub-language of S_3, since, for instance, 'p ∨ ∼p' is not valid in S_2. Nevertheless, S_3 is also, conversely, translatable into S_1. Let $\mathfrak{Q}_2$ be the converse of $\mathfrak{Q}_1$; and let $\mathfrak{Q}_3[\mathfrak{S}_1]$ be $\sim\sim\mathfrak{Q}_2[\mathfrak{S}_1]$ (if $\mathfrak{S}_1$ has the form $\sim\mathfrak{S}_2$, then $\mathfrak{S}_1$ itself can also be taken as $\mathfrak{Q}_3[\mathfrak{S}_1]$). Then $\mathfrak{Q}_3$ is a translation of S_3 into S_1 in respect of sentences. [This translation was originated by Glivenko; Gödel gives another translation in connection with it ([*Koll.* 4], p. 34).]

On the concept of translation, see also Ajdukiewicz.

§ 62. THE INTERPRETATION OF A LANGUAGE

When only the formal rules of a language, for instance our Language II, or the Latin language, are known, then, although it is possible to answer syntactical questions concerning it—to say, for example, whether a given sentence is valid or contravalid, descriptive or existential, and so on—it is not possible to use it as a language of communication, because the *interpretation* of the language is lacking. There are two ways in which anyone may learn to use a language as a language of communication: the purely practical method which is employed in the case of quite small children and at the Berlitz school of languages, and the method of theoretical statements or assertions, such as is used, for instance, in a text-book without illustrations. In the present work, by the interpretation of a language we shall always mean the second procedure, that is, the method of explicit statements. Now, what form will these interpretative statements take? To give an illustration, when we wish to state what a certain Latin sentence means in English we shall do so by equating it with another sentence which has the same meaning. Frequently the second sentence will likewise belong to the Latin language (for example, whenever we explain a new word by a familiar synonym); usually, however, it will be a sentence in English, but it may also be a sentence in any other language, such as French. The interpretation of the expressions of a language S_1 is thus given by means of a *translation* into a language S_2, the statement of the translation being effected in a syntax-language S_3; and it is possible for two of these languages, or even all three, to coincide. Sometimes, special conditions are imposed on the translation—for instance that it must depend upon a reversible transformance, or that it must be equipollent in respect of a particular language, and so on.

The interpretation of a language is a translation and therefore something which can be *formally represented*; the construction and examination of interpretations belong to formal syntax. This holds equally of an interpretation of, say, French in German when what is required is not merely some kind of transformance in respect of sentences, but, as we say, a rendering of the sense or meaning of the French sentences. We have already seen that, in the case of an individual language like German, the construction of the syntax of that language means the construction of a calculus which fulfils the condition of being in agreement with the actual historical habits of speech of German-speaking people. And the construction of the calculus must take place entirely within the domain of formal syntax, although the decision as to whether the calculus fulfils the given condition is not a logical but an historical and empirical one, which lies outside the domain of pure syntax. The same thing holds, analogously, for the relation between two languages designated as translation or interpretation. The ordinary requirement of a translation from the French into the German language is that it be in accordance with sense or meaning —which means simply that it must be in agreement with the historically known habits of speech of French-speaking and German-speaking people. The construction of every translation, and thus of every so-called *true-to-sense* translation, also takes place *within the domain of formal syntax*—although the decision as to whether a proposed translation fulfils the given requirement and can thus be called true-to-sense is an historical, extra-syntactical one. It is possible to proceed in such a way that the extra-syntactical requirement is here of the same kind as in the first case, namely, is concerned with the agreement of a syntactically constructed calculus with a certain historically given language. We first stipulate, for instance, that the French language be represented, say, by the calculus S_1, the German language by S_2; and, further, that the language which consists of the French and German languages as sub-languages be represented by the calculus S_3, of which S_1 and S_2 are sub-languages. Then a syntactically given translation, $\mathfrak{Q}_1$, of S_1 into S_2 is true-to-sense if it is equipollent in respect of S_3. Under certain circumstances it will be required in addition that $\mathfrak{Q}_1$ be a synonymous expressional translation in respect of S_3.

Sometimes the interpretation of a language S_1 in relation to an existing language S_2 is given by constructing from S_2 a more comprehensive language S_3 by means of the addition of a sub-language which is isomorphic or even congruent with S_1. The interpretation of a symbolic calculus—such as a mathematical calculus—on the basis of an existing scientific language, is, in particular, often effected in this manner.

Examples: If, for instance, the system of the calculus of vectors is first constructed as an uninterpreted mathematical calculus, the interpretation can be performed in such a manner that the original language of physics is extended by the inclusion of the calculus of vectors. Because the vector symbols are used in the new language in conjunction with the other linguistic symbols, they have themselves gained a meaning within the physical language. In the same way, any system of geometrical axioms can first be given as an isolated calculus, and the various possible interpretations may be represented as different translations into the language of physics (see § 71 e). If in this case the terminology of geometry is retained, then it is a question of a translation into a congruent sub-language of a new language constructed from the old language of physics by the inclusion of geometry.

In order to establish a particular interpretation of the language S_1, that is to say a particular translation of S_1 into S_2, it is not necessary to give the correlates of all symbols or of all sentences of S_1. *It is sufficient to state the correlates of certain expressions*; in many cases, for example, it is sufficient to state the correlates of certain descriptive sentences of a simple form, in which not even all undefined symbols of S_1 need occur. In this way, in connection with the transformation rules of S_1, the whole translation is univocally determined; or, more exactly, any two translations which have those correlates in common coincide in content. It is customary in the construction of a symbolic language, particularly in logistics, to give an interpretation by means of an expository text, and hence by means of a translation into the ordinary word-language. And generally it is also customary to state many more correlates than are necessary. This is certainly useful for facilitating comprehension; and in introducing Language I we have proceeded in this manner ourselves. But it is important to realize that interpretative statements of this kind are in most cases over-determined.

Examples: 1. Let the *descriptive Language* II contain one-termed predicates 'P_1', ... 'P_k' as the only undefined descriptive symbols. Then for a complete interpretation of Language II such stipulations as the following are sufficient: (1) '0' shall designate the initial position, and an $\mathfrak{S}$t '0$^{||\cdots|}$' with m dashes, the $(m+1)$st position in such and such a series of positions; (2) 'P_1' shall be equivalent in meaning to 'red', ... 'P_k' to 'blue'; (3) an atomic descriptive sentence of the form $\mathfrak{pr}_1(\mathfrak{S}t_1)$, where $\mathfrak{pr}_1$ is an undefined $\mathfrak{pr}_b$, shall mean that the position designated by $\mathfrak{S}t_1$ has the property designated by $\mathfrak{pr}_1$. In the sentences for which the translation is hereby determined, no defined symbols of any kind whatever occur; further, no variables ($\mathfrak{p}$, $\mathfrak{f}$, $\mathfrak{z}$, $\mathfrak{f}$), hence no operators and, finally, none of the undefined logical constants ' = ', '$\exists$', 'K', ' $\sim$ ', 'v', '.', '$\supset$'. In spite of this, the interpretation of all the remaining sentences of II is also determined by the above stipulations; that is to say, for the correlate of any other sentence of Language II, the only choice is between equipollent sentences of that sub-language of English into which Language II is reversibly transformed. Thus '$P_1(0) \vee P_1(0^|)$', for instance, must be translated into: 'the first or the second position, or both, are red' (or into a sentence which is equipollent to this one). Or again, for example: '$(x)(P_1(x))$' must be translated into 'all positions are red'; for it follows from the transformation rules of Language II that ' v ' is a symbol of proper disjunction and ' (x) ' a proper universal operator.

2. Let II$_I$ be the *logical* sub-language of II. II$_I$ is to be interpreted by means of a translation in respect of expressions into a suitable other language; and, by this translation, a correlate is to be given for every $\mathfrak{pr}$ and for every $\mathfrak{fu}$. [This requirement is intended to secure that $\mathfrak{Q}_1$ is a translation in the ordinary sense; if the requirement is not stated, then the trivial translation may be taken in which the correlate of every analytic sentence is ' $0 = 0$ ', and the correlate of every contradictory sentence ' $\sim(0=0)$ '.] We shall only give the correlates of two symbols: ' 0 ' will be translated into ' 0 ' and ' $|$ ' into ' $+1$ '. In this way, the interpretation of the whole of Language II$_I$, which contains classical mathematics, is established.

From the standpoint of interpretation, it is characteristic of the *undefined descriptive symbols* that their interpretation, even after that of the other symbols, is still *arbitrary* within a wide domain (arbitrary, that is to say, when we merely consider the syntax of the isolated language; the choice can then be limited by further conditions). Thus, for instance, it is not determined by the transformation rules of Language II and the interpretation of the other symbols, whether 'P_1' is to be interpreted, say, by 'red' or by 'green', or by the designation of any other property of positions. In most of the symbolic languages even expressions which are interpreted by their authors as logical belong to the descriptive expressions as understood in general syntax. The majority of the usual systems are interpreted by their authors as logical languages; but since commonly only d-rules are laid down, these languages are for the most part indeterminate and therefore descriptive. In consequence, for certain expressions of these languages, even if the other expressions are interpreted according to the statements of the authors, interpretations are possible that are essentially different from one another.

Example: The universal operator with a numerical variable 3 is a proper universal operator in Languages I and II, but in the usual languages—for instance, in [*Princ. Math.*]—it is an improper one (see p. 197), because these languages contain only d-rules. Thus, in the usual languages there are sentences that are indeterminate, and therefore designated by us as descriptive, although they are interpreted by their authors as logical sentences. In order to remain within the framework of our own symbolism, instead of considering one of the earlier systems, we will consider that of Language II$_d$, which results from II by limitation to the d-rules (but which must contain all the definitions stated previously in Language I). The sentence 𝔊, which is analytic but irresoluble in II (§ 36), is thus in II$_d$ an indeterminate sentence. *The universal operator* (3) *in both* [*Princ. Math.*] *and* II$_d$ *is not logical but descriptive.* By this nothing is said against the usual translation, in which the correlate of 𝔊 is a logical sentence (for example, the identically worded sentence 𝔊 in II), and the correlate of (3) is a logical expression (for example, a proper universal operator in II). The fact that 𝔊 and (3) are descriptive only means that in addition to this usual translation others are possible, amongst them some in which the correlates of 𝔊 and (3) are descriptive. We will illustrate this for the universal and existential operators by an example. Let the $^1\mathfrak{pr}^1 \mathfrak{pr}_1$ and $\mathfrak{pr}_2$ be the only undefined descriptive symbols of II$_d$ and II. We will interpret II$_d$ by means of two different translations into II, $\mathfrak{Q}_1$ and $\mathfrak{Q}_2$. For $\mathfrak{Q}_1$ and $\mathfrak{Q}_2$, we determine:

first, that the correlates of all sentential junctions shall be these junctions themselves; second, that the correlates of all atomic sentences shall be these sentences themselves. Hence the correlates of all molecular sentences are also these sentences themselves. We will now show that $\mathfrak{Q}_1$ and $\mathfrak{Q}_2$ may nevertheless still be essentially different from one another—that is to say, that they need not coincide in content. Let the $\mathfrak{Q}_1$-correlate of every sentence be that sentence itself; this is the ordinary interpretation, in which the improper universal operator $(\mathfrak{z}_1)$ of II_d is interpreted by means of a proper universal operator of II. Let $\mathfrak{S}_1$ be $(\mathfrak{z}_1)\,(\mathfrak{pr}_1(\mathfrak{z}_1))$; and let $\mathfrak{Q}_2[\mathfrak{S}_1]$ be $(\mathfrak{z}_1)\,(\mathfrak{pr}_1(\mathfrak{z}_1)) \cdot \mathfrak{pr}_2(5)$. This sentence is (in II) obviously richer in content than $\mathfrak{Q}_1[\mathfrak{S}_1]$, namely, $\mathfrak{S}_1$ itself. Let $\mathfrak{S}_2$ be $(\exists\,\mathfrak{z}_1)\,(\mathfrak{pr}_1(\mathfrak{z}_1))$; and let $\mathfrak{Q}_2[\mathfrak{S}_2]$ be $(\exists\,\mathfrak{z}_1)\,(\mathfrak{pr}_1(\mathfrak{z}_1)) \vee \sim \mathfrak{pr}_2(5)$; this sentence is (in II) obviously poorer in content than $\mathfrak{Q}_1[\mathfrak{S}_2]$, namely, $\mathfrak{S}_2$ itself. It can easily be shown that $\mathfrak{Q}_2$ is really a translation (although not an equipollent translation in respect of II), that is, that by means of $\mathfrak{Q}_2$ the consequence-relation in II_d is transformed into the consequence-relation in II. For example, let $\mathfrak{S}_3$ be $\mathfrak{pr}_1(\mathfrak{St}_1)$; then $\mathfrak{S}_3$ is a consequence of $\mathfrak{S}_1$, and $\mathfrak{S}_2$ a consequence of $\mathfrak{S}_3$; correspondingly, $\mathfrak{Q}_2[\mathfrak{S}_3]$—i.e. $\mathfrak{S}_3$—is a consequence of the previously given $\mathfrak{Q}_2[\mathfrak{S}_1]$; and the given $\mathfrak{Q}_2[\mathfrak{S}_2]$ is a consequence of $\mathfrak{Q}_2[\mathfrak{S}_3]$—i.e. $\mathfrak{S}_3$. The reason why, in addition to the ordinary interpretation, the essentially different interpretation $\mathfrak{Q}_2$, which interprets the universal and existential operators descriptively, is also possible, is that the transformation rules of II_d only determine that every sentence of the form $\mathfrak{pr}_1(\mathfrak{St})$ is a consequence of $(\mathfrak{z}_1)\,(\mathfrak{pr}_1(\mathfrak{z}_1))$, but do not determine whether this universal sentence is equipollent to (as in the usual interpretation $\mathfrak{Q}_1$), or richer in content than (as in the case of $\mathfrak{Q}_2$), the class of sentences of the form $\mathfrak{pr}_1(\mathfrak{St})$.

Other examples of descriptive symbols that are interpreted by their authors as logical are the *intensional sentential junctions* treated of by Lewis and others. (There are, however, also intensional sentential junctions that *are* logical.)

Let S be a descriptive language for which an interpretation has been given in the ordinary way in the words of an expository text. In judging of this interpretation we must, then, distinguish (as the example just examined shows) between interpretations by means of descriptive expressions and interpretations by means of logical ones. (1) Interpretations by means of descriptive expressions generally yield something new which has not already been given in the construction of the calculus; they are (to a certain extent) necessary for the establishment of an interpretation of the calculus. (2) Suppose the expression $\mathfrak{A}_1$ of the calculus is interpreted by a logical expression of the word-language. Here, there are two cases to be distinguished. (2 a) $\mathfrak{A}_1$ is a logical expression in the sense understood in general syntax; then that interpretation may already be implied in the other interpretations, and if so it only serves as an explanation, which is theoretically unnecessary, but which facilitates understanding. (2 b) $\mathfrak{A}_1$ is a descriptive expression in the sense understood in general syntax (for example: the universal operator in II$_d$). Then the interpretation of $\mathfrak{A}_1$ by means of a certain logical expression can be replaced by the erection of suitable c-rules for S, with the aid of which $\mathfrak{A}_1$ becomes a logical expression of the kind intended. [Taking our example: let II$_d$ be expanded by indefinite c-rules to II; then, in accordance with the intended interpretation, (3) will become a proper universal operator.]

General syntax proceeds according to a formal method, that is to say, in the investigation of the expressions of a language it considers only the order and syntactical kind of the symbols of an expression. We have already seen that this formal method can also represent concepts which are sometimes regarded as not formal and designated as *concepts of meaning* (or concepts of a logic of meaning), such as, for instance, consequence-relation, content, relations of content, and so on. Finally we have established the fact that even the questions which refer to the interpretation of a language, and which appear, therefore, to be the very opposite of formal, can be handled within the domain of formal syntax. Accordingly, we must acknowledge that all questions of logic (taking this word in a very wide sense, but excluding all empirical and therewith all psychological reference) belong to syntax. *As soon as logic is formulated in an exact manner, it turns out to be nothing other than the syntax either of a particular language or of languages in general.*

(e) EXTENSIONALITY

§ 63. QUASI-SYNTACTICAL SENTENCES

We are now going to introduce a number of concepts which are necessary for the discussion of the problem of extensionality, for the logic of modalities, and, later on, for the analysis of philosophical sentences. We shall first explain these concepts in an informal and inexact manner. Let B be a domain of certain objects whose properties are described in the object-language S_1. Assume that there exists in reference to B an object-property E_1, and in reference to S_1 a syntactical property of expressions E_2, such that always and only when E_1 qualifies an object, E_2 qualifies the expression which designates that object. We shall call E_2 the syntactical property correlated to E_1. E_1 is then a property which is, so to speak, disguised as an object-property, but which, according to its meaning, is of a syntactical character; we therefore call it a quasi-syntactical property (or sometimes a pseudo-object-property). A sentence which ascribes the property E_1 to an object c is called a quasi-syntactical sentence; such a sentence is translatable into the (proper) syntactical sentence which ascribes the property E_2 to a designation of c.

Examples: 1. *Irreflexiveness.* Let S_1 be a descriptive L-language (like I and II) with a symbolism similar to that of II, but a name-language, and let it be concerned with the properties and relations of the persons living in the district B on a certain day. 'Shav (a, b)' will mean: 'a shaves b' (on the day in question). We define the $^2\mathfrak{pr}^1$ 'Irr' as follows: 'Irr $(F) \equiv (x) (\sim F(x, x))$', or, in words: 'a relation P is called irreflexive when no object has this relation to itself'. 'Irr (Shav)' is thus equipollent to '$(x) (\sim \text{Shav}(x, x))$' ($\mathfrak{S}_1$). $\mathfrak{S}_1$ means that in B, on that particular day, no one shaves himself; whether that is the case or not cannot be deduced from the transformation rules of S_1; $\mathfrak{S}_1$ is synthetic. Let S_1 contain, in addition, the $^2\mathfrak{pr}^1$ 'LIrr'; 'LIrr(P)', or, in words, 'P is L-irreflexive (or logically irreflexive)', means that P is irreflexive by logical necessity, that is, 'LIrr' must be so defined that 'LIrr(P)' is only analytic when '$(x) (\sim P(x, x))$' is analytic, and otherwise it is contradictory. Then 'LIrr (Shav)' is contradictory, since $\mathfrak{S}_1$ is not analytic but synthetic. Let 'Broth' be so defined that 'Broth (a, b)' means "a is a brother of b". Then 'Irr (Broth)' is analytic, and consequently 'LIrr (Broth)' is also analytic. 'Irr' and 'LIrr' are predicates of S_1. Let the syntax-language S_2 of S_1 be a word-language; we now define the predicate 'L-irreflexive' in S_2 as follows: a two-termed predicate $\mathfrak{pr}_1$ of S_1 is called L-irreflexive when $(\mathfrak{v}_1) (\sim \mathfrak{pr}_1(\mathfrak{v}_1, \mathfrak{v}_1))$ is analytic. According to this, 'Shav' is not L-irreflexive, but 'Broth' is. In a language which contains both S_1 and S_2 as sub-languages, for any predicate 'P', the sentence 'LIrr(P)' is always equipollent to the syntactical sentence "'P' is L-irreflexive". 'L-irreflexive' is the syntactical predicate which is correlated to the predicate 'LIrr'. 'LIrr' is a quasi-syntactical predicate of S_1; on the other hand, 'Irr' is not. 'LIrr (Broth)' is a quasi-syntactical sentence of S_1; the correlated syntactical sentence of S_2 is "'Broth' is L-irreflexive"; both sentences are analytic. The same is true of '$\sim$LIrr (Shav)' and "'Shav' is not L-irreflexive". On the other hand, there are no syntactical sentences correlated to the synthetic sentences 'Irr (Shav)' and ' $\sim$ Irr (Shav)'; therefore, these are not quasi-syntactical sentences. (Concerning 'L-irreflexive', see § 71 b.)

2. *Implication*. In the descriptive L-language S_1 we shall write 'Imp (A, B)' instead of 'A $\supset$ B'. Further, let there be introduced into S_1 (by definition or by primitive sentences) a predicate 'LImp' such that, for any closed sentences 'A' and 'B', 'LImp (A, B)' is analytic if, and only if, 'Imp (A, B)' is analytic; otherwise it is contradictory. Let 'A$_1$' and 'B$_1$' be two closed sentences such that 'B$_1$' is not a consequence of 'A$_1$'. Then 'Imp (A$_1$, B$_1$)' is not analytic, and therefore 'LImp (A$_1$, B$_1$)' is contradictory. Now let 'A$_2$' and 'B$_2$' be two closed sentences of which 'B$_2$' is a consequence of 'A$_2$'. Then 'Imp (A$_2$, B$_2$)' is analytic, and consequently 'LImp (A$_2$, B$_2$)' is also analytic. Let the syntax-language S_2 of S_1 be the ordinary word-language. Then, in a language which contains S_1 and S_2 as sub-languages, for any two closed sentences, 'A' and 'B', 'LImp (A, B)' is always equipollent to the syntactical sentence "'B' is a consequence of 'A'". 'LImp' is thus a quasi-syntactical predicate of S_1 to which the syntactical predicate 'consequence' is correlated. As opposed to this, 'Imp' is not quasi-syntactical. To the quasi-syntactical sentence 'LImp (A$_2$, B$_2$)' is correlated the syntactical sentence "'B$_2$' is a consequence of 'A$_2$'"; likewise, to the quasi-syntactical sentence ' $\sim$ LImp (A$_1$, B$_1$)' is correlated the syntactical sentence "'B$_1$' is not a consequence of 'A$_1$'". On the other hand, there are no syntactical sentences correlated to the synthetic sentences 'Imp (A$_1$, B$_1$)' and ' $\sim$ Imp (A$_1$, B$_1$)'; consequently these sentences are not quasi-syntactical. The relations in this example, to which we shall return later in a discussion of the logic of modalities, are completely analogous to those of the first example.

We now pass from the informal and inexact to the syntactical discussion of these concepts. Let S_1 be any language; and let S_2 be a logical language. Let $\mathfrak{Q}_1$ be a one-one syntactical correlation between the expressions of S_1 and the expressions of a class $\mathfrak{R}_2$ in S_2, and let the expressions of $\mathfrak{R}_2$ be $^\alpha\mathfrak{Stu}$ which are all isogenous with one another. Then we shall call S_2 a **syntax-language** of S_1 (with respect to $\mathfrak{Q}_1$); and we shall call $\mathfrak{Q}_1 [\mathfrak{A}_1]$ *the syntactical designation* of $\mathfrak{A}_1$ (with respect to $\mathfrak{Q}_1$). The $\mathfrak{Sg}$, or $\mathfrak{Pr}$, of S_2 to which the expressions of $\mathfrak{R}_2$ are suitable as arguments we call syntactical $\mathfrak{Sg}$, or $\mathfrak{Pr}$ (with respect to $\mathfrak{Q}_1$). If the expressions of $\mathfrak{R}_2$ are numerical expressions, we call S_2 an *arithmetized syntax-language*. If S_2 is a sub-language of a language S_3, we say that S_3 *contains a syntax of* S_1 (with respect to $\mathfrak{Q}_1$).

An $\mathfrak{Sg}^n$, $\mathfrak{Sg}_1$, of S_1 is called a *quasi-syntactical* $\mathfrak{Sg}$ when there exist an S_2, a $\mathfrak{Q}_1$, and a logical $\mathfrak{Sg}^n$, $\mathfrak{Sg}_2$, which fulfil the following conditions: S_1 is a sub-language of S_2; S_2 contains a syntax of S_1 with respect to $\mathfrak{Q}_1$; if $\mathfrak{S}_1$ is any full sentence of $\mathfrak{Sg}_1$ in S_1, such as $\mathfrak{Sg}_1(\mathfrak{A}_1, \mathfrak{A}_2, \ldots \mathfrak{A}_n)$, in which the arguments are not $\mathfrak{B}$, then $\mathfrak{S}_1$ is equipollent in S_2 to $\mathfrak{Sg}_2(\mathfrak{Q}_1[\mathfrak{A}_1], \mathfrak{Q}_1[\mathfrak{A}_2], \ldots \mathfrak{Q}_1[\mathfrak{A}_n])$; let this be $\mathfrak{S}_2$. $\mathfrak{S}_1$ is then called **quasi-syntactical** in respect of $\mathfrak{A}_1, \ldots \mathfrak{A}_n$; $\mathfrak{S}_2$ is called a *syntactical sentence correlated to* $\mathfrak{S}_1$ (with respect to $\mathfrak{Q}_1$); $\mathfrak{Sg}_2$ is called a *syntactical* $\mathfrak{Sg}$ *correlated to* $\mathfrak{Sg}_1$ (with respect to $\mathfrak{Q}_1$). These definitions also hold for $\mathfrak{Pr}_1, \mathfrak{Pr}_2$ in the place of $\mathfrak{Sg}_1, \mathfrak{Sg}_2$.

Let $\mathfrak{Sg}_2$ be a syntactical $\mathfrak{Sg}$ which is correlated to $\mathfrak{Sg}_1$ with respect to $\mathfrak{Q}_1$. Let $\mathfrak{Sfu}_1$ have the form $\mathfrak{Sg}_1(\mathfrak{A}_1, \ldots \mathfrak{A}_n)$, where at least one of the arguments is a $\mathfrak{B}$; let $\mathfrak{Sfu}_2$ have the form $\mathfrak{Sg}_2(\mathfrak{A}'_1, \ldots \mathfrak{A}'_n)$, where $\mathfrak{A}'_i$ ($i = 1$ to n) is $\mathfrak{Q}_1[\mathfrak{A}_i]$ if $\mathfrak{A}_i$ is not a $\mathfrak{B}$; if $\mathfrak{A}_i$ is a $\mathfrak{B}_i$, let $\mathfrak{A}'_i$ be a $\mathfrak{B}$ of S_2, to the substitution-values of which belong the $\mathfrak{Q}_1$-correlates of the substitution-values of $\mathfrak{B}_i$. Then we call $\mathfrak{Sfu}_2$ *a syntactical* $\mathfrak{Sfu}$ *correlated to* $\mathfrak{Sfu}_1$ (with respect to $\mathfrak{Q}_1$). Let $\mathfrak{Sfu}_2$ be a syntactical $\mathfrak{Sfu}$ correlated to $\mathfrak{Sfu}_1$. Let $\mathfrak{S}_1$ be constructed from $\mathfrak{Sfu}_1$ by means of operators, and similarly $\mathfrak{S}_2$ from $\mathfrak{Sfu}_2$ by means of corresponding operators. Then we say that $\mathfrak{S}_2$ is a syntactical sentence correlated to $\mathfrak{S}_1$. Every sentence that contains a quasi-syntactical $\mathfrak{Sg}$, $\mathfrak{Pr}$, or $\mathfrak{Sfu}$, is called a quasi-syntactical sentence. For compound quasi-syntactical sentences, the correlated syntactical sentences are constructed in a manner analogous to the simple cases here described.

Example: Let '$P_1(F)$' and '$P_2(F, u)$' be quasi-syntactical $\mathfrak{Sfu}$ in S_1. Let the correlated syntactical $\mathfrak{Sfu}$ be '$Q_1(x)$' or '$Q_2(x, y)$', respectively. Then the syntactical sentence '$(x)[Q_1(x) \supset (\exists y)(Q_2(x, y))]$' is correlated to the quasi-syntactical sentence '$(F)[P_1(F) \supset (\exists u)(P_2(F, u))]$'.

The difference between the quasi-syntactical sentences and the others is connected with the difference between syntactical concepts and the concept 'true'. If one were to take 'true' as a syntactical term, then every sentence whatsoever, $\mathfrak{S}_1$, in relation to every partial expression, $\mathfrak{A}_1$, would be quasi-syntactical. For $\mathfrak{S}_1$ is always equipollent to the sentence '$\mathfrak{A}_1$ is such that $\mathfrak{S}_1$ is true.' If S_1 is a *logical language*, then, with respect to S_1, 'true' coincides with 'analytic' (that is to say, there are here no synthetic sentences; see Theorem 52.3). Consequently, in this case, the concept 'quasi-syntactical' becomes *trivial*. For instance, let S_1 be the logical sub-language of I. And let $\mathfrak{pr}_1$ be 'Prim'. Then, for every $\mathfrak{Z}_1$, the sentence $\mathfrak{pr}_1(\mathfrak{Z}_1)$ of S_1 is equipollent to the sentence of the syntax-language '$\mathfrak{Z}_1$ is such that $\mathfrak{pr}_1(\mathfrak{Z}_1)$ is analytic'; for either both sentences are analytic or both are contradictory. Therefore, $\mathfrak{pr}_1(\mathfrak{z}_1)$ is a quasi-syntactical sentence in respect of $\mathfrak{z}_1$. But in relation to the descriptive Language I this is not the case. If $\mathfrak{fu}_1$ is an undefined $\mathfrak{fu}_b$, then $\mathfrak{pr}_1\big(\mathfrak{fu}_1(\mathfrak{nu})\big)$ is synthetic, and therefore not equipollent to the syntactical sentence '$\mathfrak{fu}_1(\mathfrak{nu})$ is such that $\mathfrak{pr}_1\big(\mathfrak{fu}_1(\mathfrak{nu})\big)$ is analytic', for the latter is contradictory. When, in what follows, we establish the fact that certain sentences in certain languages are quasi-syntactical sentences, this means that they are still quasi-syntactical even if we expand the language so that it becomes descriptive (and in such a way that descriptive arguments for the positions in question exist). [Later, for instance, we shall assert that the $\mathfrak{Pr}$ of the logic of modalities are quasi-syntactical; by which we mean also to maintain that they are still quasi-syntactical even if we extend the calculus of the logic of modalities by admitting synthetic sentences, also, as arguments. For the consequence-predicate of the logic of modalities (e.g. for the symbol of strict implication and similar ones) this is shown by the example 'LImp' on p. 235.]

§ 64. THE TWO INTERPRETATIONS OF QUASI-SYNTACTICAL SENTENCES

Let the sentence $\mathfrak{S}_1$ of the form $\mathfrak{Sg}_1(\mathfrak{A}_1)$ be quasi-syntactical, and let the sentence $\mathfrak{S}_2$ of the form $\mathfrak{Sg}_2(\mathfrak{A}_2)$ be a correlated, and hence an equipollent, syntactical sentence. We will distinguish two possible interpretations which might here be intended. (This is only a material, non-formal investigation which serves as a preliminary to the formal definitions.) In both, $\mathfrak{A}_2$ is interpreted as a syntactical designation of the expression $\mathfrak{A}_1$, and $\mathfrak{Sg}_2$ as a designation of a syntactical property of expressions. The two cases to be distinguished are as follows: (1) where $\mathfrak{Sg}_1$ is taken as equivalent in meaning to $\mathfrak{Sg}_2$; and (2) where it is not. In the case of the first interpretation, $\mathfrak{Sg}_1$ as well as $\mathfrak{Sg}_2$ designates a syntactical property; since $\mathfrak{S}_1$ and $\mathfrak{S}_2$ are equipollent, the equivalence in meaning of the arguments follows from the equivalence in meaning of the two $\mathfrak{Sg}$. Thus, here $\mathfrak{A}_1$, like $\mathfrak{A}_2$, is to be interpreted as a syntactical designation of $\mathfrak{A}_1$; $\mathfrak{A}_1$ designates itself, and is therefore *autonymous*. [The term 'autonymous' has already been explained on p. 156; its strictly formal definition will be given later.] In the case of the second interpretation, $\mathfrak{Sg}_1$ designates not a syntactical property but an object-property, which is attributed to the object designated by $\mathfrak{A}_1$ (not to the expression $\mathfrak{A}_1$) in the sentence $\mathfrak{S}_1$. We will in general assign to the material mode of speech any sentence which (like $\mathfrak{S}_1$ in the second interpretation) is to be interpreted as attributing to an object a particular property, this property being quasi-syntactical, so that the sentence can be translated into another sentence which attributes a correlated syntactical property to a designation of the object in question. In contrast with the material mode of speech of the quasi-syntactical sentences of the second interpretation we have the *formal mode of speech* of the syntactical sentences.

Example: 1. Quasi-syntactical sentences: (a) autonymous mode of speech, "Five is a number-word"; (b) material mode of speech, "Five is a number." 2. Correlated syntactical sentence: "'Five' is a number-word." (For the sake of simplicity, in 1 a and 2 we have taken as pr that are equivalent in meaning the same word, 'number-word'.)

Our task now is to *represent formally* the difference between the two interpretations that has just been indicated materially. Which formal syntactical properties of $\mathfrak{Sg}_1$ and $\mathfrak{Sg}_2$ correspond to the fact that $\mathfrak{Sg}_1$ is intended as equivalent in meaning to $\mathfrak{Sg}_2$ and thus as a designation of a syntactical property? It is not necessary for $\mathfrak{Sg}_1$ and $\mathfrak{Sg}_2$ to be synonymous (or L-synonymous); for it may well be that, in spite of their equivalence in meaning, we intend to admit only $\mathfrak{Sg}_1$ with autonymous arguments, and not $\mathfrak{Sg}_2$. In this case $\mathfrak{Sg}_1(\mathfrak{A}_2)$ would certainly be equipollent to $\mathfrak{Sg}_1(\mathfrak{A}_1)$; but $\mathfrak{Sg}_2(\mathfrak{A}_1)$ would not—for it need not be a sentence. But if $\mathfrak{Sg}_1$ is intended to designate a syntactical property, and, further, the same syntactical property as $\mathfrak{Sg}_2$, then $\mathfrak{Sg}_1(\mathfrak{A}_2)$ is equipollent to $\mathfrak{Sg}_2(\mathfrak{A}_2)$. On the basis of this preliminary consideration, we formulate the following formal syntactical definitions (for the sake of simplicity we do so in relation to $\mathfrak{Sg}^1$; the definitions for the case of two or more arguments are analogous, likewise those referring to $\mathfrak{Pr}$).

Let the sentence $\mathfrak{S}_1$ of S_1 have the form $\mathfrak{Sg}_1(\mathfrak{A}_1)$ and be quasi-syntactical in relation to $\mathfrak{A}_1$; and let $\mathfrak{A}_1$ not be a $\mathfrak{B}$. Let S_2 contain both S_1 and a syntax of S_1 with respect to $\mathfrak{Q}_1$. Let $\mathfrak{Sg}_2(\mathfrak{Q}_1[\mathfrak{A}_1])$ be a syntactical sentence of S_2 correlated to $\mathfrak{S}_1$ with respect to $\mathfrak{Q}_1$. Two cases are to be distinguished: (1) $\mathfrak{Sg}_1(\mathfrak{Q}_1[\mathfrak{A}_1])$ is a sentence of S_2 and, in S_2, is equipollent to $\mathfrak{Sg}_2(\mathfrak{Q}_1[\mathfrak{A}_1])$; likewise, for every $\mathfrak{A}_2$ which is isogenous with $\mathfrak{A}_1$, $\mathfrak{Sg}_1(\mathfrak{Q}_1[\mathfrak{A}_2])$ is equipollent to $\mathfrak{Sg}_2(\mathfrak{Q}_1[\mathfrak{A}_2])$. In this case we call $\mathfrak{A}_1$ **autonymous** in $\mathfrak{S}_1$ (with respect to $\mathfrak{Q}_1$), and $\mathfrak{S}_1$ a sentence of the **autonymous mode of**

speech (with respect to Ω_1). (2) The given condition is not fulfilled. In this case we say that $\mathfrak{S}_1$ belongs to the **material mode of speech** (with respect to Ω_1). Let Ω_2 be a translation of S_1 into S_2 in respect of sentences; further, let the Ω_2-correlate of every quasi-syntactical (with respect to Ω_1) sentence of S_1 be a syntactical sentence correlated to it with respect to Ω_1; and let the Ω_2-correlate of every other sentence be the sentence itself. The Ω_2-translation of the sentences of the material mode of speech into correlated syntactical sentences is called *a translation from the material into the formal mode of speech.*

It is to be noted that the differentiation between autonymous and material modes of speech is concerned with interpretation. This means that this differentiation cannot be made in relation to a language S_1 which is given as an isolated calculus without any interpretation. But it does not mean that the distinction lies outside the domain of the formal, in other words, of syntax. For, even the interpretation of a language can be formally represented and thus be incorporated in the syntax. As we have seen, the interpretation of a language S_1 in relation to an assumed language S_2 can be formally represented either by the translation of S_1 into S_2, or by the incorporation of S_1 as a sub-language in a third language S_3, which is constructed from the language S_2 by extension. If $\mathfrak{S}_1$ is a quasi-syntactical sentence of S_1, and if the interpretation of S_1 is formally determined by the fact that S_1 is a sub-language of a language S_2 which contains also the syntax of S_1, then, according to the definitions just given, it can be determined whether $\mathfrak{S}_1$ belongs to the autonymous or to the material mode of speech. But in practice we are frequently not in a position to make this distinction with accuracy; namely, where it is a question of a system S_1 which another author has constructed without giving either the translation of S_1 into, or its incorporation in, another language also containing the syntax of S_1. If in such a case no interpretation whatsoever is given, then the distinction disappears. In the majority of calculi which have been constructed up to the present, although an interpretation has been given, it has usually not been done by means of strict syntactical rules (either incorporating S_1 in, or translating it into, some other formally established language S_2), but only by material explanations, that is to say, by the translation of sentences of S_1 into more or less vague sentences of a word-language. If we undertake on the basis of such explanations a translation of S_1 into a formally established language S_2, we can, at most, suppose that what was meant by the author has been more or less accurately expressed, that is, that we have proposed a translation which deviates less or more from that which the author himself would have proposed as a translation of S_1 into S_2. When in what follows we attribute certain sentences of the calculi of other authors, or of the word-language, either to the autonymous or to the material mode of speech, it must be noted that this is not intended as an exact and final classification; in the case of the sentences of other calculi, the differentiation depends upon the interpretative explanations given by their authors, and in the case of the sentences of the word-language upon consideration of the ordinary use of language. On the other hand, the decision that certain sentences are quasi-syntactical (not genuinely syntactical) can be made with the same degree of exactitude with which the language in question is itself constructed; in this we need take no heed of interpretation, whether given materially or formally.

§ 65. EXTENSIONALITY IN RELATION TO PARTIAL SENTENCES

By way of preparation for the definition of extensionality, we will first examine the definition that has been usual hitherto. An $\mathfrak{S}\mathfrak{fu}_1^1$ with one variable $\mathfrak{f}_1$ is commonly called extensional (or a truth-function) in relation to $\mathfrak{f}_1$, if for any $\mathfrak{S}_1$ and $\mathfrak{S}_2$ whatsoever, having the same truth-value, $\mathfrak{S}\mathfrak{fu}_1\left(\dfrac{\mathfrak{f}_1}{\mathfrak{S}_1}\right)$ and $\mathfrak{S}\mathfrak{fu}_1\left(\dfrac{\mathfrak{f}_1}{\mathfrak{S}_2}\right)$ have the same truth-value. If, for instance (in a symbolism like that of II), 'T(p)' is an $\mathfrak{S}\mathfrak{fu}$ of the kind in question, then 'T(p)' is called extensional, if '$(p \equiv q) \supset (\mathrm{T}(p) \equiv \mathrm{T}(q))$' ($\mathfrak{S}_1$) is true. We must formulate this definition differently; we do not use the term 'true' because it is not a genuine syntactical term; further, we will not make the limiting assumption that sentential variables and symbols of proper equivalence and implication exist in S. Since $\mathfrak{S}_1$ must be not only true (indeterminately) but valid, we can replace the given condition by the following: for any closed sentences whatsoever, say 'A' and 'B', 'T$(A) \equiv$ T(B)' ($\mathfrak{S}_3$) must be a consequence of 'A $\equiv$ B' ($\mathfrak{S}_2$). The implication having been eliminated, we will now eliminate the equivalence also. $\mathfrak{S}_2$ has the property that 'B' is a consequence of $\mathfrak{S}_2$ and 'A', and 'A' a consequence of $\mathfrak{S}_2$ and 'B'. Further, $\mathfrak{S}_2$ is the poorest in content of the sentences having this property, that is to say, if any $\mathfrak{R}_1$ likewise possesses the property in question, then $\mathfrak{S}_2$ is a consequence of $\mathfrak{R}_1$; hence, $\mathfrak{S}_3$, if a consequence of $\mathfrak{S}_2$, is also a consequence of $\mathfrak{R}_1$. These considerations lead us to the statement of the following definitions.

In analogy with the previously defined concepts—absolute concepts, as it were—of the equipollence of two $\mathfrak{R}$ (or two $\mathfrak{S}$), the coextensiveness of two $\mathfrak{Sg}$ (or $\mathfrak{Sfu}$ or $\mathfrak{Pr}$), the synonymity of two $\mathfrak{A}$, and the identity of the course of values of two $\mathfrak{Ag}$ (or $\mathfrak{Afu}$ or $\mathfrak{Fu}$), we will now define the corresponding *relative terms in relation to a sentential class*. $\mathfrak{S}_1$ and $\mathfrak{S}_2$ are called **equipollent** (to one another) **in relation to** $\mathfrak{R}_1$ if $\mathfrak{S}_2$ is a consequence of $\mathfrak{R}_1 + \{\mathfrak{S}_1\}$ and $\mathfrak{S}_1$ a consequence of $\mathfrak{R}_1 + \{\mathfrak{S}_2\}$. $\mathfrak{Sg}_1$ and $\mathfrak{Sg}_2$ are called *coextensive* (with one another) *in relation to* $\mathfrak{R}_1$ if every two full sentences with equal arguments are equipollent in relation to $\mathfrak{R}_1$; similarly for two $\mathfrak{Sfu}$ or two (isogenous) $\mathfrak{Pr}$. Two isogenous expressions $\mathfrak{A}_1$ and $\mathfrak{A}_2$ are called *synonymous in relation to* $\mathfrak{R}_1$, if every $\mathfrak{S}_1$ is equipollent to $\mathfrak{S}_1 \begin{bmatrix} \mathfrak{A}_1 \\ \mathfrak{A}_2 \end{bmatrix}$ and to $\mathfrak{S}_1 \begin{bmatrix} \mathfrak{A}_2 \\ \mathfrak{A}_1 \end{bmatrix}$ in relation to $\mathfrak{R}_1$. We say that $\mathfrak{Ag}_1$ and $\mathfrak{Ag}_2$ have the *same course of values in relation to* $\mathfrak{R}_1$ when every two full expressions with equal arguments are synonymous in relation to $\mathfrak{R}_1$; likewise for two $\mathfrak{Afu}$ or $\mathfrak{Fu}$.

Theorem 65.1. (*a*) If two $\mathfrak{S}$ are equipollent, then they are also equipollent in relation to every $\mathfrak{R}$. (*b*) Analogously for coextensiveness. (*c*) Analogously for synonymity. (*d*) Analogously for identity of the course of values.

Theorem 65.2. (*a*) If $\mathfrak{S}_1$ and $\mathfrak{S}_2$ are equipollent in relation to a valid $\mathfrak{R}_1$ then they are equipollent (absolutely). (*b*) Analogously for coextensiveness. (*c*) Analogously for synonymity. (*d*) Analogously for identity of the course of values.

Extensionality in relation to partial sentences. $\mathfrak{S}_1$ is called **extensional** in relation to the closed partial sentence $\mathfrak{S}_2$ if for any closed $\mathfrak{S}_3$ and any $\mathfrak{R}_1$ such that $\mathfrak{S}_2$ and $\mathfrak{S}_3$ are equipollent in relation to $\mathfrak{R}_1$, $\mathfrak{S}_1$ and $\mathfrak{S}_1 \begin{bmatrix} \mathfrak{S}_2 \\ \mathfrak{S}_3 \end{bmatrix}$ are always equipollent in relation to $\mathfrak{R}_1$. An $\mathfrak{Sg}_1$ to which $\mathfrak{S}$ are suitable as arguments is called *extensional* if, for any closed $\mathfrak{S}_1$ and $\mathfrak{S}_2$ and any $\mathfrak{R}_1$ such that $\mathfrak{S}_1$

and $\mathfrak{S}_2$ are equipollent in relation to $\mathfrak{R}_1$, $\mathfrak{S}\mathfrak{g}_1(\mathfrak{S}_1)$ and $\mathfrak{S}\mathfrak{g}_1(\mathfrak{S}_2)$ are always equipollent in relation to $\mathfrak{R}_1$. Correspondingly in the case of an $\mathfrak{S}\mathfrak{fu}$ or $\mathfrak{Pr}$ to which $\mathfrak{S}$ are suitable as arguments. If every sentence of S is extensional in relation to every closed partial sentence, then we call S *extensional in relation to partial sentences*. 'Intensional' is to mean the same as 'not extensional' (in the different connections). ['Intensional' as we use it means nothing more than this, and in particular it means nothing like 'related to sense', etc.; in many authors the word has a meaning of this kind, or even a mixture of the two meanings (see § 71).]

Theorem 65.3. If S is extensional in relation to partial sentences, then all $\mathfrak{S}\mathfrak{g}$, $\mathfrak{S}\mathfrak{fu}$, and $\mathfrak{Pr}$ of S to which $\mathfrak{S}$ are suitable as arguments are extensional.

Theorem 65.4. Let S be extensional in respect of partial sentences. (*a*) If two closed $\mathfrak{S}$ are equipollent in relation to $\mathfrak{R}_1$, then they are also synonymous in relation to $\mathfrak{R}_1$. (*b*) If two closed $\mathfrak{S}$ are equipollent, then they are also synonymous. (*c*) If two closed $\mathfrak{Pr}$ whose arguments are $\mathfrak{S}$ are coextensive in relation to $\mathfrak{R}_1$, then they are also synonymous in relation to $\mathfrak{R}_1$. (*d*) If two closed $\mathfrak{Pr}$ whose arguments are $\mathfrak{S}$ are coextensive, then they are also synonymous. (*e*) If two closed $\mathfrak{Fu}$ whose arguments are $\mathfrak{S}$ have the same course of values in relation to $\mathfrak{R}_1$, then they are also synonymous in relation to $\mathfrak{R}_1$. (*f*) If two closed $\mathfrak{Fu}$ whose arguments are $\mathfrak{S}$ have the same course of values, then they are also synonymous.

Theorem 65.5. *Sentential junctions.* If a $\mathfrak{Bf}$ or a $\mathfrak{vf}$ possesses a characteristic, then it is extensional; and conversely.—Thus, proper negation, proper implication, etc., are extensional.

Theorem 65.6. If S is extensional in respect of partial sentences, then all $\mathfrak{Bf}$ are extensional.

Theorem 65.7. Let $\mathfrak{Bf}_1$ be a *proper equivalence* in S. Then it is true that: (*a*) $\mathfrak{S}_1$ and $\mathfrak{S}_2$ are always equipollent in relation to $\mathfrak{Bf}_1(\mathfrak{S}_1, \mathfrak{S}_2)$. (*b*) S is extensional in relation to partial sentences if, and only if, for any closed $\mathfrak{S}_1$, $\mathfrak{S}_2$, and $\mathfrak{S}_3$, $\mathfrak{Bf}_1\left(\mathfrak{S}_3, \mathfrak{S}_3\begin{bmatrix}\mathfrak{S}_1\\\mathfrak{S}_2\end{bmatrix}\right)$ is always a consequence of $\mathfrak{Bf}_1(\mathfrak{S}_1, \mathfrak{S}_2)$. (*c*) Further, let $\mathfrak{Bf}_2$ be a proper implication in S; then S is extensional in relation to partial sentences if, and only if, for any closed $\mathfrak{S}_1$, $\mathfrak{S}_2$, and $\mathfrak{S}_3$, $\mathfrak{Bf}_2\left(\mathfrak{Bf}_1(\mathfrak{S}_1, \mathfrak{S}_2), \mathfrak{Bf}_1\left(\mathfrak{S}_3, \mathfrak{S}_3\begin{bmatrix}\mathfrak{S}_1\\\mathfrak{S}_2\end{bmatrix}\right)\right)$ is valid.

Theorem 65.8. Let ' $\equiv$ ' be a symbol of proper equivalence in S. (a) If, for closed $\mathfrak{S}_2$ and $\mathfrak{S}_3$, $\mathfrak{S}_2 \equiv \mathfrak{S}_3$ is a consequence of $\mathfrak{R}_1$, but $\mathfrak{S}_1 \equiv \mathfrak{S}_1 \begin{bmatrix} \mathfrak{S}_2 \\ \mathfrak{S}_3 \end{bmatrix}$ is not a consequence of $\mathfrak{R}_1$, then $\mathfrak{S}_1$ is intensional in relation to $\mathfrak{S}_2$. (b) If, for two closed sentences $\mathfrak{S}_2$ and $\mathfrak{S}_3$, $\mathfrak{S}_2 \equiv \mathfrak{S}_3$ is valid but $\mathfrak{S}_1 \equiv \mathfrak{S}_1 \begin{bmatrix} \mathfrak{S}_2 \\ \mathfrak{S}_3 \end{bmatrix}$ is not valid, then $\mathfrak{S}_1$ is intensional in relation to $\mathfrak{S}_2$.

$\mathfrak{Sg}_1^2$ is called an $\mathfrak{Sg}$ of *identity*, if every two possible closed arguments $\mathfrak{A}_1$ and $\mathfrak{A}_2$ are always synonymous in relation to $\mathfrak{Sg}_1 (\mathfrak{A}_1, \mathfrak{A}_2)$. An $\mathfrak{Sg}$ of identity, $\mathfrak{Sg}_1$, is called an $\mathfrak{Sg}$ of proper identity if for every two possible closed arguments $\mathfrak{A}_1, \mathfrak{A}_2$, which are synonymous in relation to $\mathfrak{R}_1$, $\mathfrak{Sg}_1 (\mathfrak{A}_1, \mathfrak{A}_2)$ is always a consequence of $\mathfrak{R}_1$; otherwise it is called an $\mathfrak{Sg}$ of improper identity. If $\mathfrak{Sg}_1$ is an $\mathfrak{Sg}$ either of proper or of improper identity, then $\mathfrak{Sg}_1 (\mathfrak{A}_1, \mathfrak{A}_2)$ is called a **sentence of** proper (or improper, respectively) **identity** (or an equation) for $\mathfrak{A}_1$ and $\mathfrak{A}_2$. A $\mathfrak{pr}_1^2$ is called a symbol of proper or improper identity (or predicate of identity, or symbol of equality) in general, or for all expressions of the class $\mathfrak{R}_1$, if the sentence $\mathfrak{pr}_1 (\mathfrak{A}_1, \mathfrak{A}_2)$ is a sentence of proper (or improper, respectively) identity for $\mathfrak{A}_1$ and $\mathfrak{A}_2$ for any closed $\mathfrak{A}$ or any closed $\mathfrak{A}$ of $\mathfrak{R}_1$ respectively. (S may, for instance, contain different symbols of identity for $\mathfrak{Z}$, $\mathfrak{S}$, and $\mathfrak{Pr}$.)

Theorem 65.9. Let $\mathfrak{S}_1$ be a sentence of identity for the closed expressions $\mathfrak{A}_1$ and $\mathfrak{A}_2$. (a) $\mathfrak{A}_1$ and $\mathfrak{A}_2$ are synonymous in relation to $\mathfrak{S}_1$. (b) If $\mathfrak{S}_1$ is valid, then $\mathfrak{A}_1$ and $\mathfrak{A}_2$ are synonymous (absolutely).

Theorem 65.10. Let S be extensional in relation to partial sentences. (a) If $\mathfrak{Bf}_1$ is a proper equivalence, then for any two closed sentences $\mathfrak{S}_1$ and $\mathfrak{S}_2$, $\mathfrak{Bf}_1 (\mathfrak{S}_1, \mathfrak{S}_2)$ is always a sentence of proper identity for $\mathfrak{S}_1$ and $\mathfrak{S}_2$. (b) A symbol of proper equivalence is a symbol of proper identity for sentences.

§ 66. EXTENSIONALITY IN RELATION TO PARTIAL EXPRESSIONS

Here we shall again start from the usual definition (using the symbolism of II). It is customary to call an $\mathfrak{Sfu}_1^1$ with a variable $\mathfrak{p}_1$, say ' $\mathrm{M}(F)$ ', extensional in relation to ' F ' if

$$'(x) \left(F(x) \equiv G(x) \right) \supset \left(\mathrm{M}(F) \equiv \mathrm{M}(G) \right)'$$

is true. We can, as previously, alter the formulation of the condition thus: for any 'P_1' and 'P_2', '$M(P_1) \equiv M(P_2)$' must always be a consequence of '$(x)(P_1(x) \equiv P_2(x))$'. With this as a basis, we now give the following definitions.

Extensionality in relation to partial expressions. Let $\mathfrak{Pr}_1$ occur in $\mathfrak{S}_1$; $\mathfrak{S}_1$ is called extensional in relation to $\mathfrak{Pr}_1$ if for any closed $\mathfrak{Pr}_2$, and any $\mathfrak{K}_1$ such that $\mathfrak{Pr}_1$ and $\mathfrak{Pr}_2$ are coextensive in relation to $\mathfrak{K}_1$, $\mathfrak{S}_1$ and $\mathfrak{S}_1 \left[\begin{matrix} \mathfrak{Pr}_1 \\ \mathfrak{Pr}_2 \end{matrix} \right]$ are always equipollent in relation to $\mathfrak{K}_1$. Let $\mathfrak{Fu}_1$ occur in $\mathfrak{S}_1$; $\mathfrak{S}_1$ is called extensional in relation to $\mathfrak{Fu}_1$ if, for any closed $\mathfrak{Fu}_2$ and any $\mathfrak{K}_1$ such that $\mathfrak{Fu}_1$ and $\mathfrak{Fu}_2$ have the same course of values in relation to $\mathfrak{K}_1$, $\mathfrak{S}_1$ and $\mathfrak{S}_1 \left[\begin{matrix} \mathfrak{Fu}_1 \\ \mathfrak{Fu}_2 \end{matrix} \right]$ are equipollent in relation to $\mathfrak{K}_1$. If $\mathfrak{S}_1$ is extensional in relation to all the closed $\mathfrak{S}$, $\mathfrak{Pr}$, and $\mathfrak{Fu}$ which occur in $\mathfrak{S}_1$, $\mathfrak{S}_1$ is called *extensional*. An $\mathfrak{Sg}_1$, to which $\mathfrak{Pr}$, $\mathfrak{Fu}$, or $\mathfrak{S}$ are suitable as arguments, is called extensional if every full sentence of $\mathfrak{Sg}_1$ with closed arguments is extensional in relation to every argument. Correspondingly for every $\mathfrak{Sfu}_1$ or $\mathfrak{Pr}_1$ to which $\mathfrak{Pr}$, $\mathfrak{Fu}$, or $\mathfrak{S}$ are suitable as arguments.

If every sentence of S is extensional in relation to every closed partial expression $\mathfrak{Pr}$ (or $\mathfrak{Fu}$) then S is called *extensional in relation to* $\mathfrak{Pr}$ (or $\mathfrak{Fu}$, respectively). If S is extensional in relation to partial sentences, to $\mathfrak{Pr}$, and to $\mathfrak{Fu}$, then S is called **extensional**.

Theorem 66.1. (*a*) If S is extensional in relation to $\mathfrak{Pr}$, then two closed $\mathfrak{Pr}$ which are coextensive (absolutely or in relation to $\mathfrak{K}_1$) are always (absolutely or in relation to $\mathfrak{K}_1$, respectively) synonymous. (*b*) If S is extensional in relation to $\mathfrak{Fu}$, then two closed $\mathfrak{Fu}$ which have the same course of values (absolutely or in relation to $\mathfrak{K}_1$) are always (absolutely or in relation to $\mathfrak{K}_1$, respectively) synonymous.

Examples: The languages of Russell and of Hilbert and our own Languages I and II are *extensional in relation to partial sentences.* That is shown, for instance, by the criterion of Theorem 65.7 *c* (cf. Hilbert [*Logik*], p. 61). The symbols of equivalence in these languages are symbols of proper equivalence and hence, according to Theorem 65.10 *b*, they are also symbols of proper identity for $\mathfrak{S}$. The form of the language will be simpler if only one symbol of identity is used (as in I and II, and in contrast with Russell and Hilbert), the same for $\mathfrak{S}$ as for $\mathfrak{Z}$, $^0\mathfrak{A}$ and so on. If from Russell's language R we construct a new language R′, by extending the rules of formation to admit of undefined $\mathfrak{pr}_b$ with $\mathfrak{S}$ as arguments, then

R' is no longer necessarily extensional in relation to partial sentences; in order to guarantee extensionality here also, we can proceed, for example, by admitting $\mathfrak{S} = \mathfrak{S}$ as a sentence, and (in analogy with PSII 22, see below) stating a new primitive sentence as follows: '$(p \equiv q) \supset (p = q)$'. If the extended language II' is constructed from II in the same way, then it is extensional in relation to partial sentences. Here no new primitive sentence is necessary, since we use the symbol of identity as symbol of equivalence, so that the above sentence of implication is demonstrable.

Languages I and II are also *extensional* in general. In II the extensionality in relation to $\mathfrak{Pr}$ and $\mathfrak{Fu}$ is guaranteed by PSII 22 and 23 (see p. 92). In the case of the other languages, the question of extensionality in relation to $\mathfrak{Pr}$ and $\mathfrak{Fu}$ can only be decided after further stipulations have been made, especially regarding what undefined $^{n}\mathfrak{pr}_{b}$ (for $n > 1$) are to be admitted.

The languages of Lewis, Becker, Chwistek, and Heyting are *intensional*, for partial sentences as well as for the rest (see § 67).

§ 67. THE THESIS OF EXTENSIONALITY

Wittgenstein ([*Tractatus*], pp. 102, 142, 152) put forward the thesis that every sentence is "a truth-function of the elementary sentences" and therefore (in our terminology) extensional in relation to partial sentences. Following Wittgenstein, Russell ([*Introd. Wittg.*], pp. 13 ff.; [*Princ. Math.*] Vol. 1, 2nd edition, pp. xiv and 659 ff.) adopted the same view with regard to partial sentences and predicates; as I also did, but from rather a different standpoint ([*Aufbau*], pp. 59 ff.). In so doing, however, we all overlooked the fact that there is a multiplicity of possible languages. Wittgenstein, especially, speaks continually of "the" language. From the point of view of general syntax, it is evident that the thesis is incomplete, and must be completed by stating the languages to which it relates. In any case it does not hold for all languages, as the well-known examples of intensional languages show. The reasons given by Wittgenstein, Russell, and myself, in the passages cited, argue not for the necessity but merely for the possibility of an extensional language. For this reason we will now formulate the *thesis of extensionality* in a way which is at the same time more complete and less ambitious, namely: *a universal language of science may be extensional*; or, more exactly: for every given intensional language S_1, an extensional language S_2 may be constructed such that S_1 can be translated into S_2. In what follows we shall discuss the most important examples of intensional sentences and demonstrate the possibility of their translation into sentences of an extensional language.

Let us enumerate some of the most important *examples of intensional sentences*. 'A' and 'B' are abbreviations (not designations) for sentences, e.g. "It is raining now in Paris", etc. 1. Russell ([*Princ. Math.*], Vol. I, p. 73 and [*Math. Phil.*], pp. 187 ff., and similarly Behmann [*Logik*], p. 29) gives examples of approximately the following kind: "Charles says A", "Charles believes A", "it is strange that A", "A is concerned with Paris". Incidentally Russell himself later, influenced by Wittgenstein's opinions, rejected these examples, and asserted that their intensionality was only apparent ([*Princ. Math.*], Vol. I, 2nd edition, Appendix C). We prefer to say instead that these sentences are genuinely intensional but are translatable into extensional ones. 2. Intensional sentences concerning being-contained-in and substitution in relation to expressions: "(The expression) Prim(3) contains (the expression) 3"; "Prim(3) results from Prim(x) by substituting 3 for x". Sentences of this kind (but written in symbols) occur in the languages of Chwistek and Heyting. 3. Intensional sentences of the logic of modalities: "A is possible"; "A is impossible"; "A is necessary"; "B is a consequence of A"; "A and B are incompatible". Sentences of this kind (in symbols) occur in the systems of the logic of modalities constructed by Lewis, Becker, and others. 4. The following intensional sentences are akin to those of the logic of modalities: "Because A, therefore B"; "Although A, nevertheless B"; and the like. That any sentence $\mathfrak{S}_1$ of the examples given is intensional in relation to 'A' and 'B' follows easily from the criterion of Theorem 65.8 a. If, for instance, 'A' is analytic and 'C' is synthetic, then 'A ≡ C' is a consequence of 'C'; but the false sentence "A is necessary ≡ C is necessary" is not a consequence of 'C'. These examples will be discussed in greater detail in what follows.

The above examples appear at first glance to be very different in kind. But, as a closer examination will show, they agree with one another in one particular feature, and this feature is the *reason for their intensionality: all these sentences are quasi-syntactical sentences* and, in particular, they are quasi-syntactical with respect to those expressions in relation to which they are intensional. With the establishment of this characteristic, *the possibility of their translation into an extensional language* is at once given, inasmuch, namely, as *every quasi-syntactical sentence is translatable into a correlative syntactical sentence*. That the syntax of any language (even an intensional one) can be formulated in an extensional language is easy to see. For arithmetic can be formulated to any desired extent in an extensional language, and hence an arithmetized syntax also. Incidentally this is equally true of a syntax in axiomatic form.

What we have said holds for all examples of intensional sentences so far known. Since we are ignorant of whether there exist intensional sentences of quite another kind than those known, we are also ignorant of whether the methods described, or others, are applicable to the translation of all possible intensional sentences. For this reason the *thesis of extensionality* (although it seems to me to be a fairly plausible one) is presented here *only as a supposition*.

§ 68. Intensional Sentences of the Autonymous Mode of Speech

Some of the known examples of intensional sentences belong to the autonymous mode of speech. When translated into an extensional language, they are transformed into the correlated syntactical sentences. We will first of all examine the converse process, namely, the construction from an extensional syntactical sentence of an intensional sentence with an autonymous expression. By this means the nature of these intensional sentences will become clear.

Let S_1 and S_2 be extensional languages; and let S_2 contain S_1 as a sub-language and the syntax of S_1 by virtue of $\mathfrak{Q}_1$. Let $\mathfrak{A}_1$ be an $\mathfrak{S}$, $\mathfrak{Pr}$, or $\mathfrak{Fu}$ of S_1, and $\mathfrak{S}_2$ (in S_2) have the form $\mathfrak{Pr}_2(\mathfrak{Q}_1[\mathfrak{A}_1])$. In material interpretation: $\mathfrak{Q}_1[\mathfrak{A}_1]$ is a syntactical designation of $\mathfrak{A}_1$; $\mathfrak{S}_2$ ascribes to $\mathfrak{A}_1$ a certain syntactical property expressed by $\mathfrak{Pr}_2$. $\mathfrak{Pr}_2(\mathfrak{A}_1)$ is in general not a sentence of S_2. Now, out of S_2, we construct an extended language S_3 (that is to say, S_2 is a proper sub-language of S_3). The rules of formation are extended as follows: in S_3, for every $\mathfrak{A}_3$ which is isogenous with $\mathfrak{A}_1$ in S_1, $\mathfrak{Pr}_2(\mathfrak{A}_3)$ is a sentence, and hence $\mathfrak{Pr}_2(\mathfrak{A}_1)$ also (let this be $\mathfrak{S}_1$); further, the rules of transformation are extended as follows: in S_3, for every $\mathfrak{A}_3$ which is isogenous with $\mathfrak{A}_1$ in S_1, $\mathfrak{Pr}_2(\mathfrak{A}_3)$ is equipollent to $\mathfrak{Pr}_2(\mathfrak{Q}_1[\mathfrak{A}_3])$, and therefore $\mathfrak{S}_1$ is also equipollent to $\mathfrak{Pr}_2(\mathfrak{Q}_1[\mathfrak{A}_1])$ (this is $\mathfrak{S}_2$). Then, according to the criterion given earlier (p. 238), $\mathfrak{A}_1$ is *autonymous* in $\mathfrak{S}_1$. A sentence which is formulated like $\mathfrak{S}_1$ is in general intensional in respect of $\mathfrak{A}_1$.

Example: Let S_1 be I. As syntax-language in S_2 we will take the word-language. Let the $\mathfrak{Q}_1$-correlates (the syntactical designations) be formed with inverted commas. Let $\mathfrak{A}_1$ be '$0^{||}=2$', and accordingly $\mathfrak{A}_2$, ''$0^{||}=2$''. Let $\mathfrak{S}_2$ be ''$0^{||}=2$' is an equation'. Then $\mathfrak{S}_1$ is '$0^{||}=2$ is an equation'. For S_3 we stipulate that $\mathfrak{S}_1$ and $\mathfrak{S}_2$ be mutual consequences of one another; and likewise, corresponding other sentences with the same $\mathfrak{Pr}$. Then '$0^{||}=2$' is autonymous in $\mathfrak{S}_1$, and, according to Theorem 65.8b, $\mathfrak{S}_1$ is intensional in relation to '$0^{||}=2$'. For let $\mathfrak{A}_3$ be 'Prim (3)'; then $\mathfrak{A}_2 \equiv \mathfrak{A}_3$ is analytic but 'Prim (3) is an equation' ($\mathfrak{S}_4$), because it is equipollent to ''Prim (3)' is an equation', is contradictory; hence, since $\mathfrak{S}_1$ is analytic, $\mathfrak{S}_1 \equiv \mathfrak{S}_4$ is contradictory.

Now some of the examples of intensional sentences previously mentioned have the same character as the intensional sentences constructed in the way here described: their intensionality is due to the occurrence of an autonymous expression. We will cite some examples of this, at the same time giving the correlated syntactical sentences. The latter may belong to an extensional language. [Sentences 1 b and 2 b belong to descriptive syntax, 3 b, 4 b, and 5 b to pure syntax. The preceding investigations and definitions have all been given in relation to pure syntax only; they may, however, be correspondingly extended to apply to descriptive syntax.] To interpret these sentences as belonging to the autonymous mode of speech seems to me to be the natural thing, especially in the case of 4 a and 5 a. However, if anyone prefers not to ascribe one of them (say 2 a or 3 a) to the autonymous mode of speech, he is at liberty to do so; the sentence in question will then belong to the material mode of speech. The only essential points are: (1) these intensional sentences are quasi-syntactical; and (2) they can (together with all other sentences of the same language) be translated into extensional sentences, namely, into the correlated syntactical sentences.

Intensional sentences of the autonymous mode of speech	*Extensional sentences* of syntax
Let 'A' be an abbreviation (not a designation) of some sentence.	
1 a. Charles says (writes, reads) A.	1 b. Charles says 'A'.
2 a. Charles thinks (asserts, believes, wonders about) A.	2 b. Charles thinks 'A'.

[Of the same kind is the following: "it is astounding that...", that is to say: "many wonder about the fact that...".]

3 *a*. A has to do with Paris.	3 *b*. 'Paris' occurs in a sentence which results from 'A' by the elimination of defined symbols.
4 *a*. Prim (3) contains 3.	4 *b*. '3' occurs in 'Prim (3)'.
5 *a*. Prim (3) results from Prim (*x*) by the substitution of 3 for *x*.	5 *b*. 'Prim (3)' results from 'Prim (*x*)' by the substitution of '3' for '*x*'.

We have here interpreted the previously mentioned (p. 246) examples of intensional sentences put forward by Russell, Chwistek, and Heyting, as sentences of the *autonymous mode of speech*. This interpretation is suggested by the relevant indications given by the authors themselves. Russell's sentences are already presented in the word-language; and for the sentences of Chwistek and Heyting, which are formulated in symbols, the authors themselves give paraphrases in the word-language corresponding to 4 *a* and 5 *a*.

Chwistek's system of so-called *semantics* is, on the whole, dedicated to the same task as our syntax. But Chwistek throughout employs the autonymous mode of speech (apparently without being aware of it himself). He uses as the designation of an expression with which a sentence of semantics is concerned either this expression itself or, alternatively, a symbol which is synonymous with it (and is thus, originally, not a designation but an abbreviation for it). As a result of the employment of the autonymous mode of speech, many sentences of Chwistek's semantics are intensional. Because of this, he has come to the conclusion that every formal (Chwistek says "nominalistic") theory of linguistic expressions must make use of intensional sentences. This view is refuted by the counter-example of our syntax, which, although strictly formal, is consistently extensional (this is most clearly seen in the formalized syntax of I in I, in Part II). The fact that Chwistek believed himself forced to abandon the simple rule of types for his semantics and to return to the branched rule (see § 60·a), was also, in my opinion, only a consequence of his use of the autonymous mode of speech.

Heyting gives as the word-translation of certain symbolic expressions of his language: "the expression which results from *a* when the variable *x* is replaced wherever it appears by the combination of symbols *p*" ([*Math.* 1], p. 4) and: "*g* does not contain *x*" ([*Math.* 1], p. 7). Such formulations, like our examples 4 *a* and 5 *a*, belong, without any doubt, to the autonymous mode of speech. But even the sentential calculus of Heyting's system [*Logik*] contains intensional sentences; sentential junctions which can be shown to possess no characteristic are used (see p. 203). These circumstances make it natural to suppose not only that the whole system can be translated by us into a system of syntactical sentences, but also that this was in a certain sense the author's intention. "In a certain sense" only, because the distinction between the object- and the syntax-languages is nowhere explicitly made; so that it is not even clear which language it is whose syntax is supposed to be represented in the system. According to [*Grundlegung*], p. 113, the assertion of a sentence (which is formulated symbolically by placing the symbol of assertion in front of the sentence) is "the establishment of an empirical fact, namely the fulfilment of the intention expressed by the sentence" or of the expectation of a possible experience. Such an assertion may mean, for example, the historical circumstance that I have a proof of the proposition in question lying in front of me. According to this, the assertions in Heyting's system should be interpreted as sentences of descriptive syntax. On the other hand, Gödel [*Kolloquium* 4], p. 39, gives an interpretation of Heyting's system in which the sentences of the system would be purely syntactical sentences about demonstrability; "'A' is demonstrable' is formulated by means of 'BA', and consequently in the autonymous mode of speech.

§ 69. Intensional Sentences of the Logic of Modalities

We shall now give some further examples of *intensional* sentences together with their *translation into extensional syntactical sentences*. By means of this translation the *intensional sentences* are shown to be *quasi-syntactical*. Sentences 1a to 4a contain terms that are usually known as *modalities* ['possible', 'impossible', 'necessary', 'contingent' (in the sense of 'neither necessary nor impossible')]. Sentences 5a to 7a contain terms that are similar in character to these modalities, and are therefore treated by the newer systems of the logic of modalities (Lewis, Lukasiewicz, Becker, and others) together with them. In these systems, the modal sentences are symbolically formulated in approximately the same way as our examples 1b to 7b. Examples 8a are intensional sentences of the ordinary word-language which we add here because, as the syntactical translation shows, they are akin to the modal sentences. 'A' and 'B' are here sentences—i.e. abbreviations (not designations) of certain sentences (such as synthetic sentences) either of the word-language or of a symbolic language.

Intensional sentences of the logic of modalities		*Extensional* sentences of syntax
1 a. A is possible.	1 b. P(A).	1 c. 'A' is not contradictory.
2 a. A . ∼A is impossible.	2 b. I(A . ∼A); ∼P(A . ∼A).	2 c. 'A . ∼A' is contradictory.

3 a. A $\vee \sim$A is *necessary*.	3 b. N(A $\vee \sim$A); $\sim$P$\sim$(A $\vee \sim$A).	3 c. 'A $\vee \sim$A' is analytic.
4 a. A is *contingent*.	4 b. $\sim$N(A) . $\sim$ I(A); P(A) . P($\sim$A).	4 c. 'A' is synthetic. ('A' is neither analytic nor contradictory; neither 'A' nor '$\sim$A' is contradictory.)
5 a. A *strictly implies* B; B is a consequence of A.	5 b. A < B.	5 c. 'B' is an L-consequence of 'A'.
6 a. A and B are strictly equivalent.	6 b. A = B.	6 c. 'A' and 'B' are L-equipollent (i.e. mutual L-consequences).
7 a. A and B are compatible.	7 b. C(A, B); $\sim$(A < $\sim$B).	7 c. 'A' and 'B' are L-compatible. ('$\sim$B' is not an L-consequence of 'A'.)
8 a. Because A, therefore B; A, hence B.		8 c. 'A' is analytic, 'B' is an L-consequence of 'A', 'B' is analytic. ('A' is valid, 'B' is a consequence of 'A', 'B' is valid.)

Since the terms used in the logic of modalities are somewhat vague and ambiguous, it is also possible to choose other syntactical terms for the translations; in 2 c, for instance, instead of 'contradictory' we may put 'contravalid', 'L-refutable', or 'refutable'. Similarly in the other cases, instead of the L-c-term we can take the general c-term, the L-d-term, or the d-term. With regard to 8 c, in the majority of cases the general c-term (or the P-term) is perhaps more natural as an interpretation of 8 a than the L-term. The difference between the so-called *logical* and the so-called *real* modalities can be represented in the translation by the difference between L- and general c-terms (or even P-terms):

9 a. A is logically impossible.	9 c. 'A' is contradictory.
10 a. A is really impossible.	10 c_1. 'A' is contravalid.
	10 c_2. 'A' is P-contravalid.

The translation of 10 a depends upon the meaning of 'really impossible'. If this term is so meant that it is also to be applied to cases of logical impossibility, then the translation 10 c_1 must be chosen; otherwise 10 c_2. Analogous translations may be given for the three other modalities—for 'logically (or "really", respectively) possible', 'necessary', and 'contingent'.

That sentences 1 a to 10 a and 1 b to 7 b are *intensional* is easily seen. [*Example:* Let 'Q' be an undefined $\mathfrak{pr}_\mathfrak{b}$, and ' $\equiv$ ' a symbol of proper equivalence. Let $\mathfrak{S}_1$ be 'Prim (3) $\equiv$ Q (2)'; $\mathfrak{S}_2$ be: 'Prim (3) is necessary'; and $\mathfrak{S}_3$: 'Q (2) is necessary'. Then $\mathfrak{S}_2 \equiv \mathfrak{S}_3$ cannot be a consequence of $\mathfrak{S}_1$ (for $\mathfrak{S}_1$ is synthetic, $\mathfrak{S}_2$ analytic, and $\mathfrak{S}_3$ contradictory, and hence $\mathfrak{S}_2 \equiv \mathfrak{S}_3$ is contradictory). Therefore (by Theorem 65.7 b) $\mathfrak{S}_2$ is intensional in relation to 'Prim (3)'.]

Since the sentences given here are quasi-syntactical, we can interpret them as sentences either of the autonymous or of the material mode of speech. In the case of the sentences of § 68, the verbal formulations, or the verbal paraphrases given by the authors, suggest interpretation in the autonymous mode of speech. On the other hand, in the case of the symbolic sentences 1 *b* to 7 *b*, it is not clear which of the two interpretations is intended—in spite of the fact that paraphrases (of the same kind as sentences 1 *a* to 7 *a*), and sometimes even detailed material explanations as well, are given by the authors. In relation to a particular example, the decisive question (as formulated in the material mode) is the following: Are 'I (A)' and 'A is impossible' to refer to the sentence 'A', or to that which is designated by 'A'? In the formal mode: Is "A' is impossible' also to be a sentence? [If so, it must undoubtedly be equipollent to 'A is impossible.'] If the answer is in the affirmative, then 'I (A)' and 'A is impossible' both belong to the autonymous mode of speech; if in the negative, then they belong to the material mode of speech. The authors do, it is true, say that the sentences of modality are concerned with propositions, but this assertion would decide the question only if it were quite clear what was meant by the term 'proposition'. We will discuss the two possibilities separately.

1. Suppose that by the term 'proposition' the authors mean what we mean by 'sentence'. Then the term 'proposition' is a syntactical term, namely, the designation either of certain physical objects in descriptive syntax or of certain expressional designs in pure syntax. Then 'A is impossible' is concerned with the sentence 'A', hence is equipollent to "A' is impossible', and belongs to the *autonymous mode of speech*. In this case the intensionality of the modal sentences does not depend upon the fact that they speak about expressions (in the examples, about sentences, in other cases, also about predicate-expressions) but upon the fact that they do so according to the autonymous and not according to the syntactical method.

2. Suppose that by a 'proposition' the authors mean not a sentence (in our sense) but that which is designated by a sentence. [For instance, in Lewis's [*Logic*], pp. 472 ff., the distinction between 'proposition' and 'sentence' is possibly to be understood in this way.] We will leave aside the question of what it is that is

designated by a sentence (some people say thoughts or the content of thoughts, others, facts or possible facts); it is a question that easily leads to philosophical pseudo-problems. So we shall simply say neutrally "that which is designated by a sentence". In this interpretation, the sentence 'A is impossible' ascribes impossibility not to the sentence 'A' but to the A which is designated by the sentence. Here the impossibility is not a property of sentences. "'A' is impossible' is not a sentence; it is therefore a case not of the autonymous but of the *material* mode of speech. 'A is impossible' ascribes to the A which is designated by the sentence a quasi-syntactical property, instead of to the sentence 'A' the correlated syntactical property (here 'contradictory'). [In this example, the second interpretation is perhaps the more natural. It is the only possible one in the case of the formulation 'the process (or: state of affairs, condition) A is impossible'; see § 79, Examples 33 to 35. On the other hand, we are perhaps more inclined to relate a sentence about the consequence-relation or about derivability to sentences rather than to that which is designated by them, and accordingly to choose the first interpretation.] We shall see later that, in general, the use of the material mode of speech, though it is not inadmissible, brings with it the danger of entanglement in obscurities and pseudo-problems that are avoided by the application of the formal mode. So also here, the systems of the logic of modalities are (on the whole) formally correct. But if they are (in the accompanying text) interpreted in the second way, that is, in the material mode of speech, then pseudo-problems easily arise. This may perhaps explain the strange and, in part, unintelligible questions and considerations which are to be found in some treatises on the logic of modalities.

C. I. Lewis was the first to point out that in Russell's language [*Princ. Math.*] there is no way of expressing the fact that a certain proposition necessarily holds or that a particular proposition is a consequence of another. As against this, Russell can rightly maintain that, in spite of it, his system is adequate for the construction both of logic and of mathematics, that in it necessarily valid sentences can be proved and a sentence which follows from another can be derived from the former.

Although Lewis's contention is correct, it does not exhibit any lacuna *within* Russell's language. The requirement that a language be capable of expressing necessity, possibility, the consequence-relation, etc., is in itself justifiable; it is fulfilled by us for instance in the case of our Languages I and II, not by means of anything supplementary to these languages, but by the formulation of their syntax. On the other hand, both Lewis and Russell—they are agreed on this point—look upon the consequence-relation and implication as terms on the same footing as sentential connections, of which the first is the narrower. For this reason, Lewis found himself obliged to extend Russell's language by introducing, in addition to Russell's symbol of implication ' ⊃ ' (so-called material implication; in our terminology: proper implication), a new symbol ' < ' for what is called *strict implication* (in our terminology: an intensional symbol of improper implication without characteristic). This is intended to express the consequence-relation (or derivability-relation), that is to say, in Lewis's language, ' A < B ' is demonstrable if ' B ' is a consequence of ' A '. Lewis rightly pointed out that Russell's implication does not correspond to this interpretation, and that, moreover, none of the so-called truth-functions (in our terminology: the extensional sentential junctions) can express the consequence-relation at all. He therefore believed himself compelled to introduce intensional sentential junctions, namely, those of strict implication and of the modality-terms. In this way his system of the logic of modalities arose as an intensional extension of Russell's language. The system is set forth by Lewis in [*Survey*], pp. 291 ff., following MacColl, and later presented in an improved form in [*Logic*], pp. 122 ff., profiting by the researches of Becker and others. To Russell's system are added, as new primitive symbols, symbols for 'possible' and 'strictly equivalent', and with the help of these, 'impossible', 'necessary', 'strict implication', 'compatible', etc., are defined. Similar systems have been constructed by Lewis's pupils—by Parry ([*Koll.*], p. 5), for example, and Nelson ([*Intensional*]). Becker ([*Modalitätslogik*]), starting out from Lewis's [*Survey*], has made some interesting investigations using the same method. Before this Lukasiewicz had already worked out so-called many-valued systems of the sentential calculus (see his [*Aussagenkalkül*]). In [*Mehrwertige*] he interprets the sentences of the three-valued calculus by a translation into the modal sentences; these are, as are Lewis's, formulated in accordance with the quasi-syntactical method.

It is important to note the *fundamentally different nature of implication and the consequence-relation*. Materially expressed: the consequence-relation is a relation between sentences; *implication is not a relation between sentences*. [Whether, for example, Russell's opinion that it is a relation between propositions is erroneous or not, depends upon what is to be understood by a "proposition". If we are going to speak at all of 'that which is designated by a sentence', then implication is a relation between what is so designated; but the consequence-relation is not.] ' A ⊃ B ' ($\mathfrak{S}_1$)—as opposed to the syntactical sentence "'B' is a consequence of 'A'" ($\mathfrak{S}_2$)—means, not something about the sentences 'A' and 'B', but, with the help of these sentences and of the junction-symbol '⊃', something about the objects to which 'A' and 'B' refer. Formally expressed: '⊃' is a symbol of the object-language, and 'consequence' a predicate of the syntax-language. Of course, between the two sentences $\mathfrak{S}_1$ and $\mathfrak{S}_2$ there is an important relation (see Theorem 14.7). $\mathfrak{S}_2$ cannot, however, be inferred from $\mathfrak{S}_1$ but only from the (equally syntactical) sentence '$\mathfrak{S}_1$ is valid (or analytic)'. The majority of the symbolic languages (for example, Russell's [*Princ. Math.*]) are (after a suitable extension of the rules of inference) logical languages, and therefore contain no indeterminate sentences. Hence, in these systems, $\mathfrak{S}_2$ can be inferred from $\mathfrak{S}_1$. This explains why the sentences of implication are in general erroneously interpreted as sentences about consequence-relations. [This is one of the points which shows clearly how unfortunate it is that the indeterminate sentences have, for the most part, been disregarded in logical investigations.] The relation of the *intensional symbols of implication* in the systems of the logic of modalities, for instance that of the symbol of strict implication to '⊃' and to 'consequence', will become clear with the aid of the earlier example on p. 235; this relation corresponds exactly to that subsisting between 'LImp', 'Imp', and 'consequence'. [We can ignore here the differences between the intensional implications in the various systems; they correspond to the different definitions of the syntactical concept of 'consequence'.]

Russell's choice of the designation 'implication' for the sentential junction with the characteristic TFTT has turned out to be a very unfortunate one. The words 'to imply' in the English language mean the same as 'to contain' or 'to involve'. Whether the choice of the name was due to a confusion of implication with the consequence-relation, I do not know; but, in any case, this nomenclature has been the cause of much confusion in the minds of many, and it is even possible that it is to blame for the fact that a number of people, though aware of the difference between implication and the consequence-relation, still think that the symbol of implication ought really to express the consequence-relation, and count it as a failure on the part of this symbol that it does not do so. If we have retained the term 'implication' in our system, it is, of course, in a sense entirely divorced from its original meaning; it serves in the syntax merely as the designation of sentential junctions of a particular kind.

§ 70. The Quasi-Syntactical and the Syntactical Methods in the Logic of Modalities

All the foregoing systems of the logic of modalities (within the province of modern logic, in symbolic language) have, it seems, applied the *quasi-syntactical method*. This is not a matter of conscious choice between syntactical and quasi-syntactical methods; rather the method applied is held to be the natural one. All intensional sentences of the previously existing systems of the logic of modalities are, in any case, quasi-syntactical sentences, independently of which of the two interpretations earlier discussed is intended or (by a suitable incorporation in a more comprehensive language) carried into effect. [Incidentally, it should be noted that for each of the systems one of the two interpretations can be arbitrarily chosen and carried out, provided no attention is paid to the authors' indications regarding interpretation. Accordingly, it is, in particular, possible to interpret every sentence $\mathfrak{S}_1$ of the logic of modalities that is intensional in respect of a partial expression $\mathfrak{A}_1$, in such a way that $\mathfrak{A}_1$ is autonymous in $\mathfrak{S}_1$.] *Every intensional system of the logic of modalities* (and that even when synthetic sentences are admitted as arguments) *can be translated into an extensional syntactical language*, whereby every intensional sentence, since it is quasi-syntactical, is translated into the correlated syntactical sentence. In other words: *syntax already contains the whole of the logic of modalities*, and the construction of a special intensional logic of modalities is not required.

Whether, for the construction of a logic of modalities, the quasi-syntactical or the syntactical method is chosen is solely a question of expedience. We will not here decide the question but will only state the properties of both methods. The use of the quasi-syntactical method leads to intensional sentences, while the syntactical method can also be carried into effect in an extensional language. In a certain sense, the quasi-syntactical method is the simpler; and it may be that it will prove to be the appropriate one for the solution of certain problems. It will only be possible to pronounce judgment on its fruitfulness as a whole when the method is further developed. Hitherto, if I am not mistaken, it has in the main only been applied to the domain of the sentential calculus which, on account of the resolubility of its sentences, is quite a simple one (see Parry [*Koll.*], pp. 15 f.). It cannot be said that the logic of modalities does not necessitate any syntactical terms and is therefore simpler. For the construction of every calculus, and therefore also of the logic of modalities, a syntax-language is required in which the statement of the rules of inference and of the primitive sentences is formulated (see § 31); it is usual simply to take the word-language for this purpose. Now, as soon as this syntax-language is obtained, everything that it is desired to express by the sentences of modality—and, in general, far more—can be defined and formulated within it. That is the reason why we have here given preference to the syntactical method. It is, however, in any case, a worth-while task to develop the quasi-syntactical method in general, and its use in the logic of modalities in particular, and to investigate its possibilities in comparison with the syntactical method.

Even if in the construction of a logic of modalities we wish to use, not the syntactical but the ordinary method hitherto employed, the realization that this method is a quasi-syntactical one can help us to overcome a number of uncertainties. These, for example, have manifested themselves at various points in the fact that, wishing to start from evident axioms, logicians have found themselves in doubt about the evidence of certain sentences; it has even happened that sentences which had previously been individually regarded as evident have turned out later to be incompatible. As soon, however, as it is seen that the concepts of modality—even when they are formulated quasi-syntactically—are concerned with syntactical properties, their relativity is recognized. They must always be referred to a particular language (which may be other than that in which they are formulated). In this way the problems regarding the evident character of *absolute* relations between the modality-concepts disappear.

§ 71. IS AN INTENSIONAL LOGIC NECESSARY?

Some logicians take the view that the ordinary logic (for instance, that of Russell) is deficient in some respects and must therefore be supplemented by a new logic, which is designated as intensional logic or the logic of meaning (e.g. Lewis, Nelson

17

[*Intensional*], Weiss, and Jörgensen [*Ziele*], p. 93). Is this requirement justified? A close examination shows that two different
questions, which should be treated separately, are here involved.

1. Russell's language is an extensional language. It is required
that it be supplemented by an *intensional language* for the purpose
of expressing the concepts of modality ('consequence', 'necessary',
etc.). We have dealt with this question before, and have seen that
the concepts of modality may also be expressed in an extensional
language, and that their formulation only led to intensional sentences because the quasi-syntactical method was used. Neither for
an object-language concerned with any domain of objects nor for
the syntax-language of any object-language is it necessary to go
outside the framework of an extensional language.

2. As opposed to the ordinary formal logic, a *logic of content* or
a *logic of meaning* is demanded. And, further, it is believed that
this second requirement also will be fulfilled by the construction
of an intensional logic of modalities; thus it often happens that the
designations 'intensional logic' and 'logic of meaning' are used
synonymously. It is thought, that is, that the concepts of modality,
since they are not dependent merely upon the truth-values of
the arguments, are therefore dependent upon the *meaning* of the
arguments. This is often especially emphasized in connection with
the consequence-relation (e.g. Lewis [*Survey*], p. 328: "Inference
depends upon meaning, logical import, intension"). If all that is
meant by this is merely that, if the meanings of two sentences are
given, the question of whether one is a consequence of the other
or not is also determined, I will not dispute it (although I prefer to
regard the connection from the opposite direction, namely, the
relations of meaning between the sentences are given by means of
the rules of consequence; see § 62). But the decisive point is the
following: *in order to determine whether or not one sentence is a
consequence of another, no reference need be made to the meaning of
the sentences. The mere statement of the truth-values is certainly too
little; but the statement of the meaning is, on the other hand, too
much. It is sufficient that the syntactical design of the sentences be
given.* All the efforts of logicians since Aristotle have been directed
to the formulation of the rules of inference as *formal rules*, that is to
say, as rules which refer only to the form of the sentences (for the
development of the formal character of logic, see Scholz [*Ge-*

schichte]). It is theoretically possible to establish the logical relations (consequence-relation, compatibility, etc.) between two sentences written in Chinese without understanding their sense, provided that the syntax of the Chinese language is given. (In practice this is only possible in the case of the simpler artificially constructed languages.) The two requirements (1) and (2), which are usually blended into one, are entirely independent of one another. Whether we wish to speak merely of the forms of the language S_1 or of the sense (in some meaning of the word) of the sentences of S_1, in either case an intensional language may be used; but we can also use an extensional language for both these purposes. *The difference between the extensionality and intensionality of a language has nothing to do with the difference between the formal and the material treatment.* Now, is it the business of logic to be concerned with the sense of sentences at all (no matter whether they are given in extensional or in intensional languages)? To a certain extent, yes; namely, in so far as the sense and relations of sense permit of being formally represented. Thus, in the syntax, we have represented the formal side of the sense of a sentence by means of the term 'content'; and the formal side of the logical relations between sentences by means of the terms 'consequence', 'compatible', and the like. All the questions which it is desired to treat in the required logic of meaning are nothing more than questions of syntax; in the majority of cases, this is only concealed by the use of the material mode of speech (as is demonstrated by many examples in Part V). Questions about something which is not formally representable, such as the conceptual content of certain sentences, or the perceptual content of certain expressions, do not belong to logic at all, but to psychology. All questions in the field of logic can be formally expressed and are then resolved into syntactical questions. *A special logic of meaning is superfluous*; 'non-formal logic' is a *contradictio in adjecto. Logic is syntax.*

Sometimes the demand for an intensional logic is made in a third connection: it is maintained that hitherto logic has only dealt with the *extension of concepts*, whereas it should also deal with the intension of concepts. But, actually, the newer systems of logic (Frege, as early as 1893, followed by Russell and Hilbert) have got far beyond the stage of development of the mere logic of extension in this sense. Frege himself was the first to define in an exact way the old distinction between the intension and the extension of a concept (namely, by means of his distinction between a sentential function and its course of values). One can rather maintain the reverse, that modern logic, in its latest phase of development, has completely suppressed extension in favour of intension (cf. the elimination of classes, § 38). This misunderstanding has already been cleared up many times (see Russell [*Princ. Math.*], I, p. 72; Carnap [*Aufbau*], p. 58, Scholz [*Geschichte*], p. 63); it is always reappearing, however, amongst philosophers who are not thoroughly acquainted with modern logic (and amongst psychologists, who, in addition, confuse the logical and the psychological content of a concept).

(f) RELATIONAL THEORY AND AXIOMATICS

§ 71a. RELATIONAL THEORY

In the *theory of relations*, the properties of relations are investigated, particularly the structural properties—that is to say those which are retained in isomorphic transformation. A theory of this kind is nothing more than the syntax of many-termed predicates. We have abandoned the usual distinction between the one-termed predicates and the class-symbols appertaining to them, and designate both class and property by pr^1 (see §§ 37, 38). Similarly we no longer differentiate the n-termed predicates for $n > 1$ from the relational symbols which have hitherto been correlated with them as symbols of extension. In this section, we shall indicate briefly how the most important terms of the theory of relations may be incorporated in the general syntax of the predicates.

With regard to the terms used in the theory of relations (such as 'symmetrical', 'transitive', 'isomorphic', etc.), it is important to distinguish between their formulation in the object-language and their formulation in the syntax-language. By means of this distinction—the necessity of which is usually disregarded—certain paradoxes in connection with the question of the multiplicity of the transfinite cardinal numbers and the possibility of non-denumerable aggregates are, as we shall see, clarified.

We will call an n-termed predicate **homogeneous** when, from a sentence constructed from it and n arguments, another sentence always arises as a result of any permutation of the arguments. The majority of the terms of relational theory refer to homogeneous two-termed predicates.

The relational properties of symmetry, reflexiveness, and so on are expressed, according to the ordinary method introduced by Russell, by means of predicates of the second level (or, in Russell's own symbolism, by class symbols of the second level). We will write the definitions in the following form (employing the symbolism of Language II, but leaving open the question as to whether the expressions of the zero level are numerical expressions or designations of objects):

(Non-emptiness):* $\qquad \mathrm{Erf}(F) \equiv (\exists x)(\exists y)\big(F(x,y)\big)$ (1)

(Emptiness): $\qquad \mathrm{Leer}(F) \equiv \sim \mathrm{Erf}(F)$ (2)

(Symmetry):
$$\mathrm{Sym}(F) \equiv \big[\mathrm{Erf}(F) \bullet (x)(y)\,\big(F(x,y) \supset F(y,x)\big)\big] \qquad (3)$$

(Asymmetry): $\mathrm{As}(F) \equiv (x)(y)\,\big(F(x,y) \supset \sim F(y,x)\big)$ (4)

(Reflexiveness):
$$\mathrm{Refl}(F) \equiv \big[\mathrm{Erf}(F) \bullet (x)(y)\big((F(x,y) \vee F(y,x)) \supset F(x,x)\big)\big] \qquad (5)$$

(Total reflexiveness):
$$\mathrm{Reflex}(F) \equiv \big[\mathrm{Erf}(F) \bullet (x)\,\big(F(x,x)\big)\big] \qquad (6)$$

(Irreflexiveness): $\qquad \mathrm{Irr}(F) \equiv (x)\,\big(\sim F(x,x)\big)$ (7)

(Transitivity):
$$\mathrm{Trans}(F) \equiv \big[(\exists x)(\exists y)(\exists z)\,(F(x,y) \bullet F(y,z)) \bullet$$
$$(x)(y)(z)\big((F(x,y) \bullet F(y,z)) \supset F(x,z)\big)\big] \qquad (8)$$

(Intransitivity):
$$\mathrm{Intr}(F) \equiv (x)(y)(z)\,\big[(F(x,y) \bullet F(y,z)) \supset \sim F(x,z)\big] \qquad (9)$$

We have altered the usual forms of the definitions (see Russell [*Princ. Math.*]; Carnap [*Logistik*]) by introducing in the definiens of (3), (5), (6), and (8) an existential sentence or 'Erf(F)' as a conjunction-term. According to the definitions hitherto given, transitivity and intransitivity do not exclude one another; and similarly, neither do symmetry and asymmetry, reflexiveness and irreflexiveness. If, for instance, a relation has no intermediary term (that is to say, no term which occurs in one pair of the relation as second term, and in another pair as first term) then it is simultaneously both transitive and intransitive (because the implicans in the definiens of (9) is always false); and for the same reason a null relation is at the same time transitive, intransitive, symmetrical, asymmetrical, reflexive and irreflexive. On this account we introduce conditions which require for symmetrical, reflexive, and transi-

---

* *Erfülltheit.*

tive relations the property of non-emptiness, and further, for a transitive relation, the occurrence of an intermediary term (non-emptiness of the second power of the relation). On the basis of our definition, the two terms of each of the three pairs exclude one another. [The term 'Erf(F)' in (6) can be left out if the individual domain is non-empty, that is to say, if in the language in question, '$(\exists x)(x=x)$' is demonstrable, as is the case in the ordinary languages of logistics.]

§ 71b. Syntactical Terms of Relational Theory

We will now introduce *syntactical terms of relational theory* as opposed to the terms of relational theory of the object-language which have been defined in the foregoing. The difference between these two kinds of terms must be very carefully noted. Let us take as an example the sentence 'As(P)'—or, in the word-language: 'The relation P is an asymmetrical relation.' This sentence—we will call it $\mathfrak{S}_1$—is equipollent to the sentence

$$'(x)(y)\left[P(x,y) \supset \sim P(y,x)\right]'.$$

In contradistinction to this, we will say that the predicate 'P' (not the relation P) is (systemically asymmetrical or) S-asymmetrical, when $\mathfrak{S}_1$ is not merely true, but systemically true, i.e. valid; and that 'P' is (logically asymmetrical or) L-asymmetrical when $\mathfrak{S}_1$ is (not merely valid but) analytic. In the material mode: The object-sentence 'As(P)' or 'P is asymmetrical' expresses the fact that the relation P does not hold in both directions in any pair; on the other hand the syntactical sentence "'P' is S-asymmetrical" means that this fact can be inferred from the transformation rules of the language-system S (hence, for example, from the natural laws, if they are formulated as primitive sentences); and the syntactical sentence "'P' is L-asymmetrical" means that this is not a genuinely synthetic fact, but is already determined by the L-rules of S, and hence is given in substance by the definition of 'P'.

We will formulate the definitions indicated here in a somewhat different manner, so as to avoid the limiting assumption that universal operators and symbols of proper negation and implication occur in the object-language S. The following are our *syntactical definitions*. Let $\mathfrak{pr}_1$ be a homogeneous two-termed predicate. [The definitions can easily be transferred to any homogeneous $\mathfrak{Pr}^2$, $\mathfrak{Sfu}^2$, and $\mathfrak{Sg}^2$.] Then $\mathfrak{pr}_1$ is called **S-null** (or **L-null**) if always (that is, here and in what follows, for any closed arguments, $\mathfrak{A}_1, \mathfrak{A}_2$), $\mathrm{pr}_1(\mathfrak{A}_1, \mathfrak{A}_2)$ is contravalid (or contradictory, respectively). pr_1 is called S-*fulfilled* (or L-*fulfilled*, respectively) when a valid (or analytic) sentence of the form $\mathrm{pr}_1(\mathfrak{A}_1, \mathfrak{A}_2)$ exists. pr_1 is called **S-symmetrical** (or **L-symmetrical**) when pr_1 is not S-null (or L-null, respectively) and $\mathrm{pr}_1(\mathfrak{A}_2, \mathfrak{A}_1)$ is always a consequence (or L-consequence) of $\mathrm{pr}_1(\mathfrak{A}_1, \mathfrak{A}_2)$. pr_1 is called S-*asymmetrical* (or L-*asymmetrical*, respectively) when $\mathrm{pr}_1(\mathfrak{A}_2, \mathfrak{A}_1)$ and $\mathrm{pr}_1(\mathfrak{A}_1, \mathfrak{A}_2)$ are always incompatible (or L-incompatible) with one another. pr_1 is called S-*reflexive* (or L-*reflexive*) when pr_1 is not S-null (or L-null) and $\mathrm{pr}_1(\mathfrak{A}_1, \mathfrak{A}_1)$ is always a consequence (or L-consequence) of $\mathrm{pr}_1(\mathfrak{A}_1, \mathfrak{A}_2)$ and always a consequence (or L-consequence) of $\mathrm{pr}_1(\mathfrak{A}_2, \mathfrak{A}_1)$; pr_1 is called S-*totally reflexive* (or L-*totally reflexive*) when $\mathrm{pr}_1(\mathfrak{A}_1, \mathfrak{A}_1)$ is always valid (or analytic, respectively); pr_1 is called S-*irreflexive* (or L-*irreflexive*) when $\mathrm{pr}_1(\mathfrak{A}_1, \mathfrak{A}_1)$ is always contravalid (or contradictory, respectively). pr_1 is called S-*transitive* (or L-*transitive*) when the two sentences $\mathrm{pr}_1(\mathfrak{A}_1, \mathfrak{A}_2)$ and $\mathrm{pr}_1(\mathfrak{A}_2, \mathfrak{A}_3)$ are not always incompatible (or L-incompatible, respectively) with one another, and when $\mathrm{pr}_1(\mathfrak{A}_1, \mathfrak{A}_3)$ is always a consequence (or L-consequence, respectively) of those two sentences; pr_1 is called S-*intransitive* (or L-*intransitive*) when the above-mentioned three sentences are always incompatible (or L-incompatible, respectively) with one another.

In the case of all these terms, corresponding P-*terms* can be defined; pr_1 is called **P-null** when pr_1 is S-null but not L-null; and so forth.

We will again make clear the difference between the terms of relational theory of the object-language and those of the syntax-language by means of a juxtaposition.

The property of *symmetry* appertains to certain relations.	The property of S-*symmetry* appertains to certain predicates (namely, to symbols of relations). (The same holds for L-symmetry.)
This property is expressed by the symbol 'Sym', or by the word 'symmetrical'; these symbols belong to the *object-language*.	This property is expressed by the word 'S-symmetrical'; this word belongs to the *syntax-language*.

Assuming appropriate definitions for the predicates in a suitable language S, the following examples hold. The predicate 'brother' is L-irreflexive, but it is neither S-symmetrical nor S-asymmetrical. If it follows from the rules of transformation of S that, in the district B, at least one man has a brother but no man has a sister, then 'brother in B' is S-symmetrical, but not L-symmetrical, and is therefore P-symmetrical. 'Father' is L-irreflexive, L-asymmetrical and L-intransitive.

Theorem 71b.1. (*a*) If the predicate 'P' is L-symmetrical or P-symmetrical, then it is also S-symmetrical. (*b*) If 'P' is S-symmetrical, then P (not 'P') is symmetrical; the converse is not universally true. (*c*) Let S be an L-language (which may also be a descriptive language like I and II); then if 'P' is L-symmetrical in S, it is also S-symmetrical; and conversely. (*d*) Let S be a logical language (hence an L-language); then if 'P' is S-symmetrical or L-symmetrical in S, P is symmetrical; and conversely. Corresponding theorems are true for the remaining terms. For 1*b* and 1*d*, it is assumed that the language S contains its own syntax; S is here taken as a word-language, in which 'P is symmetrical' is written for 'Sym(P)'.

It would be equally possible to express the syntactical terms here defined by means of second level predicates of the *object-language*—for example: ''P' is S-irreflexive' by 'SIrr(P)' and ''P' is L-irreflexive' by 'LIrr(P)'. But in 'SIrr(P)' and 'LIrr(P)', 'P' would be *autonymous*, which is not the case in 'Irr(P)' (in so far as descriptive arguments are admitted; see p. 237). Those sentences are *quasi-syntactical*, but 'Irr(P)' is not (see Example 1 on p. 234).

§ 71*c*. Isomorphism

We will define a few more terms of relational theory leading up to the particularly important term 'isomorphism'. First we will give, as before, definitions of symbols of an object-language (with a symbolism like that of Language II).

(Converse): $\operatorname{cnv}(F)(x,y) \equiv (F(y,x))$ (1)

(One-many):
$$\operatorname{Un}(F) \equiv (x)(y)(z)\left[(F(x,z) \bullet F(y,z)) \supset (x=y)\right]$$ (2)

(One-one): $\operatorname{Unun}(F) \equiv (\operatorname{Un}(F) \bullet \operatorname{Un}[\operatorname{cnv}(F)])$ (3)

(Correlator):

$$\mathrm{Korr}\,(H, F, G) \equiv \big(\mathrm{Unun}\,(H) \bullet (u) \left[(\exists\, v)\,(F(u,v) \vee F(v,u)) \equiv \right.$$
$$(\exists\, x)\,(H\,(u,\,x))\big] \bullet (x) \left[(\exists\, y)\,(G\,(x,y) \vee G\,(y,x)) \equiv (\exists\, u) \right.$$
$$(H\,(u,x))\big] \bullet (u)(v)(x)(y)\left[(H(u,x)\bullet H(v,y)) \supset (F(u,v) \equiv \right.$$
$$G\,(x,y))\big]\big) \tag{4}$$

(Isomorphism):

$$\mathrm{Is}\,(F, G) \equiv (\exists\, H)\,(\mathrm{Korr}\,(H, F, G)) \tag{5}$$

These definitions correspond (in a somewhat different formulation) to the usual ones. (4) is here formulated for two-termed predicates, but can easily be transferred to n-termed predicates for $n > 2$. Just as, earlier, we opposed the terms of relational theory of the object-language (such as 'Irr') to corresponding syntactical terms (such as 'S-irreflexive' and 'L-irreflexive'), so here also we must contrast the *terms of the object-language* that are defined in (1) to (5) with *syntactical terms* that have previously been either ignored or confused with the former. Let pr_1 be a homogeneous two-termed predicate (the definitions can easily be transferred to $\mathfrak{Pr}$, $\mathfrak{Sfu}$, or $\mathfrak{Sg}$). pr_2 is called the S-*converse* of pr_1 if always (that is to say, here and in the following, for any closed arguments) $\mathrm{pr}_2\,(\mathfrak{A}_1, \mathfrak{A}_2)$ is equipollent to $\mathrm{pr}_1\,(\mathfrak{A}_2, \mathfrak{A}_1)$. pr_1 is called S-*one-many* if $\mathfrak{A}_1$ and $\mathfrak{A}_2$ are always synonymous in relation to $\{\mathrm{pr}_1\,(\mathfrak{A}_1, \mathfrak{A}_3), \mathrm{pr}_1\,(\mathfrak{A}_2, \mathfrak{A}_3)\}$. pr_1 is called S-*one-one* if pr_1 and the S-converse of pr_1 are S-one-many. Let pr_1 and pr_2 be homogeneous n-termed predicates; then pr_3 is called an S-*correlator* for pr_1 and pr_2 if the following conditions are fulfilled: (1) pr_3 is S-one-one; (2) if $\mathfrak{A}_1$ is a suitable argument for pr_1 then it is also a suitable argument of the first place for pr_3, and conversely; (3) if $\mathfrak{A}_1$ is a suitable argument for pr_2 then it is also a suitable argument of the second place for pr_3, and conversely; (4) $\mathrm{pr}_1\,(\mathfrak{A}_1, \mathfrak{A}_2, \ldots \mathfrak{A}_n)$ and $\mathrm{pr}_2\,(\mathfrak{A}_1', \mathfrak{A}_2', \ldots \mathfrak{A}_n')$ are always equipollent in relation to $\{\mathrm{pr}_3\,(\mathfrak{A}_1, \mathfrak{A}_1'), \mathrm{pr}_3\,(\mathfrak{A}_2, \mathfrak{A}_2'), \ldots \mathrm{pr}_3\,(\mathfrak{A}_n, \mathfrak{A}_n')\}$. Two homogeneous n-termed predicates, pr_1 and pr_2, are called **S-isomorphic** if there is an S-correlator of pr_1 and pr_2. For each one of these terms there is to be defined an analogous L-term and P-term.

Theorem 71c.1. Let the language S contain its own syntax. [Here we will take a word-language and will write "P and Q are isomorphic" (not 'P' and 'Q') instead of 'Is(P,Q)'.] Then (analogously to Theorem 71 *a*.1 *b* and 1 *d*) it is true that: if 'P' and

'Q' are S- (or L-) isomorphic, then P and Q are isomorphic; if S is a logical language, then the converse is also true.

An S-correlator for pr_1 and pr_2 is a predicate of the object-language. As distinguished from this, we mean by a *syntactical correlation* of two homogeneous n-termed predicates, pr_1 and pr_2, a one-one syntactical correlation, $\mathfrak{Q}_1$, which fulfils the following conditions: (1) if $\mathfrak{A}_1$ is a suitable argument for pr_1, then $\mathfrak{Q}_1[\mathfrak{A}_1]$ is a suitable argument for pr_2; (2) if $\mathfrak{A}_2$ is a suitable argument for pr_2 then there is a suitable argument $\mathfrak{A}_1$ for pr_1 such that $\mathfrak{Q}_1[\mathfrak{A}_1]$ is $\mathfrak{A}_2$; (3) $pr_1(\mathfrak{A}_1,\mathfrak{A}_2)$ is always equipollent to $pr_2(\mathfrak{Q}_1[\mathfrak{A}_1], \mathfrak{Q}_1[\mathfrak{A}_2])$. Two homogeneous n-termed predicates, pr_1 and pr_2, are called **syntactically isomorphic** when there is a syntactical correlation for them (that is to say, when such a correlation can be defined in the syntax-language, assuming it to be sufficiently rich).

We will make the difference between the concepts of isomorphism quite clear by means of a contrasting table; this is analogous to the earlier one, but here a third kind of concept, namely, syntactical isomorphism, is introduced.

The relation of *isomorphism* subsists between certain (homogeneous, two- or many-termed) *relations*.	1. The relation of S-*isomorphism* subsists between certain (homogeneous, two- or many-termed) *predicates* (namely, symbols of relations). (The same holds for L-isomorphism.)
This relation is expressed by the symbol 'Is', or by the word 'isomorphic'; these symbols belong to the *object-language*.	This relation is expressed by the word 'S-isomorphic'; this word belongs to the *syntax-language*.
	2. The relation of *syntactical isomorphism* likewise subsists between certain predicates. It is expressed by the words 'syntactically isomorphic'; these words belong to the *syntax-language*.

S-isomorphism and syntactical isomorphism are thus both syntactical concepts which refer to predicates of the object-language. The difference between the two concepts consists in the fact that in S-isomorphism the one-one correlation is brought about by means of a predicate of the object-language, and in syntactical isomorphism, on the other hand, by any syntactical terms. Thus it may happen that two predicates, although they are syntactically isomorphic, are not S-isomorphic; namely, when the object-language contains no suitable correlator. Since the majority of mathematical calculi (when their rules of transformation have, if necessary, been suitably completed) contain only logical symbols, in their case, in accordance with Theorem (1), isomorphism ('Is') and S-isomorphism coincide. [To be more exact, they appertain to corresponding pairs: isomorphism to a pair of relations, S-isomorphism to the corresponding pair of predicates. Formally expressed: 'Is' is in this case quasi-syntactical; 'S-isomorphic' is the correlated syntactical predicate.] But even here, the difference between S-isomorphism and syntactical isomorphism must be noted.

Theorem 71c.2. If two predicates are S- (or L-) isomorphic, then they are also syntactically isomorphic. The converse is not universally true (even if S is a logical language).

§ 71*d*. THE NON-DENUMERABLE CARDINAL NUMBERS

If due attention is paid to the difference between S-isomorphism and syntactical isomorphism, certain paradoxes in connection with the Theory of Aggregates can be explained. We may consider as an example the theorem of the multiplicity of transfinite cardinal numbers, which is one of the main supports of the Theory of Aggregates. The one-termed predicates are designations of aggregates; the isomorphism of two such predicates corresponds to equality of their cardinal numbers ('similarity' or 'equivalence' in the terminology of the Theory of Aggregates). Let us take as object-language S the system of axioms used in Fraenkel's Theory of Aggregates ([*Mengenlehre*], § 16) supplemented by a sentential and a functional calculus (in the word-language). The theorem that more than one transfinite cardinal number exists depends upon the theorem that the aggregate U (M) of the sub-aggregates of an aggregate M has a higher cardinal number than has M; this theorem is based upon what is known as Cantor's theorem, which maintains that M and U(M) cannot have the same cardinal number. Fraenkel [*Untersuchungen*] has given a proof of this theorem which remains valid for his system S even though it contains the so-called Axiom of Limitation ([*Mengenlehre*], p. 355). On the other hand, however, we arrive at a contrary result as a consequence of the following argument. The Axiom of Limitation means that in the aggregate-domain which is treated in S—let us call it B—only those aggregates occur of which the existence is required by the other axioms. Therefore, only the following aggregates are existent in B: in the first place, two initial aggregates, namely, the null-aggregate and the denumerably infinite aggregate, Z, required by Axiom VII; and secondly, those aggregates which can be constructed on the basis of these initial aggregates by applying an arbitrary but finite number of times certain constructional procedures. There are only six kinds of these constructional steps (namely, the formation of the pair-aggregate, of the sum-aggregate, of the aggregate of sub-aggregates, of the aggregate of *Aussonderung*, of the aggregate of selection, and of the aggregate of replacement). Since only a denumerable multiplicity of aggregates can be constructed in this way, there is in B, according to the Axiom of Limitation, only a denumerable multiplicity of aggregates, and consequently, at the most, only a denumerable multiplicity of sub-aggregates of Z. Therefore U(Z) cannot have a higher cardinal number than Z. Actually, on the basis of the two initial aggregates and the six constructional steps, it is easy to give a method of denumerating all the aggregates of B, and hence also the sub-aggregates of Z, and in this way the sub-aggregates of Z can be univocally correlated with the elements of Z. Therefore U(Z) and Z have the same cardinal number.

This result appears to contradict Cantor's theorem; but *the contradiction disappears as soon as we differentiate between equality of cardinal numbers and syntactical equality of cardinal numbers.* [Since S is a logical language, equality of cardinal numbers and S-equality of cardinal numbers coincide.] According to Fraenkel's definition ([*Mengenlehre*], p. 314) two (mutually exclusive) aggregates M and N have the same cardinal number only if (in B) there is a transforming aggregate (i.e. a correlator) Q—that is, an aggregate of mutually exclusive pairs $\{m, n\}$ where m is an element of M and n of N such that the pairs exhaust M and N. Now if

M is denumerably infinite, a one-one correlation of the kind mentioned before can be effected between the elements of M and those of U (M), and hence between the elements and the sub-aggregates of M. This correlation, however, is not a correlator in S but a syntactical correlation. In B there is no aggregate Q which could be a correlator for M and U (M); that is shown by Fraenkel's proof. But now Fraenkel's proof and our own findings are no longer in contradiction with one another: M and U (M), *although they have different cardinal numbers are nevertheless syntactically of the same cardinal number.*

In syntax it is always possible to effect a denumeration of ex-pressions of any kind (in an arithmetized syntax, for instance, by means of the series-numbers of the expressions). Thus in relation to a fixed syntax-language (which must be presupposed for the construction of the system S) *every aggregate of Fraenkel's domain of aggregates B is syntactically denumerable; two transfinite aggre-gates are always syntactically of the same cardinal number.* This is the element of truth in the criticism brought by the Intuitionists against the concept of the non-denumerable aggregates. [Poincaré ([*Gedanken*], pp. 108 ff., 134 ff.) bases his rejection of the non-denumerably infinite—subsequently maintained by Brouwer [*In-tuitionism*] and others—on this nominalistic view, which he him-self, not very happily, designates as idealistic.] It must, however, be noted that the syntactical equivalence of all transfinite aggre-gates of B (from the standpoint of a fixed syntax-language) is not in contradiction with their non-equivalence (within the system S), and that therefore the *distinction* between *different transfinite cardinal numbers within a system of the Theory of Aggregates is justified.* And indeed, in Fraenkel's system of axioms, which, because of the Axiom of Limitation, is, in a broad sense, a con-structive system, the inequivalence of certain aggregates—for instance that of Z and U (Z)—follows from a certain poverty of the system: it does not contain any aggregate which in the given cases could serve as a correlator. In non-constructive axiom-systems—for instance, in a system which contains no Axiom of Limitation, and which, on the other hand, operates with existential axioms to greater extent—the inequivalence, say, of M and U (M) can be attributed, conversely, to a certain richness of the system: U (M) contains so many element-aggregates that they cannot be correlated in a one-one correspondence with the elements of M. Of course, this does not mean that such a wealth of aggregate-*designations* exists within the system; obviously the number of aggregate-designations is denumerable in every system. The richness is only assumed by means of axioms, and is not demonstrable by designations (names or descriptions).

Further it must be noted that the difference between the aggregates of the natural numbers, of the real numbers, of the functions of real numbers, and so on, which Cantor has pointed out and formulated by attributing to them different cardinal numbers, is also syntactically representable. This distinction is particularly significant for the syntactical investigation of a series of languages each of which is contained in the next as a proper sub-language. That characteristic of the class of the logical numerical functors which Cantor designates as the non-denumerability of the aggregate of the real numbers is expressed, for instance, in an increasing series of languages by the fact that every language of the series, in addition to the denumerably many such functors of the previous languages, can always contain new ones (on this point, see our earlier remarks on the diagonal method, on Richard's antinomy, and on the defectiveness of arithmetic; compare Theorems $60c.3$ and $60d.1$).

As a result of the distinction between denumerability (in the system under consideration) and syntactical denumerability, the paradox in connection with the famous Löwenheim-Skolem theorem (Skolem [*Erfüllbarkeit*]; cf. Fraenkel [*Mengenlehre*], p. 333) also disappears. This theorem means approximately that for a non-contradictory axiom-system S of the Theory of Aggregates there is always already a model in a denumerable domain. Such a model, however, is not constructed by means of terms of S, but by means of discussions about S, that is to say, by means of syntactical terms. And the denumerability of the domain whose elements constitute the model is not demonstrated by the production of a correlator in S, but by the proof of the constructibility of a syntactical correlation. It is, accordingly, not the denumerability (in S) of a model which is proved, but only the syntactical denumerability. Thus the Skolem theorem does not contradict Cantor's theorem (or Fraenkel's proof).

§71e. THE AXIOMATIC METHOD

An axiom-system (abbreviation 'AS') is usually regarded as a system of sentences, the so-called axioms, from which other sentences, the so-called theorems or conclusions, may be deduced. The axioms consist partly of symbols whose meaning is assumed to be known already (for the most part, logical symbols), and partly of symbols which are introduced for the first time by the AS, the so-called primitive symbols of the AS. It is customarily said that no meaning is presupposed for the latter, but, that the AS—as a sort of implicit definition—determines their meaning. In order to draw conclusions from the axioms, obviously the rules of formation and transformation of the language concerned must be known. These rules are usually tacitly assumed, but in an exact formulation of the AS this tacit assumption must be replaced by an explicit statement. Further, it is characteristic of the axiomatic method that the primitive symbols are, to a certain extent, determined by the AS only in relation to one another. Hence there is sometimes the possibility of interpreting the primitive symbols in several different ways. The statement of a certain interpretation of the primitive symbols is designated as the establishment of correlative definitions (see p. 78). If it is proved that the axioms are fulfilled for a certain interpretation, or at least that their fulfilment is not excluded, we say that by this interpretation a model for the AS is constructed.

Example: In drawing up an AS of Geometry, it is usual merely to state the specifically geometrical axioms. In order to render deductions possible, the sentential and functional calculus, together with elementary arithmetic, must be added.

Usually the AS is formulated in the word-language without any precise statement of the syntactical rules, particularly the rules of inference. Now there are several quite different possibilities of putting such an AS into the exact form of a calculus. We will state briefly the most important methods of formulation. It is desirable to choose a different terminology for each of the three methods, so that it may always be clear which one is the subject of discussion. Therefore we shall speak of "axioms" only in connection with the first method, of "primitive sentences" in connection with the second (in accordance with our regular usage in this book), and of "premisses" in connection with the third.

First method: the axioms as sentential functions.

For the representation of the AS, a language S with a sentential and a functional calculus will be taken. (For the examples in the following, we shall use the symbolism of Language II.) Each of the k primitive symbols of the AS is represented by a $\mathfrak{v}$ (or $\mathfrak{B}$); we call these $\mathfrak{v}$ the *primitive variables*. Each of the m axioms is then formulated as an $\mathfrak{Sfu}$, and, specifically, as an $\mathfrak{Sfu}^i$ if the axiom contains i different primitive symbols. The same holds of the conclusions. In the deductions, however, there is no substitution for the free primitive variables. (In the material mode of speech: the primitive variables do not express universality, but indeterminateness.) $\mathfrak{Sfu}_n$ is called a conclusion from the m axioms $\mathfrak{Sfu}_1, \ldots$ $\mathfrak{Sfu}_m$, if the universal implication-sentence

$$(\mathfrak{v}_1) \ldots (\mathfrak{v}_k) \left[(\mathfrak{Sfu}_1 \bullet \mathfrak{Sfu}_2 \bullet \ldots \mathfrak{Sfu}_m) \supset \mathfrak{Sfu}_n \right]$$

is analytic (or L-demonstrable) in S. According to this method, a model for the AS is to be understood as a series of k substitution-values $\mathfrak{A}_1, \ldots \mathfrak{A}_k$ for the primitive variables. If

$$(\mathfrak{Sfu}_1 \bullet \mathfrak{Sfu}_2 \bullet \ldots \mathfrak{Sfu}_m) \begin{pmatrix} \mathfrak{v}_1 \\ \mathfrak{A}_1 \end{pmatrix} \ldots \begin{pmatrix} \mathfrak{v}_k \\ \mathfrak{A}_k \end{pmatrix}$$

is valid (or not contravalid, or not contradictory, respectively) in S, then the model is called a real (or a really possible, or a logically possible) model. If at least one of the substitution-values is descriptive, then the model is called descriptive; otherwise, logical (or mathematical).

The advantage of this method consists in the fact that by it a common language may be used for all AS's, and for all AS's of the usual kind a simple language of the usual kind having a sentential and a functional calculus. The primitive variables in this connection are usually $^0\mathfrak{v}$ or $\mathfrak{p}$; in the ordinary AS only $^0\mathfrak{v}$, $^1\mathfrak{p}$ and $^2\mathfrak{p}$ occur, and for the most part $^1\mathfrak{p}$.

Example: If Hilbert's AS of Euclidean geometry ([*Grundl. Geom.*], p. 1) is presented in accordance with the first method, seven different primitive variables appear: 'point', 'straight line', 'plane' will each be represented by a $^1\mathfrak{p}^1$; 'lies upon', by a $^1\mathfrak{p}^2$; 'between', by a $^1p^3$; and 'congruence of segments' and 'congruence of angles' each by a $^1p^4$.

On the first method, see Carnap ([*Logistik*], pp. 71 ff., [*Axiomatik*]).

Second method: the axioms as primitive sentences.

The axioms of the AS are formulated as the primitive sentences of a language S_1. Sometimes, in this case, the axioms of a given AS are the only primitive sentences of S_1, so that only rules of inference have to be added. But sometimes not only the rules of inference but also the L-primitive sentences of S_1 are tacitly assumed, so that the given axioms must be formulated as *additional primitive sentences* of S_1 (for the most part descriptive P-sentences). The conclusions of the AS are the sentences that are valid (or demonstrable) in S_1. The primitive symbols of the AS are here primitive symbols of S_1; and either they are the only primitive symbols of S_1 or they are *additional primitive symbols* (mostly descriptive) added to the original logical primitive symbols of S_1 (which in the ordinary formulation of the AS are tacitly assumed). The primitive symbols are not $\mathfrak{B}$. Hence, the construction of a model can here not be effected by substitution. It is achieved by means of a translation, $\mathfrak{Q}_1$, of S_1 into another language S_2 (usually a language of science which has a practical use). In the majority of cases this will be an expressional translation; the statement of the model consists, as a rule, only of the statement of the $\mathfrak{Q}_1$-correlates of the additional primitive symbols, the translation of the logical primitive symbols being assumed to be established and well known. The model is said to be real (or really possible, or logically possible) if the class of the $\mathfrak{Q}_1$-correlates of the axioms of the AS is valid (or not contravalid, or not contradictory, respectively) in S_2. If this class is descriptive, the model is called descriptive; if it is logical, the model is called logical (or mathematical).

Example: On a system of geometrical axioms in accordance with the second method, see § 25, II A "Axiomatic Geometry"; arithmetical geometry (I) constitutes a logical model, physical geometry (II B) a descriptive model.

The second method affords a greater freedom in interpretation, and thus in the construction of models, than the first. In the first method, the domain of the interpretations of a certain primitive symbol is the domain of the substitution-values of the primitive variable. If, as is usual, it is a case of primitive variables within a system of types, then the same relations of types must hold between the symbols of the model as hold between the corresponding primitive variables. In the second method, the place of substitution is taken by the far more elastic operation of translation; here, for instance, isogenous primitive symbols can have correlates which are not isogenous.

Examples: 1. Let S_1, S_2, and S_3 be presentations of AS's of Euclidean geometry in accordance with the second method. Let S_1 take straight lines as classes of points (see Carnap [*Logistik*], § 34); let S_2 take straight lines as relations between points (see Carnap [*Logistik*], § 35); and let S_3 take straight lines and points as individuals (as does Hilbert [*Grundl. Geom.*]). Three AS's of this kind, formulated in accordance with the first method, cannot have a common model. On the other hand, by the second method this is possible, in the sense that S_1, S_2, and S_3 can all be translated into the same sub-language of a logical language, in which a point is interpreted in the usual way as a triad of real numbers, a plane as a class of such triads which satisfy a linear equation, and so on. Thus, by this method, it is easy to portray formally the relationship of the three AS's, which is what is meant when it is said that they represent the same geometry. 2. Let an AS of the Theory of Aggregates be given which takes all aggregates as individuals (as, for instance, Fraenkel does [*Mengenlehre*], § 16) but in which only homogeneous aggregates occur (so that, for example, as opposed to the AS of Fraenkel, m and $\{m\}$ cannot be elements of the same aggregate). If an AS of such a kind is presented in accordance with the second method, it can be interpreted as a theory of classes, and, in spite of the equal level of the aggregates, as a theory of classes of all levels. $^0\mathfrak{a}$ and certain $\mathfrak{Pr}^1$ of all levels (for instance in Language II) are taken as correlates of the aggregate-expressions.

Third method: the axioms as premisses.

The AS is represented by means of a (usually indeterminate) *sentential class* of an assumed language S. The conclusions are here the L-consequences of this class, and hence the axioms appear as premisses of derivations (or of consequence-relations). In this, as in the second method, an interpretation consists of a translation; and, as in the first method, it is possible to formulate several AS's within the same language.

Special and general *axiomatics*, that is, the theory of certain individual AS's or of AS's in general, is nothing more than *the syntax of the AS's*. The investigations in axiomatics, which have been conducted chiefly and intensively by mathematicians, thus contain a great number of syntactical discussions and definitions, many of which we have already been able to apply in this outline of a general syntax. We have defined some terms, in accordance with the second method, as properties of languages, and some (in part, the same ones), in accordance with the third method, as properties of sentential classes. [For instance, the terms 're-futable', 'L-refutable', 'contravalid', and 'contradictory', which refer to sentential classes, correspond to the terms 'contradictory', 'L-contradictory', 'inconsistent', and 'L-inconsistent', which refer to languages.] Conversely, it will be possible to make use of the findings and definitions of general syntax for axiomatics. But we cannot go more fully into this subject in the present work.

Full bibliographical references on the subject of axiomatics up to the year 1928 are given by Fraenkel [*Mengenlehre*], § 18. Some new works on the subject are as follows: Hertz [*Axiom.*], Lewis and Langford [*Logic*], and Tarski [*Methodologie*], [*Widerspruchsfr.*].

PART V

PHILOSOPHY AND SYNTAX

A. ON THE FORM OF THE SENTENCES BELONGING TO THE LOGIC OF SCIENCE

§ 72. PHILOSOPHY REPLACED BY THE LOGIC OF SCIENCE

The questions dealt with in any theoretical field—and similarly the corresponding sentences and assertions—can be roughly divided into *object-questions* and *logical questions*. (This differentiation has no claim to exactitude; it only serves as a preliminary to the following non-formal and inexact discussion.) By object-questions are to be understood those that have to do with the objects of the domain under consideration, such as inquiries regarding their properties and relations. The logical questions, on the other hand, do not refer directly to the objects, but to sentences, terms, theories, and so on, which themselves refer to the objects. (Logical questions may be concerned either with the meaning and content of the sentences, terms, etc., or only with the form of these; of this we shall say more later.) In a certain sense, of course, logical questions are also object-questions, since they refer to certain objects—namely, to terms, sentences, and so on—that is to say, to objects of logic. When, however, we are talking of a non-logical, proper object-domain, the differentiation between object-questions and logical questions is quite clear. For instance, in the domain of zoology, the object-questions are concerned with the properties of animals, the relations of animals to one another and to other objects, etc.; the logical questions, on the other hand, are concerned with the sentences of zoology and the logical connections between them, the logical character of the definitions occurring in that science, the logical character of the theories and hypotheses which may be, or have actually been, advanced, and so on.

According to traditional usage, the name 'philosophy' serves as a collective designation for inquiries of very different kinds.

Object-questions as well as logical questions are to be found amongst these inquiries. The object-questions are in part concerned with supposititious objects which are not to be found in the object-domains of the sciences (for instance, the thing-in-itself, the absolute, the transcendental, the objective idea, the ultimate cause of the world, non-being, and such things as values, absolute norms, the categorical imperative, and so on); this is especially the case in that branch of philosophy usually known as metaphysics. On the other hand, the object-questions of philosophy are also concerned with things which likewise occur in the empirical sciences (such as mankind, society, language, history, economics, nature, space and time, causality, etc.); this is especially the case in those branches that are called natural philosophy, the philosophy of history, the philosophy of language, and so on. The logical questions occur principally in logic (including applied logic), and also in the so-called theory of knowledge (or epistemology), where they are, however, for the most part, entangled with psychological questions. The problems of the so-called philosophical foundations of the various sciences (such as physics, biology, psychology, and history) include both object-questions and logical questions.

The logical analysis of philosophical problems shows them to vary greatly in character. As regards those object-questions whose objects do not occur in the exact sciences, critical analysis has revealed that they are pseudo-problems. The supposititious sentences of metaphysics, of the philosophy of values, of ethics (in so far as it is treated as a normative discipline and not as a psycho-sociological investigation of facts) are pseudo-sentences; they have no logical content, but are only expressions of feeling which in their turn stimulate feelings and volitional tendencies on the part of the hearer. In the other departments of philosophy the psychological questions must first of all be eliminated; these belong to psychology, which is one of the empirical sciences, and are to be handled by it with the aid of its empirical methods. [By this, of course, no veto is put upon the discussion of psychological questions within the domain of logical investigation; everyone is at liberty to combine his questions in the way which seems to him most fruitful. It is only intended as a warning against the disregard of the difference between proper logical (or epistemological)

questions and psychological ones. Very often the formulation of a
question does not make it clear whether it is intended as a psychological or a logical one, and in this way a great deal of confusion
arises.] The remaining questions, that is, in ordinary terminology,
questions of logic, of the theory of knowledge (or epistemology), of
natural philosophy, of the philosophy of history, etc., are sometimes designated by those who regard metaphysics as unscientific
as questions of scientific philosophy. As usually formulated, these
questions are in part logical questions, but in part also object-
questions which refer to the objects of the special sciences. Philosophical questions, however, according to the view of philosophers,
are supposed to examine such objects as are also investigated by
the special sciences from quite a different standpoint, namely,
from the purely philosophical one. As opposed to this, we shall
here maintain that all these remaining philosophical questions are
logical questions. Even the supposititious object-questions are
logical questions in a misleading guise. The supposed peculiarly
philosophical point of view from which the objects of science are
to be investigated proves to be illusory, just as, previously, the
supposed peculiarly philosophical realm of objects proper to metaphysics disappeared under analysis. Apart from the questions of
the individual sciences, only the questions of the logical analysis of
science, of its sentences, terms, concepts, theories, etc., are left as
genuine scientific questions. We shall call this complex of questions the *logic of science*. [We shall not here employ the expression
'theory of science'; if it is to be used at all, it is more appropriate
to the wider domain of questions which, in addition to the logic
of science, includes also the empirical investigation of scientific
activity, such as historical, sociological, and, above all, psychological inquiries.]

According to this view, then, once philosophy is purified of all
unscientific elements, only the logic of science remains. In the
majority of philosophical investigations, however, a sharp division
into scientific and unscientific elements is quite impossible. For
this reason we prefer to say: *the logic of science takes the place of the
inextricable tangle of problems which is known as philosophy*. Whether,
on this view, it is desirable to apply the term 'philosophy' or
'scientific philosophy' to this remainder, is a question of expedience which cannot be decided here. It must be taken into

consideration that the word 'philosophy' is already heavily burdened, and that it is largely applied (particularly in the German language) to speculative metaphysical discussions. The designation 'theory of knowledge' (or 'epistemology') is a more neutral one, but even this appears not to be quite unobjectionable, since it mis- leadingly suggests a resemblance between the problems of our logic of science and the problems of traditional epistemology; the latter, however, are always permeated by pseudo-concepts and pseudo-questions, and frequently in such a way that their dis- entanglement is impossible.

The view that, as soon as claims to scientific qualifications are made, all that remains of philosophy is the logic of science, cannot be established here and will not be assumed in what follows. In this part of the book we propose to examine the character of the sentences of the logic of science, and to show that they are syn- tactical sentences. For anyone who shares with us the anti- metaphysical standpoint it will thereby be shown that all philo- sophical problems which have any meaning belong to syntax. The following investigations concerning the logic of science as syntax are not, however, dependent upon an adherence to this view; those who do not subscribe to it can formulate our results simply as a statement that the problems of that part of philosophy which is neither metaphysical nor concerned with values and norms are syntactical.

Anti-metaphysical views have often been put forward in the past, especially by Hume and the Positivists. The more exact thesis that philosophy can be nothing other than a logical analysis of scientific concepts and sentences (in other words, what we shall call the logic of science) is represented in particular by Wittgenstein and the Vienna Circle, and has been both established in detail and in- vestigated in all its consequences by them; see Schlick [*Metaphysik*], [*Wende*], [*Positivismus*]; Frank [*Kausalgesetz*]; Hahn [*Wiss. Weltauff.*]; Neurath [*Wiss. Weltauff.*], [*Wege*]; Carnap [*Meta- physik*]; further bibliographical references are given by Neurath [*Wiss. Weltauff.*] and in *Erkenntnis*, I, 315 ff. Neurath is definitely opposed to the continued use of the expressions 'philosophy', 'scientific philosophy', 'natural philosophy', 'theory of knowledge', etc.

The term '*logic of science*' will be understood by us in a very wide sense, namely, as meaning the domain of all the questions which are usually designated as pure and applied logic, as the logical analysis of the special sciences or of science as a whole, as epistemology, as problems of foundations, and the like (in so far as these questions are free from metaphysics and from all reference to norms, values, transcendentals, etc.). To give a concrete illustration we assign the following investigations (with very few exceptions) to the logic of science: the works of Russell, Hilbert, Brouwer, and their pupils, the works of the Warsaw logicians, of the Harvard logicians, of Reichenbach's Circle, of the Vienna Circle centring around Schlick, the majority of the works cited in the bibliography of this book (and others by the same authors), the articles in the journals *Erkenntnis* and *Philosophy of Science*, the books in the collections "Schriften zur wissenschaftlichen Weltauffassung" (edited by Schlick and Frank), "Einheitswissenschaft" (edited by Neurath), and finally the works mentioned in the following bibliographies: *Erkenntnis*, I, 315 ff. (general), 335 ff. (Polish logicians); II, 151 ff. (foundations of mathematics), 189 f. (causality and probability); V, 185 ff. (general), 195 ff. (American authors), 199 ff. (Polish authors), 409 ff. (general).

§ 73. THE LOGIC OF SCIENCE IS THE SYNTAX OF THE LANGUAGE OF SCIENCE

In what follows we shall examine the nature of the questions of the logic of science in the wide sense, including, as already indicated, the so-called philosophical problems concerning the foundations of the individual sciences, and we shall show that these questions are questions of syntax. In order to do this, it must first be shown that the object-questions which occur in the logic of science (for example, questions concerning numbers, things, time and space, the relations between the psychical and the physical, etc.) are only pseudo-object-questions—i.e. questions which, because of a misleading formulation, appear to refer to objects while actually they refer to sentences, terms, theories, and the like—and are, accordingly, in reality, logical questions. And secondly, it must be shown that all logical questions are capable of formal presentation, and can, consequently, be formulated as syntactical questions. According to the usual view, all logical investigation comprises two parts: a formal inquiry which is concerned only with the order and syntactical kind of the linguistic expressions, and an inquiry of a material character, which has to do not merely with the formal design but, over and above that, with questions of meaning and sense. Thus the general opinion is that the formal problems constitute, at the most, only a small section of the domain of logical problems. As opposed to this, our discussion of general syntax has already shown that the formal method, if carried far enough, embraces all logical problems, even the so-called problems of content or sense (in so far as these are genuinely logical and not psychological in character). Accordingly, when we say that the logic of science is nothing more than the syntax of the language of science, we do not mean to suggest that only a certain number of the problems of what has hitherto been called the logic of science (as they appear, for example, in the works previously mentioned) should be regarded as true problems of the logic of science. The view we intend to advance here is rather that all problems of the current logic of science, as soon as they are exactly formulated, are seen to be syntactical problems.

It was Wittgenstein who first exhibited the close connection between the logic of science (or "philosophy", as he calls it) and syntax. In particular, he made clear the formal nature of logic and emphasized the fact that the rules and proofs of syntax should have no reference to the meaning of symbols ([*Tractatus*], pp. 52, 56, and 164). Further, he has shown that the so-called sentences of metaphysics and of ethics are pseudo-sentences. According to him philosophy is "critique of language" (*op. cit.* p. 62), its business is "the logical clarification of ideas" (p. 76), of the sentences and concepts of science (natural science), that is, in our terminology, the logic of science. Wittgenstein's view is represented, and has been further developed, by the Vienna Circle, and in this part of the book I owe a great deal to his ideas. If I am right, the position here maintained is in general agreement with his, but goes beyond it in certain important respects. In what follows my view will sometimes be contrasted with his, but this is done only for the sake of greater clarity, and our agreement on important fundamental questions must not therefore be overlooked.

There are two points especially on which the view here presented differs from that of Wittgenstein, and specifically from his negative theses. The first of these theses (*op. cit.* p. 78) states: "Propositions cannot represent the logical form: this mirrors itself in the propositions. That which mirrors itself in language, language cannot represent. That which expresses *itself* in language, we cannot express by language.... If two propositions contradict one another, this is shown by their structure; similarly, if one follows from another, etc. What *can* be shown *cannot* be said.... It would be as senseless to ascribe a formal property to a proposition as to deny it the formal property." In other words: There are no sentences about the forms of sentences; there is no expressible syntax. In opposition to this view, our construction of syntax has shown that it can be correctly formulated and that syntactical sentences do exist. It is just as possible to construct sentences about the forms of linguistic expressions, and therefore about sentences, as it is to construct sentences about the geometrical forms of geometrical structures. In the first place, there are the analytic sentences of pure syntax, which can be applied to the forms and relations of form of linguistic expressions (analogous to the analytic sentences of arithmetical geometry, which can be applied to the relations of form of the abstract geometrical structures); and in the second place, the synthetic physical sentences of descriptive syntax, which are concerned with the forms of the linguistic expressions as physical structures (analogous to the synthetic empirical sentences of physical geometry, see § 25). *Thus syntax is exactly formulable in the same way as geometry is.*

Wittgenstein's second negative thesis states that the logic of science ("philosophy") cannot be formulated. (For him, this thesis does not coincide with the first, since he does not consider the logic of science and syntax to be identical; see below.) "Philosophy is not a theory, but an activity. A philosophical work consists essentially of elucidations. The result of philosophy is not a number of 'philosophical propositions,' but to make propositions clear" (p. 76). Consistently Wittgenstein applies this view to his own work also; at the end he says: "My propositions are elucidatory in this way: he who understands me finally recognizes them as senseless, when he has climbed out through them, on them, over them. (He must, so to speak, throw away the ladder, after he has climbed up on it.) He must surmount these propositions; then he sees the world rightly. Whereof one cannot speak, thereof one must be silent" (p. 188). According to this, the investigations of the logic of science contain no sentences, but merely more or less vague explanations which the reader must subsequently recognize as pseudo-sentences and abandon. Such an interpretation of the logic of science is certainly very unsatisfactory. [Ramsey first raised objections to Wittgenstein's conception of philosophy as nonsense, but important nonsense ([*Foundations*], p. 263), and then Neurath, in particular, ([*Soziol. Phys.*], pp. 395 f. and [*Psychol.*], p. 29) definitely rejected it.] When in what follows it is shown that the logic of science is syntax, it is at the same time shown that the logic of science can be formulated, and formulated not in senseless, if practically indispensable, pseudo-sentences, but in perfectly correct sentences. The difference of opinion here indicated is not merely theoretical; it has an important influence on the practical form of philosophical investigations. Wittgenstein considers that the only difference between the sentences of the speculative metaphysician and those of his own and other researches into the logic of science is that the sentences of the logic of science—which he calls philosophical elucidations—in spite of their theoretical lack of sense, exert, practically, an important psychological influence upon the philosophical investigator, which the properly metaphysical sentences do not, or, at least, not in the same way. Thus there is only a difference of degree, and that a very vague one. The fact that Wittgenstein does not believe in the possibility of the exact formulation of the sentences of the logic of science has as its consequence that he does not demand any scientific exactitude in his own formulations, and that he draws no sharp line of demarcation between the formulations of the logic of science and those of metaphysics. In the following discussion we shall see that translatability into the formal mode of speech—that is, into syntactical sentences—is the criterion which separates the proper sentences of the logic of science from the other philosophical sentences —we may call them metaphysical. In some of his formulations, Wittgenstein has clearly overstepped this boundary; this consequence of his belief in the two negative theses is psychologically quite understandable.

In spite of this difference of opinion, I agree with Wittgenstein that there are no special sentences of the logic of science (or philosophy). The sentences of the logic of scier e are formulated as syntactical sentences about the language of science; but no new domain in addition to that of science itself is thereby created. The sentences of syntax are in part sentences of arithmetic, and in part sentences of physics, and they are only called syntactical because they are concerned with linguistic constructions, or, more specifically, with their formal structure. Syntax, pure and descriptive, is nothing more than the mathematics and physics of language.

Wittgenstein says of the rules of logical syntax (see above) that they must be formulated without any reference to sense or meaning. According to our view the same thing holds also for the sentences of the logic of science. But Wittgenstein, as it appears, thinks that these sentences (the so-called philosophical elucidations) go beyond the formal and refer to the sense of the sentences and terms. Schlick ([*Wende*] p. 8) interprets Wittgenstein's position as follows: philosophy "is that activity by which the meaning of propositions is established or discovered"; it is a question of "what the propositions actually *mean*. The content, soul, and spirit of science naturally consist in what is ultimately *meant* by its sentences; the philosophical activity of rendering significant is thus the alpha and omega of all scientific knowledge".

§ 74. Pseudo-Object-Sentences

We have already distinguished (in an inexact manner) between object-sentences and logical sentences. We will now contrast instead (at first also in an inexact manner) the two domains of *object-sentences* and *syntactical sentences*, only those logical sentences which are concerned with form being here taken into account and included in the second domain. Now there is an intermediate field between these two domains. To this intermediate field we will assign the sentences which are formulated as though they refer (either partially or exclusively) to objects, while in reality they refer to syntactical forms, and, specifically, to the forms of the designations of those objects with which they appear to deal. Thus these sentences are syntactical sentences in virtue of their content, though they are disguised as object-sentences. We will call them *pseudo-object-sentences*. If we attempt to represent in a formal way the distinction which is here informally and inexactly indicated, we shall see that these pseudo-object-sentences are simply *quasi-syntactical sentences of the material mode of speech* (in the sense already formally defined, see § 64).

To this middle territory belong many of the questions and sentences relating to the investigation of what are called philosophical foundations. We will take a simple example. Let us suppose that in a philosophical discussion about the concept of number we want to point out that there is an essential difference between numbers and (physical) things, and thereby to give a warning against pseudo-questions concerning the place, weight, and so on of numbers. Such a warning will probably be formulated as a sentence of, say, the following kind: "Five is not a thing but a number" ($\mathfrak{S}_1$). Apparently this sentence expresses a property of the number five, like the sentence "Five is not an even but an odd number" ($\mathfrak{S}_2$). In reality, however, $\mathfrak{S}_1$ is not concerned with the number five, but with the word 'five'; this is shown by the formulation $\mathfrak{S}_3$ which is equipollent to $\mathfrak{S}_1$: "'Five' is not a thing-word but a number-word." While $\mathfrak{S}_2$ is a proper object-sentence, $\mathfrak{S}_1$ is a pseudo-object-sentence; $\mathfrak{S}_1$ is a quasi-syntactical sentence (material mode of speech), and $\mathfrak{S}_3$ is the correlated syntactical sentence (formal mode of speech).

We have here left out of account those logical sentences which assert something about the *meaning*, *content*, or *sense* of sentences or linguistic expressions of any domain. These also are pseudo-object-sentences. Let us consider as an example the following sentence, $\mathfrak{S}_1$: "Yesterday's lecture was about Babylon." $\mathfrak{S}_1$ appears to assert something about Babylon, since the name 'Babylon' occurs in it. In reality, however, $\mathfrak{S}_1$ says nothing about the town Babylon, but merely something about yesterday's lecture and the word 'Babylon'. This is easily shown by the following non-formal consideration: for our knowledge of the properties of the town of

Babylon it does not matter whether $\mathfrak{S}_1$ is true or false. Further, that $\mathfrak{S}_1$ is only a pseudo-object-sentence is clear from the circumstance that $\mathfrak{S}_1$ can be translated into the following sentence of (descriptive) syntax: "In yesterday's lecture either the word 'Babylon' or an expression synonymous with the word 'Babylon' occurred" ($\mathfrak{S}_2$).

Accordingly, we distinguish *three kinds of sentences*:

1. Object-sentences	2. Pseudo-object-sentences = quasi-syntactical sentences	3. Syntactical sentences
	Material mode of speech	*Formal mode of speech*
Examples: "5 is a prime number"; "Babylon was a big town"; "lions are mammals."	Examples: "Five is not a thing, but a number"; "Babylon was treated of in yesterday's lecture." ("Five is a number-word" is an example belonging to the autonymous mode of speech.)	Examples: "'Five' is not a thing-word, but a number-word"; "the word 'Babylon' occurred in yesterday's lecture"; "'A . ∼A' is a contradictory sentence."

The intermediate field of the pseudo-object-sentences, the boundaries of which have so far been only materially and inexactly indicated, can also be exactly, and moreover formally, demarcated. The pseudo-object-sentences are, namely, quasi-syntactical sentences of the material mode of speech. [We can leave the autonymous mode of speech out of account here, since there is practically no danger of a sentence belonging to this mode of speech being mistaken for an object-sentence.] The criterion of the material mode of speech assumes a simpler form when we are concerned with an object-language S_1 which contains its own syntax-language S_2 as a sub-language. For instance, let S_1 be the English language representing the whole language of science; then the syntax-language S_2, in which the syntax of S_1 is formulated, is a sub-language of S_1. This expresses the fact that we regard syntax not as a special domain outside that of the rest of science but as a sub-domain of science as a whole, which forms a single system (Neurath: *Einheitswissenschaft*) having a single language S_1. *That a language may contain its own syntax without contradiction* we have already shown. Even if the syntax-language S_2 is a sub-language of S_1 it is, of course, both possible and necessary to distinguish between a sentence $\mathfrak{S}_1$, of S_1 (which may also belong to S_2), and a syntactical sentence $\mathfrak{S}_2$, concerning $\mathfrak{S}_1$, which belongs to S_2 and therefore also to S_1. For simplicity's sake, we will formulate the criterion of the material mode of speech for the simplest sentential form only (and further, for the sake of brevity and clarity, we will formulate it for a symbolic sentence) (see § 64). Let $\mathfrak{S}_1$ be 'P(a)'; $\mathfrak{S}_1$ is called *quasi-syntactical* in respect of 'a', if there exists a syntactical predicate 'Q' such that 'P(a)' is equipollent to 'Q('a')' ($\mathfrak{S}_2$) and 'P(b)' is equipollent to 'Q('b')', and correspondingly for every expression isogenous with 'a'. Now 'P' may possibly be a syntactical predicate which is equivalent in meaning to 'Q' (this would be shown formally by the fact that 'P('a')' would also be a sentence, and moreover a sentence equipollent to 'Q('a')', and that, further, 'P('b')' would be equipollent to 'Q('b')', and correspondingly for every expression isogenous with 'a'); if this is not the case, we call $\mathfrak{S}_1$ a sentence of the *material mode of speech*. 'Q' is called a syntactical predicate correlated to the quasi-syntactical predicate 'P'; and $\mathfrak{S}_2$ is called a syntactical sentence correlated to the quasi-syntactical sentence $\mathfrak{S}_1$. *In the translation from the material to the formal mode of speech, $\mathfrak{S}_1$ is translated into $\mathfrak{S}_2$.*

In order to make it clearer and facilitate its practical application to the following examples, we will formulate the criterion (still for the simplest form of sentence) once more, in a less exact, non-formal way (the examples of sentences which come later, especially those of the logic of science, belong almost entirely to the word-language; in consequence, they are themselves not formulated sufficiently exactly to make possible the application to them of exact concepts). $\mathfrak{S}_1$ is called a sentence of the material mode of speech if $\mathfrak{S}_1$ asserts a property of an object which has, so to speak, correlated to it, another, and syntactical, property; that is to say, when there is a syntactical property which belongs to a designation of an object if, and only if, the original property belongs to the object.

It is easy to see that in the previous example concerning 'Babylon' this criterion is fulfilled for the sentence $\mathfrak{S}_1$: the syntactical (in this case the descriptive-syntactical) property which is asserted in $\mathfrak{S}_2$ of the word 'Babylon' is parallel to that property which is asserted in S_1 of the town of Babylon; for if, and only if, yesterday's lecture was concerned with a certain object, did a designation of that object occur in the lecture. The criterion of the material mode of speech is likewise fulfilled for the sentence S_1 of the example concerning 'five'; for if, and only if, the property expressed in S_1—that of being not a thing but a number—belongs to some object (for instance, to the number five) does the property expressed in S_2—that of being not a thing-word but a number-word—belong to a designation of this object (in the example, to the word 'five').

§ 75. Sentences about Meaning

In this section, we shall consider various kinds of sentences of the material mode of speech, especially those kinds which occur frequently in philosophical discussions. On the basis of these investigations we shall be better able to diagnose the material mode of speech in subsequent cases. Further, by this means the whole character of philosophical problems will become clearer to us. The obscurity with regard to this character is chiefly due to the deception and self-deception induced by the application of the material mode of speech. The disguise of the material mode of speech conceals the fact that the so-called problems of philosophical foundations are nothing more than questions of the logic of science concerning the sentences and sentential connections of the language of science, and also the further fact that the questions of the logic of science are formal—that is to say, syntactical—questions. The true situation is revealed by the translation of the sentences of the material mode of speech, which are really quasi-syntactical sentences, into the correlated syntactical sentences and thus into the formal mode. We do not mean by this that the material mode of speech should be entirely eliminated. Since it is in general use and often easier to understand, it may well be retained in its place. But it is a good thing to be conscious of its use, so as to avoid the obscurities and pseudo-problems which otherwise easily result from it.

In a sentence S_1 of the material mode of speech, the illusion that a genuine object-sentence is present is most easily dissipated if S_1 belongs in part to the syntax-language S_2, but contains at the same time elements of S_1 which do not belong to S_2. [Not all sentences of this kind are sentences of the material mode of speech. For example, the sentence "The University of Freiburg bears the inscription 'the truth will make you free'" is not a quasi-syntactical sentence but a simple sentence of descriptive syntax.] Especially important here are those sentences which express a relation of designation, that is to say, those in which one of the following expressions occurs: 'treats of', 'speaks about', 'means', 'signifies', 'names', 'is a name for', 'designates', and the like. We shall now give a series of such sentences concerning *meaning*, and, along with them, the correlated syntactical sentences. The first of these examples has already been discussed. [It is, of course, of no importance whether or not the sentences in the examples are true.]

Material mode of speech	*Formal mode of speech*
(quasi-syntactical sentences)	(the correlated syntactical sentences)
1 *a*. Yesterday's lecture treated of Babylon.	1 *b*. In yesterday's lecture the word 'Babylon' (or a synonymous designation) occurred.
2 *a*. The word 'daystar' *designates* (or: *means*; or: *is a name for*) the sun.	2 *b*. The word 'daystar' is synonymous with 'sun'.
3 *a*. The sentence S_1 *means* (or: *asserts*; or: *has the content*; or: *has the meaning*) that the moon is spherical.	3 *b*. S_1 is equipollent to the sentence 'The moon is spherical.'
4 *a*. The word 'luna' in the Latin language *designates* the moon.	4 *b*. There is an equipollent expressional translation of the Latin into the English language in which the word 'moon' is the correlate of the word 'luna'.
5 *a*. The sentence '…' of the Chinese language *means* that the moon is spherical.	5 *b*. There is an equipollent sentential translation of the Chinese into the English language in which the sentence 'The moon is spherical' is the correlate of the sentence '…'.

The following examples, 6 and 7, show how the difference between the *meaning of an expression* and the *object designated by the expression* can be formally represented. [This difference is emphasized by the phenomenologists, but explained only in a psychological, not in the logical, sense.]

6 a. The expressions 'merle' and 'blackbird' have the same *meaning* (or: *mean* the same; or: have the same *intensional object*).

6 b. 'Merle' and 'blackbird' are L-synonymous.

7 a. 'Evening star' and 'morning star' have a different meaning, but they *designate* the same object.

7 b.   'Evening star' and 'morning star' are not L-synonymous, but P-synonymous.

[With respect to a symbolic (P-) language, the above correlates may also be formulated thus: 6 b. $\mathfrak{A}_1 = \mathfrak{A}_2$ is analytic. 7 b. $\mathfrak{A}_1 = \mathfrak{A}_2$ is not analytic but P-valid.]

In the case of sentences *the formal representation of the difference between the fact designated and the meaning* is analogous. [The usual formulations like 'mean the same' or 'have the same content' are ambiguous; in some cases 8 b is intended, in others 9 b, and in many the intention remains obscure.]

8 a. The sentences $\mathfrak{S}_1$ and $\mathfrak{S}_2$ have the same meaning.

8 b. $\mathfrak{S}_1$ and $\mathfrak{S}_2$ are L-equipollent.

9 a. $\mathfrak{S}_1$ and $\mathfrak{S}_2$ have a different *meaning* but they *represent* (or: describe) the same fact.

9 b. $\mathfrak{S}_1$ and $\mathfrak{S}_2$ are not L-equipollent but P-equipollent.

[With respect to a symbolic language: 8 b. $\mathfrak{S}_1 \equiv \mathfrak{S}_2$ is analytic. 9 b. $\mathfrak{S}_1 \equiv \mathfrak{S}_2$ is not analytic but P-valid.]

10 a. The sentences of arithmetic *state* (or: express) certain properties of numbers and certain relations between numbers.

10 b. The sentences of arithmetic are composed of numerical expressions and one- or many-termed numerical predicates combined in such and such a way.

11 a. A particular sentence of physics *states* the condition of a spatial point at a given time.

11 b. A particular sentence of physics consists of a descriptive predicate and spatio-temporal co-ordinates as arguments.

The following examples 12 a, 13 a, and 14 a appear at first to be of the same kind as 1 a and 4 a. Actually, however, they demonstrate particularly clearly the danger of error which is involved in the use of the material mode of speech.

12 a. This letter *is about* the son of Mr. Miller.

12 b. In this letter a sentence $\mathfrak{Pr}(\mathfrak{A}_1)$ occurs in which $\mathfrak{A}_1$ is the description 'the son of Mr. Miller'.

13 a. The expression 'le cheval de M' *designates* (or: means) the horse of M.

13 b. There is an equipollent expressional translation from the French into the English language in which 'the horse of M' is the correlate of 'le cheval de M'.

14 a. The expression 'un éléphant bleu' *means* a blue elephant.

14 b. (Analogous to 13 b.)

Let us assume that Mr. Miller has no son; even in this case the sentence 12 a may still be true; the letter will then merely be telling a lie. Now, from the true sentence 12 a, according to the ordinary logical rules of inference, a false sentence can be derived. In order to make the derivation more exact, we will use a symbolism in place of the word-language. Instead of 'this letter' we will write 'b'; instead of 'b is about a' we will write 'H (b, a)'; and instead of 'the son of a' we will write 'Son'a' (description in Russell's symbolism, see § 38c). Hence for 12 a will be written: 'H (b, Son' Miller)' ($\mathfrak{S}_1$). According to a well-known theorem of logistics (see my [*Logistik*], § 7 c: L 7.2), from a sentence $\mathfrak{Pr}(\mathfrak{Arg})$ in which a description occurs as argument, a sentence is derivable which asserts that there exists something which has the descriptional property. Accordingly, from $\mathfrak{S}_1$ would be derivable '$(\exists x)\,(\mathrm{Son}\,(x, \mathrm{Miller}))$' ($\mathfrak{S}_2$); or, in words: "a son of Mr. Miller exists". This, however, is a false sentence. Similarly the possibly false sentence "There is a horse of M" is derivable from 13 a, and the false sentence "there is a blue elephant" from 14 a. On the other hand, by the usual rules no false sentences can be derived from the sentences 12 b, 13 b, and 14 b of the formal mode of speech. These examples show that the use of the material mode of speech leads to contradictions if the methods of inference which are correct for other sentences are thoughtlessly used also in connection with it. [It cannot be maintained that the formulations 12 a, 13 a, and 14 a are incorrect, or that the use of the material mode of speech leads necessarily to contradictions; for, after all, the word-language is not bound by the rules of logistics. If, therefore, one wishes to admit the material mode of speech, one must apply to it a system of rules which is not only more complicated than that of logistics but is also more complicated than that which governs the rest of the sentences of the word-language.]

Some sentences contain a relation of meaning which is to some extent concealed. With sentences of this kind it is not obvious, at first sight, that they belong to the material mode of speech. The most important examples of this are the sentences which use the so-called *indirect* or oblique mode of speech (that is to say, sentences which say something about a spoken, thought, or written sentence, but which do so not by a statement of the original wording but instead by means of a 'that', 'whether', or other 'w...' sentence, or of a subordinate sentence without a connective word, or of an infinitive with 'to'). In the following examples, 15 a and 16 a, the formulations 15 b and 16 b show that the sentences in which the indirect mode of speech occurs are of the same kind as the examples previously discussed, and hence also belong to the material mode of speech.

I. *Material mode of speech*		II. *Formal mode of speech*
1. *Sentences in indirect speech*	2. *Sentences about meaning*	
15 *a*. Charles said (wrote, thought) Peter was coming tomorrow (or: that Peter was coming tomorrow).	15 *b*. Charles said a sentence which means that Peter is coming tomorrow.	15 *c*. Charles said the sentence 'Peter is coming tomorrow'(or: a sentence of which this is a consequence).
16 *a*. Charles said *where* Peter is.	16 *b*. Charles said a sentence which states where Peter is.	16 *c*. Charles said a sentence of the form 'Peter is —' in which a spatial designation takes the place of the dash.

The use of the indirect mode of speech is admittedly short and convenient; but it contains the same dangers as the other sentences of the material mode. For instance, sentence 15 *a*, as contrasted with sentence 15 *c*, gives the false impression that it is concerned with Peter, while in reality it is only concerned with Charles and with the word 'Peter'. When the direct mode of speech is used, this danger does not occur. For instance, the sentence: "Charles says 'Peter is coming tomorrow'" does not belong to the material mode of speech: it is a sentence of descriptive syntax. The direct mode of speech is the ordinary form used in the word-language for the formal syntactical mode. (On the construction of the syntactical designation of an expression with the help of inverted commas, see § 41.)

The examples so far given suffice to show that, with certain formulations in the material mode of speech, there is the danger of obscurity or of contradictions. It is true that in such simple cases as these the danger is easy to avoid. But in less obvious cases of essentially the same kind, especially in philosophy, the application of the material mode of speech has time and again led to inconsistencies and confusions.

§ 76. UNIVERSAL WORDS

We will call a predicate of which every full sentence is an analytic sentence a *universal predicate*, or, if it is a word in the word-language, a **universal word**. [For every genus of predicates a universal predicate can easily be defined. For instance, if pr_1 is a pr^1 of any genus whatsoever, we define the universal predicate pr_2, of the same genus, as follows: $pr_2(v_1) \equiv (pr_1(v_1) \lor \sim pr_1(v_1))$.] The investigation of universal words is especially important for the analysis of philosophical sentences. They occur very often in such sentences both in metaphysics and in the logic of science, and are for the most part in the material mode of speech. In order to facilitate the practical application of the criterion for 'universal word', let us also formulate it in an informal way. A word is called a universal word if it expresses a property (or relation) which belongs analytically to all the objects of a genus, any two objects being assigned to the same genus if their designations belong to the same syntactical genus. Since the rules of syntax of the word-language are not exactly established, and since linguistic usage varies considerably on just this point of the generic classification of words, our examples of universal words must always be given with the reservation that they are valid only for one particular use of language.

Examples: 1. 'Thing' is a universal word (provided that the designations of things constitute a genus). In the word-series 'dog', 'animal', 'living creature', 'thing', every word is a more comprehensive predicate than the previous one, but only the last is a universal predicate. In the corresponding series of sentences, 'Caro is a dog', '... is an animal', '... a living creature', 'Caro is a thing', the content is successively diminished. But the final sentence is fundamentally different from the preceding ones, in that its L-content is null and it is analytic. If in 'Caro is a thing', 'Caro' is replaced by any other thing-designation, the result is again an analytic sentence; but if 'Caro' is replaced by an expression which is not a thing-designation, the result is not a sentence at all.

2. 'Number' is a universal word (provided that the numerical expressions constitute a genus, as for instance in Languages I and II, as opposed to Russell's language where they form a part of the class-expressions of the second level). In the series of predicates, 'number of the form $2^n + 1$', 'odd number', 'number', only the last is a universal predicate. In the series of sentences '7 has the form $2^n + 1$', '7 is odd', '7 is a number', the second is already analytic, but only the third has the property that every sentence which results from it if '7' is replaced by another $\mathfrak{Z}$ is again analytic. If '7' is replaced by an expression which is not a $\mathfrak{Z}$, then no sentence results (on the assumptions made at the beginning).

Examples of universal words: 'thing', 'object', 'property', 'relation', 'fact', 'condition', 'process', 'event', 'action', 'spatial point', 'spatial relation', 'space' (system of spatial points connected by spatial relations), 'temporal point', 'temporal relation', 'time' (system of temporal points connected by temporal relations); 'number', 'integer' (in I and II), 'real number' (in some systems), 'function', 'aggregate' (or 'class'); 'expression' (in a language of pure syntax); and many others.

We all use such universal words in our writings in almost every sentence, especially in the logic of science. That the use of these words is necessary is, however, only due to the deficiencies of the word-languages, i.e. to their inadequate syntactical structure. Every language can be transformed in such a way that universal words no longer occur in it, and this without any sacrifice either of expressiveness or conciseness.

We will now distinguish *two methods of employing* universal words (without making an exact and formal differentiation). The second method involves the material mode of speech, and will be dealt with later. The *first method* has to do with genuine object-sentences. Here a universal word serves to point out the syntactical genus of another expression. In some cases the syntactical genus of the other expression is already univocally determined by its form alone; the special indication of it by means of the added universal word is then only of use in making it more prominent, as an aid to the comprehension of the reader. In other cases, however, the addition of the universal word is necessary, since without it the other expression would be ambiguous. In all these cases of the first way of using it, the universal word is, so to speak, *dependent*; it is an *auxiliary grammatical symbol* added to another expression, something like an index.

Examples: 1. "By means of the process of crystallization...." Since crystallization belongs without any ambiguity to the genus of the processes, one might simply say: "By means of crystallization...." Here the universal word 'process' only serves to point out the genus to which the word 'crystallization' belongs. Similarly in the following examples: 2. "The condition of fatigue...." 3. "The number five...."

In the following sentences the universal word is necessary for univocality. It can be rendered superfluous by the use of a suffix ('7' and '7r') or by introducing various explicit expressions in place of the ambiguous one. 4a. "The integer 7...." 4b. "The real number 7...." 5a. "The condition of friendship...." 5b. "The relation of friendship...."

In the word-language universal words are especially needed as *auxiliary symbols for variables*, that is, in the formulation of universal and existential sentences, for the purpose of showing from which genus the substitution-values are to be taken. The word-language employs as variables words ('a', 'some', 'every', 'all', 'any', and so on) to which no particular genus is correlated as their realm of values. If, as is usual in the symbolic languages, different kinds of variables were used for the different genera of substitution-values, the addition of a universal word would be superfluous. Accordingly, the universal word here serves to some extent as an index to a variable, which indicates the genus of its substitution-values.

Examples: We will contrast the formulations of the word-language with those of the symbolic language of logistics. 6*a*. "If any number..., then...." 6*b*. "$(x)(...\supset...)$" (where 'x' is a $\mathfrak{z}$). 7*a*. "There is a number...." 7*b*. "$(\exists x)(...)$" (where 'x' is a $\mathfrak{z}$). 8*a*. "I know a thing which...." 8*b*. "$(\exists x)(...)$" (where 'x' is a thing-variable). 9*a*. "Every numerical property...." 9*b*. "$(F)(...)$" (where 'F' is a $\mathfrak{p}$ of which the values are $\mathfrak{z}\mathfrak{pr}^1$). 10*a*. "There is a relation...." 10*b*. "$(\exists F)(...)$" (where 'F' is a $\mathfrak{p}^2$).

Wittgenstein [*Tractatus*] p. 84 says: "So the variable name 'x' is the proper sign of the pseudo-concept *object*. Wherever the word 'object' ('thing', 'entity', etc.) is rightly used, it is expressed in logical symbolism by the variable name.... Wherever it is used otherwise, i.e. as a proper concept-word, there arise senseless pseudo-propositions.... The same holds of the words 'complex', 'fact', 'function', 'number', etc. They all signify formal concepts and are presented in logical symbolism by variables, not by functions or classes (as Frege and Russell thought). Expressions like ' 1 is a number', 'there is only one number nought', and all like them are senseless." Here the correct view is taken that the universal words designate formal (in our terminology: syntactical) concepts (or, more exactly: are not syntactical but quasi-syntactical predicates) and that in the translation into a symbolic language they are translated into variables (or, again more exactly: they determine the kind of variables by which the words 'a', 'every', and so on, are translated; it is only the kind of variables that is determined, and not their design; in the examples given above, 'y' or 'z' can equally well be taken instead of 'x'). On the other hand, I do not share Wittgenstein's opinion that this method of employing the universal words is the only admissible one. We shall see later that, precisely in the most important cases, there is another method of use in which the universal word is employed in dependently ("as a proper concept-word"). There it is a question of sentences of the material mode of speech which are to be translated into syntactical sentences. Sentences of this kind with a universal word are held by Wittgenstein to be nonsense, because he does not consider the correct formulation of syntactical sentences to be possible.

The use of universal words in questions in connection with one of the w... interrogatives ('what', 'who', 'where', 'which', etc.) is akin to their use in universal and existential sentences. Here also, in translation into a symbolic language, the universal word determines the choice of the kind of variable. A yes-or-no question demands either the affirmation or the denial of a certain sentence $\mathfrak{S}_1$, that is to say, the assertion of either $\mathfrak{S}_1$ or $\sim \mathfrak{S}_1$. [*Example:* The question "Is the table round?" requires us to assert in answer either: "the table is round" or: "the table is not round."] As contrasted with this, a w... question demands in reference to a certain sentential function (or sentential framework) the assertion of a closed full sentence. In a symbolic question, the genus of the arguments requested is determined by the kind of the argument variables. In the word-languages this genus is indicated by means either of a specific w... interrogative (such as 'who', 'where', 'when') or of an unspecific w... interrogative (such as 'what', 'which') with an auxiliary universal word. Hence here also the universal word is, so to speak, an index to a variable.

Examples: 1. Suppose I want to ask someone to make an assertion of the form "Charles was — in Berlin", where a time-determination of which I am ignorant but which I wish to learn from the assertion is to take the place of the dash. Now the question must indicate by some means that the missing expression is to be a time-determination. If symbols are used this can be effected by giving a sentential function in which in the place of the argument a variable 't', which is established as a temporal variable, occurs. [To symbolize the question, the variable whose argument is requested must be bound by means of a question-operator, e.g. '($?t$) (Charles was t in Berlin)'.] In the word-language the kind of argument requested is made known either by means of the specific question-word 'when' ("When was Charles in Berlin?") or by means of the universal word 'time' or 'temporal point' attached to an unspecific question-word ("At what time was Charles in Berlin?").

2. I wish to ask someone to make me an assertion of the form "Charles is — of Peter", where a relation-word is to take the place of the dash ('father', 'friend', 'teacher', or the like). The symbolic formulation of this question, by means of the relational variable 'R', is: '($?R$) (R (Charles, Peter))'. Its formulation in the word-language by means of the addition of the universal word 'relation' to an unspecific question-word is: "What relation is there between Charles and Peter?"

§ 77. UNIVERSAL WORDS IN THE MATERIAL MODE OF SPEECH

In the first use of a universal word, which we have up to now been discussing, it appears as an auxiliary symbol determining the genus of another expression; it was found that, if in place of this other expression a symbol indicating its own genus was introduced, then the universal word could be dispensed with. As opposed to this, *in the second use the universal word appears as an independent expression*, which in the simplest form occupies the place of the predicate in the sentence in question. Sentences of this kind belong to the *material mode of speech*; for a universal word is here a quasi-syntactical predicate; the correlated syntactical predicate is that which designates the appertaining expressional genus. [*Example:* 'number' is a universal word because it belongs analytically to all the objects of a genus of objects, namely, that of the numbers; the correlated syntactical predicate is 'numerical expression' (or 'number-word'), since this applies to all expressions which designate a number. The sentence "Five is a number" is a quasi-syntactical sentence of the material mode of speech; a correlated syntactical sentence is "'Five' is a number-word".]

Sentences with universal words	*Syntactical sentences*
(Material mode of speech)	(Formal mode of speech)
17 a. The moon is a *thing*; five is not a thing, but a *number*.	17 b. 'Moon' is a thing-word (thing-name); 'five' is not a thing-word, but a number-word.

In 17 a, as contrasted with sentences like "the thing moon...", "the number five...", the universal words 'thing' and 'number' are independent.

18 a. A property is not a *thing*.	18 b. An adjective (property-word) is not a thing-word.

That the formulation 18 a is open to objection is shown by the following consideration. 18 a violates the ordinary rule of types. This comes out particularly clearly when an attempt is made to formulate it symbolically, either by means of '(F) $(\mathrm{Prop}\,(F) \supset\; \sim \mathrm{Thing}\,(F))$' or by means of '$(x)$ $(\mathrm{Prop}\,(x) \supset\; \sim \mathrm{Thing}\,(x))$'; in the first case, '$\mathrm{Thing}\,(F)$', and in the second case '$\mathrm{Prop}\,(x)$', is inconsistent with the rule of types. Therefore, if 18 a is admitted as a sentence (it makes no difference whether true or false), by the usual syntax of logistics Russell's antinomy can be constructed. If this is to be avoided, special complicated syntactical rules are necessary.

19 a. Friendship is a *relation*. | 19 b. 'Friendship' is a rela-
       | tion-word.
20 a. Friendship is not a *pro-* | 20 b. 'Friendship' is not a
perty. | property-word.

19 a corresponds to the sentential form used by Russell '... ε Rel'; the analogous symbolic formulation of 20 a would, however, violate the rule of types. On the other hand, the correlated sentences of the formal mode of speech, 19 b and 20 b, are, even without any special preliminary adjustments, of the same kind and equally correct. In contrast with the pseudo-object-sentence 19 a, a sentence of the form "Friendship ensues if...", for instance, is a genuine object-sentence, and therefore not a sentence of the material mode of speech.

It is frequently said that the rule of types (even the simple one) restricts the expressiveness of a language to an inconvenient extent, and that one is often tempted to use formulations which would not be allowed by it. Such formulations, however, are often (like the examples given) only pseudo-object-sentences with universal words. If, in such cases, instead of the object-terms which one would like to, but must not, combine, one uses the correlated syntactical terms, the restrictive effect of the rule of types disappears.

Independent universal words appear very often in philosophical sentences, in the logic of science as well as in traditional philosophy. Most of the examples of philosophical sentences which will be given later belong to the material mode of speech by reason of the employment of independent universal words.

§ 78. Confusion in Philosophy Caused by the Material Mode of Speech

The fact that, in philosophical writings—even in those which are free from metaphysics—obscurities so frequently arise, and that in philosophical discussions people so often find themselves talking at cross purposes, is in large part due to the use of the material instead of the formal mode of speech. The habit of formulating in the material mode of speech causes us, in the first place, to deceive ourselves about the objects of our own investigations: pseudo-object-sentences mislead us into thinking that we are dealing with extra-linguistic objects such as numbers, things, properties, experiences, states of affairs, space, time, and so on; and the fact that, in reality, it is a case of language and its connections (such as numerical expressions, thing-designations, spatial co-ordinates, etc.) is disguised from us by the material mode of speech. This fact only becomes clear by translation into the formal mode of speech, or, in other words, into syntactical sentences about language and linguistic expressions.

Further, the use of the material mode of speech gives rise to obscurity by employing absolute concepts in place of the syntactical concepts which are relative to language. With regard to every sentence of syntax, and consequently every philosophical sentence that it is desired to interpret as syntactical, the language or kind of language to which it is to be referred must be stated. If the language of reference is not given, the sentence is incomplete and ambiguous. Usually a syntactical sentence is intended to hold in one of the following ways:

1. for all languages;

2. for all languages of a certain kind;

3. for the current language of science (or of a sub-domain of science, such as physics, biology, etc.);

4. for a particular language whose syntactical rules have been stated beforehand;

5. for at least one language of a certain kind;

6. for at least one language in general;

7. for a language (not previously stated) which is proposed as a language of science (or of a sub-domain of science);

8. for a language (not previously stated) whose formulation and investigation is proposed (apart from the question whether it is to serve as a language of science or not).

If the formal syntactical mode of speech is used, then linguistic expressions are being discussed. This makes it quite clear that the language intended must be stated. In the majority of cases, however, even if the language is not expressly named, it will be understood from the context which interpretation (say, of those just given) is intended. The use of the *material mode of speech* leads, on the other hand, to a *disregard of the relativity to language of philosophical sentences*; it is responsible for an *erroneous conception of philosophical sentences as absolute*. It is especially to be noted that the statement of a philosophical thesis sometimes (as in interpretation 7 or 8) represents not an *assertion* but a *suggestion*. Any dispute about the truth or falsehood of such a thesis is quite mistaken, a mere empty battle of words; we can at most discuss the utility of the proposal, or investigate its consequences. But even in cases where a philosophical thesis presents an assertion, obscurity and useless controversy are liable to arise through the possibility of several interpretations (for instance, 1 to 6). A few examples may serve to make this clear. (For the sake of brevity, we shall formulate these sample theses in a more elementary manner than would be done in an actual discussion.)

Philosophical sentences	*Syntactical sentences*
(Material mode of speech)	(Formal mode of speech)
21 a. *Numbers* are classes of classes of things.	21 b. Numerical expressions are class-expressions of the second level.
22 a. *Numbers* belong to a special primitive kind of objects.	22 b. Numerical expressions are expressions of the zero-level.

Let us assume that a logicist holds thesis 21 a, and a formalist thesis 22 a. Then between these two there can be endless fruitless discussion as to which of them is right and what numbers actually *are*. The uncertainty disappears as soon as the formal mode of speech is applied. First of all, theses 21 a and 22 a should be translated into 21 b and 22 b. But these sentences are not yet complete, because the statement of the language intended is lacking. Various interpretations—such, for instance, as those mentioned previously—are still possible. Interpretation 3 is obviously not intended. Under interpretation 1 both parties would be wrong. Under the minimum interpretation, 6, both would be right, and the controversy would be at an end; for it is possible to construct a language of arithmetic either in such a way that 21 b is true or in such a way that 22 b is true. Perhaps, however, the two disputants agree that they intend their theses as proposals in the sense of 7, for instance. In that case, the question of truth or falsehood cannot be discussed, but only the question whether this or that form of language is the more appropriate for certain purposes.

23 a. Some *relations* belong to the primitive data.	23 b. Some two- (or more-) termed predicates belong to the undefined descriptive primitive symbols.
24 a. *Relations* are never primitive data, they depend upon the properties of their members.	24 b. All two- and more-termed predicates are defined on the basis of the one-termed predicates.

In the case of theses 23 a and 24 a, discussion is again fruitless and deluded until the disputants pass over to the formal mode of speech and agree as to which of the interpretations 1 to 8 is intended for sentences 23 b and 24 b.

| 25 a. A *thing* is a complex of sense-data. | 25 b. Every sentence in which a thing-designation occurs is equipollent to a class of sentences in which no thing-designations but sense-data designations occur. |
| 26 a. A thing is a complex of atoms. | 26 b. Every sentence in which a thing-designation occurs is equipollent to a sentence in which space-time co-ordinates and certain descriptive functors (of physics) occur. |

Suppose that a positivist maintains thesis 25 a, and a realist thesis 26 a. Then an endless dispute will arise over the pseudo-question of what a thing actually is. If we transfer to the formal mode of speech, it is in this case possible to reconcile the two theses, even if they are interpreted in the sense of 3, that is, as assertions about the whole language of science. For the various possibilities of translating a thing-sentence into an equipollent sentence are obviously not incompatible with one another. *The controversy between positivism and realism is an idle dispute about pseudo-theses which owes its origin entirely to the use of the material mode of speech.*

Here again we want to emphasize the fact that it does not follow from the given examples that all sentences of the material mode of speech are necessarily incorrect. But they are usually incomplete. Even this does not prevent their correct use; for in every domain incomplete, abbreviated modes of speech may frequently be employed with profit. But the examples show how important it is in using the material mode of speech, especially in philosophical discussions, to be fully aware of its character, so as to be able to avoid the dangers inherent in it. As soon as, in a discussion, obscurities and doubts of the kind here described arise, it is advisable to translate at least the principal thesis involved in the controversy into the formal mode of speech, and to render it more precise by stating whether it is meant as an assertion or as a suggestion, and to which language it refers. If the exponent of a thesis refuses to make these statements concerning it, the thesis is incomplete and therefore ineligible for discussion.

§ 79. Philosophical Sentences in the Material and in the Formal Mode of Speech

We will now give a series of further examples of sentences in the material mode of speech, together with their translations into the formal mode. These are sentences such as commonly occur in philosophical discussions, sometimes in those of the traditional sort, sometimes in investigations which are already expressly oriented in accordance with the logic of science. [For the sake of brevity, the sentences are, to a certain extent, formulated in a simplified way.] These illustrative sentences (as also those of § 78) have not, for the most part, the simple form of those for which we formulated the criterion of the material mode of speech in an earlier section. But they have the general feature which is characteristic of the material mode of speech; they speak about objects of some kind, but in such a way that it is possible to construct correlated sentences of the formal mode of speech which make corresponding assertions about the designations of these objects. Since the original sentence, in most cases, cannot be understood univocally, a particular translation into the formal mode of speech cannot univocally be given; it cannot even be stated with certainty that the sentence in question is a pseudo-object-sentence and, hence, a sentence of the material mode of speech. The translation given here is accordingly no more than a suggestion and is in no way binding. It is the task of anyone who wishes to maintain the philosophical thesis in question to interpret it by translating it into an exact sentence. This latter may sometimes be a genuine object-sentence (that is to say, not a quasi-syntactical sentence); and, in that case, no material mode of speech occurs. Otherwise it must be possible to give the interpretation by means of translation into a syntactical sentence. The syntactical sentences of the following examples—like those of the preceding ones—must further be completed by stating the language which is referred to; from this statement it can then be seen whether the sentence is an assertion or a proposal, e.g. a new rule. We have omitted these statements in the examples which follow, because as a rule it is impossible to obtain them univocally from the philosophical sentences of the material mode of speech. [Here, as in the earlier examples, it obviously makes no difference to our investigations whether the illustrative sentences are true or not.]

Philosophical sentences (Material mode of speech)	*Syntactical sentences* (Formal mode of speech)

A. *Generalities* (about things, properties, facts, and so on). Here belong also Examples 7, 9, 17–20.

27 a. A property of a thing-property is not itself a thing-property.	27 b. A ^{2}pr is not a ^{1}pr.
28 a. A property cannot possess another property. (As opposed to 27 a.)	28 b. There is no pr of a level higher than the first. (As opposed to 27 b.)
29 a. The world is the totality of facts, not of things.	29 b. Science is a system of sentences, not of names.
30 a. A fact is a combination of objects (entities, things).	30 b. A sentence is a series of symbols.
31 a. If I know an object, then I also know all the possibilities of its occurrence in facts.	31 b. If the genus of a symbol is given, then all the possibilities of its occurrence in sentences are also given.
32 a. Identity is not a relation between objects.	32 b. The symbol of identity is not a descriptive symbol.

Sentences 29 a to 32 a come from Wittgenstein. Similarly many other sentences of his which at first appear obscure become clear when translated into the formal mode of speech.

33 a. This circumstance (or: fact, process, condition) is logically necessary; ...logically impossible (or: inconceivable); ... logically possible (or: conceivable).	33 b. This sentence is analytic; ...contradictory; ...not contradictory.
34 a. This circumstance (or: fact, process, condition) is really (or: physically, in accordance with natural laws) necessary; ... really impossible; ...really possible.	34 b. This sentence is valid; ...contravalid; ...not contravalid.
35 a. The circumstance (or fact, process, condition) C_1 is a logically (or really) necessary condition for the circumstance C_2.	35 b. $\mathfrak{S}_1$ is an L-consequence (or a P-consequence, respectively) of $\mathfrak{S}_2$.

33 a to 35 a are sentences of modality; see § 69.

36 a. A property of an object c is called an *essential* (or: *internal*) property of c, if it is inconceivable that c should not possess it (or: if c necessarily possesses it); otherwise it is an *inessential* (or: *external*) property. (Correspondingly for a relation.)

36 b. $\mathfrak{pr}_1$ is called an analytic (or, if desired: an essential or internal) predicate in relation to an object-designation $\mathfrak{A}_1$ if $\mathfrak{pr}_1(\mathfrak{A}_1)$ is analytic. (Correspondingly for a two- or more-termed predicate.)

The uncertainty of the formulation 36 a is shown by the fact that it leads to obscurities and contradictions. Let us take as the object c, for example, the father of Charles. According to definition 36 a, being related to Charles is an essential property of c, since it is inconceivable that the father of Charles should not be related to Charles. But being a landowner is not an essential property of the father of Charles. For, even if he is a landowner, it is conceivable that he might not be one. On the other hand, being a landowner is an essential property of the owner of this piece of land. For it is inconceivable that the owner of this piece of land should not be a landowner. Now, however, it happens to be the father of Charles who is the owner of this piece of land. On the basis of definition 36 a, it has just been proved that it is both an essential and not an essential property of this man to be a landowner. Thus 36 a leads to a contradiction; but 36 b does not, because 'landowner' is an analytic predicate in relation to the object-designation 'the owner of this piece of land', but it is not an analytic predicate in relation to the object-designation 'the father of Charles'. Hence the fault of definition 36 a lies in the fact that it is referred to the one *object* instead of to the *object-designations*, which may be *different* even when the object is the same.

This example shows (as will easily be confirmed by a closer investigation) that the numerous discussions and controversies about *external and internal properties and relations* are idle, if, as is usual, they are based on a definition of either the form indicated or one resembling it, or, at any rate, on one which is formulated in the material mode of speech. [Such investigations are especially to be found in the work of Anglo-Saxon philosophers, and it was through them that Wittgenstein, although it is to him that we owe the detection of many other pseudo-questions, was himself misled into enquiries of this nature.] If instead of the usual sort of definition, a definition in the formal mode is given, then the situation in these commonly disputed cases becomes unambiguous, and moreover so simple that no one can any longer be tempted to raise philosophical problems about it.

B. *The so-called philosophy of numbers; logical analysis of arithmetic.*

Here belong also Examples 10, 17, 21, and 22.

37 a. God created the natural numbers (integers); fractions

37 b. The natural-number symbols are primitive symbols;

and real numbers, on the other hand, are the work of man. (Kronecker.)

38 a. The natural numbers are not given; only an initial term of the process of counting and the operation of progression from one term to the next are given; the other terms are created progressively by means of this operation.

39 a. The mathematical *continuum* is a series of a certain structure; the terms of the series are the *real numbers*.

40 a. The mathematical continuum is not composed of atomic elements, but is a whole which is analysable into ever further analysable sub-intervals. A real number is a series of intervals contained one inside the other.

the fractional expressions and the real-number expressions are introduced by definition.

38 b. The natural number expressions are not primitive symbols (as opposed to 37 b); only '0' and '1' are primitive symbols; an St has the form nu or St¹. (Languages I and II.)

39 b. A pr^2_1, to which certain structural properties (density, continuity, etc.) are attributed in the axioms, is a primitive symbol. The arguments which are suitable to pr_1—they are expressions of the zero-level—are called real-number expressions.

40 b. A pr^2_1, to which certain structural properties (namely, those of a part-whole relation of a certain kind) are attributed in the axioms, is a primitive symbol. An $\mathfrak{Fu}^1$ whose arguments are natural-number expressions and whose value-expressions are suitable as arguments to pr_1 is called a real-number expression. [A so-called becoming ("werdende") sequence of selections is then represented by an $\mathfrak{Fu}_b$; see p. 148.]

39 a and 40 a present (in a simplified formulation) the antithesis between *the usual mathematical conception of the continuum of real numbers, based on the theory of aggregates,* and *the intuitionist conception of the continuum represented by Brouwer and Weyl,* which rejects the former as atomistic. 39 b and 40 b may be interpreted as suggestions for the construction of two different calculi.

C. *Problems of the so-called given or primitive data (epistemology, phenomenology); logical analysis of the protocol sentences.*

Here belong also Examples 23 and 24.

41 a. The only *primitive data* are relations between experiences.

41 b. Only two- or more-termed predicates whose arguments belong to the genus of the experience-expressions occur as descriptive primitive symbols.

42 a. A temporal series of visual fields is given as primitive datum; every visual field is a two-dimensional system of positions which are occupied by colours. (As opposed to 41 a.)

42 b. A descriptive atomic sentence consists of a time co-ordinate, two space co-ordinates and a colour expression.

43 a. The sense-qualities, such as colours, smells, etc., belong to the primitive data.

43 b. Symbols of sense-qualities, such as colour-symbols, smell-symbols, etc., belong to the descriptive primitive symbols.

44 a. The fact that the system of colours arranged according to similarity (the so-called colour-pyramid) is three-dimensional, is known a priori (or: is to be apprehended by intuition of essence; or: is an internal property of that arrangement).

44 b. A colour-expression consists of three co-ordinates; the values of each co-ordinate form a serial order according to syntactical rules; on the basis of these syntactical rules, therefore, the colour-expressions constitute a three-dimensional order.

45 a. The colours are not originally given as members of an order, but as individuals; an empirical relation of similarity exists between them, however, on the basis of which the colours can be arranged empirically in a three-dimensional order.

45 b. The colour expressions are not compound; they are primitive symbols; further, a symmetrical, reflexive, but not transitive, pr_0^2 to which the colour-expressions are suitable as arguments, occurs as a primitive symbol; the theorem of the three-dimensionality of the order determined by this pr is P-valid.

The much-disputed philosophical question as to whether the knowledge of the *three-dimensionality of the colour-pyramid* is *a priori* or *empirical* is thus, by reason of the use of the material mode of speech, incomplete. The answer is dependent upon the form of the language.

46 a. Every *colour* possesses three components: colour-tone, saturation, and intensity (or: colour-tone, white-content, and black-content).

46 b. Every colour-expression consists of three partial expressions (or: is synonymous with an expression composed in this way): one colour-tone expression, one saturation-expression, and one intensity-expression.

47 a. Every colour is at a place.

47 b. A colour-expression is always accompanied in a sentence by a place-designation.

48 a. Every *tone* has a certain pitch.

48 b. Every tone-expression contains an expression of pitch.

D. *The so-called natural philosophy; logical analysis of the natural sciences.*

Here belong also Examples 11, 25, and 26.

49 a. *Time* is continuous.	49 b. The real-number expressions are used as time-co-ordinates.

See Wittgenstein on this point ([*Tractatus*] p. 172): "All propositions such as the law of causation, the law of continuity in nature, . . . are *a priori* intuitions of the possible forms of the propositions of science." (Instead of "*a priori* intuitions of" we would prefer to say: "conventions concerning".)

50 a. *Time* is one-dimensional; *space* is three-dimensional.	50 b. A time-designation consists of one co-ordinate; a space-designation consists of three co-ordinates.
51 a. Time is infinite in both directions, forwards and backwards.	51 b. Every positive or negative real-number expression can be used as a time-co-ordinate.

The opposition between the *determinism* of classical physics and the probability determination of quantum physics concerns a syntactical difference in the system of natural laws, that is, of the P-rules of the physical language (already formulated or still to seek); this is shown by the two following examples.

52 a. Every process is univocally determined by its causes.	52 b. For every particular physical sentence $\mathfrak{S}_1$ there is, for any time-co-ordinate $\mathfrak{A}_1$ which has a smaller value than the time-co-ordinate which occurs in $\mathfrak{S}_1$, a class $\mathfrak{R}_1$ of particular sentences with $\mathfrak{A}_1$ as time-co-ordinate, such that $\mathfrak{S}_1$ is a P-consequence of $\mathfrak{R}_1$.
53 a. The position and velocity of a particle is not univocally but only probably determined by a previous constellation of particles.	53 b. If $\mathfrak{S}_1$ is a particular sentence concerning particles and $\mathfrak{A}_1$ a time-co-ordinate of smaller value than that which occurs in $\mathfrak{S}_1$, then $\mathfrak{S}_1$ is not a P-consequence of a class of such sentences with $\mathfrak{A}_1$ as time-co-ordinate, however comprehensive, but only a probability-consequence of such a class with a coefficient of probability smaller than 1.

§ 80. The Dangers of the Material Mode of Speech

If we wish to characterize the *material mode of speech* by one general term, we may say, for instance, that it is *a special kind of transposed mode of speech*. By a transposed mode of speech we mean one in which, in order to assert something about an object *a*, something corresponding is asserted about an object *b* which stands in a certain relation to the object *a* (this does not pretend to be an exact definition). For example, every metaphor is a transposed mode of speech; but other kinds also occur frequently in ordinary language —far more frequently than one may at first believe. The use of a transposed mode of speech can easily lead to obscurities; but when systematically carried into effect, it is non-contradictory.

Examples of different kinds of *transposed mode of speech*. 1. An artificial example. The term 'marge' (as a term parallel to 'large') is introduced by means of the following rule: if a place *a* has more than 10,000 inhabitants, then we shall say that the place *b*, whose name precedes that of *a* in the alphabetical list of places, is marge. A rule of this kind can be carried into effect without any contradiction; for instance, according to it, the place Berlichingen is marge, since, in the alphabetical list of places, its name is followed by 'Berlin'. The definition seems absurd, since it makes no difference to the properties (in the ordinary sense) of a place whether it is marge or not. But the same thing holds for the ordinary material mode of speech also (see below, Example 5), even (as one finds on examination, in opposition, of course, to the view commonly held) for Examples 2, 3, and 4. 2. According to the ordinary use of language, a man is called *famous* if other people make assertions of a certain kind about him. 3. According to the ordinary use of language, an action *a* of a certain person is called *legal crime* if the penal law of the country in which that person lives places the description of a kind of action to which *a* belongs in the list of crimes. 4. According to the ordinary use of language, an action *a* of a certain person is called a *moral crime* if, in the minds of the majority of other persons, the thought of someone (but not themselves) committing an action of this kind calls forth the feeling of moral indignation. 5. According to the ordinary use of language, it is said of a city (for instance, of Babylon; see the example in § 74) that it has been treated of in a certain lecture (material mode of speech) if a designation of the city has occurred in this lecture. For the qualities (in the ordinary sense) of the city in question, it is not of the least importance whether it has the property of having been treated of in yesterday's lecture or not. This property is therefore a transposed property.

The material mode of speech is a transposed mode of speech. In using it, in order to say something about a word (or a sentence) we say instead something parallel about the object designated by the word (or the fact described by the sentence, respectively). The origin of a transposed mode of speech can sometimes be explained psychologically by the fact that the conception of the substituted object b is for some reason more vivid and striking, stronger in feeling-tone, than the conception of the original object a. This is the case with the material mode of speech. The image of a word (for instance, of the word 'house') is often much less vivid and lively than that of the object which the word designates (in the example, that of the house). Further, the fact, which is perhaps a consequence of the psychological fact just mentioned, that the approach and method of syntax have hitherto not been sufficiently known, and that, in consequence, the majority of the necessary syntactical terms have not been a part of ordinary language, may have contributed to the origin of the material mode of speech. For this reason, instead of saying: "The sentence 'a has three books, b has two books, and a and b together have seven books' is contradictory", we say: "It is impossible (or inconceivable) for a to have three books, b two books, and a and b together seven books"; or (which has an even stronger resemblance to an object-sentence): "If a has three books, and b two, then a and b together cannot possibly have seven books." People are not accustomed to direct their attention to the sentence instead of the fact; and it is apparently much more difficult to do so. In addition, there is the circumstance that, in ordinary language, we have no syntactical expression which is equivalent in meaning to 'contradictory', while the quasi-syntactical expression 'impossible' is ready to hand.

How difficult it is even for scientists to adopt the syntactical point of view, that is to say, to pay attention to the sentences instead of to the facts, is shown especially clearly in the typical misunderstandings which one encounters again and again in discussing logical questions even with scientists, and still more with philosophers. For instance, when we of the Vienna Circle criticize, in accordance with our anti-metaphysical view, certain sentences of metaphysics (such as: "There is a God") or of metaphysical epistemology (such as: "The external world is real") we are interpreted by the majority of our opponents as denying those object-sentences and consequently affirming others (such as: "There is no God" or: "The external world is not real ", etc.). These misunderstandings are always occurring in spite of the fact that we have already explained them many times (see, for instance, Carnap [*Scheinprobleme*], Schlick [*Positivismus*], Carnap [*Metaphysik*]), and are constantly pointing out that we are not talking about the (supposititious) facts, but about the (supposititious) sentences; in the mode of expression of this book: the thesis maintained by us is not an object-sentence but a syntactical sentence.

The suggestions we have given are intended only to throw light upon, and not by any means to answer, the question of the psychological explanation of transposed modes of speech in general, and of the material mode in particular. To investigate it more closely would be well worth while; but we must leave that task to the psychologists. What we must here take into account is the fact that the material mode of speech is a part of ordinary linguistic usage, and that it will continue to be frequently employed, even by ourselves. Therefore it behoves us to pay special attention to the dangers connected with its use.

Most of the ordinary formulations in the material mode of speech depend upon the use of universal words. *Universal words very easily lead to pseudo-problems*; they appear to designate kinds of objects, and thus make it natural to ask questions concerning the nature of objects of these kinds. For instance, philosophers from antiquity to the present day have associated with the universal word '*number*' certain pseudo-problems which have led to the most abstruse inquiries and controversies. It has been asked, for example, whether numbers are real or ideal objects, whether they are extra-mental or only exist in the mind, whether they are the creation of thought or independent of it, whether they are potential or actual, whether real or fictitious. The question of the origin of numbers has been raised, and has been found to be due to a division of the self, to an original primitive intuition of duality in unity, and so forth. Similarly, innumerable questions have been put concerning *the nature of space and time*, not only by speculative metaphysicians (up to recent times), but also by many philosophers whose epistemological theses are ostensibly (as with Kant) oriented in accordance with empirical science. As opposed to all this, an inquiry which is free from metaphysics and concerned with the logic of science can only have as its object the syntax of the spatio-temporal expressions of the language of science, in the form, say, of an axiomatics of the space-time system of physics (as, for instance, the researches of Reichenbach [*Axiomatik*]). Further, mention should be made of the many pseudo-problems concerning the nature of the *physical* and the *psychical*. Again, the pseudo-questions concerning *properties and relations* and with them *the whole controversy about universals* rests on the misleading use of universal words. All pseudo-questions of this kind disappear if the formal instead of the material mode of speech is used, that is, if in the formulation of questions, instead of universal words (such as 'number', 'space', 'universal'), we employ the corresponding syntactical words ('numerical expression', 'space-co-ordinate', 'predicate', etc.).

We have already met with a number of examples in which the use of the material mode of speech leads to contradictions. The danger of the occurrence of such contradictions is especially great in the case of languages which are mutually translatable, or, from the standpoint of one language of science, of two sub-languages between the sentences of which certain relations of equipollence (not necessarily of L-equipollence) hold. This applies, for instance, to *the language of psychology and the language of physics.* If the material mode of speech is employed in relation to the psychological language (by the use, for instance, of universal words like 'the psychical', 'psyche', 'psychical process', 'mental process', 'act', 'experience', 'content of experience', 'intentional object', and so on), and if, in the same investigation, it is also used in relation to the physical language (either the everyday language or the scientific language), hopeless confusion frequently ensues.

The danger here indicated has been described by us in detail on other occasions ([*Phys. Sprache*] pp. 453 ff., [*Unity*]). Compare also [*Psychol.*] p. 186, where attention is drawn to the obscurities which arise from the use of the material mode of speech in the sentences of a psychologist; further, see [*Psychol.*] p. 181 for the origin of a pseudo-problem due to the material mode of speech. The examples on p. 314 under I also belong in part here. On the psycho-physical problem, see p. 324.

From the earlier examples, which could easily be multiplied, it is clear that the use of the material mode of speech often gives rise to an obscurity, an ambiguity, which is manifested, for instance, in the fact that essentially different translations into the formal mode of speech are possible. In more extreme cases, contradictions also appear. These contradictions are, however, frequently not at all obvious, for the reason that the consequences are not derived by means of formal rules, but by means of material considerations, in which it is often possible to avoid the traps that one has set oneself by this dubious formulation. Even where no contradictions or ambiguities occur, the use of the material mode of speech has the disadvantage of leading easily to self-deception as regards the object under discussion: one believes that one is investigating certain objects and facts, whereas one is, in reality, investigating their designations, i.e. words and sentences.

§ 81. THE ADMISSIBILITY OF THE MATERIAL MODE OF SPEECH

We have spoken of dangers and not of errors of the material mode of speech. *The material mode of speech is not in itself erroneous*; it only readily lends itself to wrong use. But if suitable definitions and rules for the material mode of speech are laid down and systematically applied, no obscurities or contradictions arise. Since, however, the word-language is too irregular and too complicated to be actually comprehended in a system of rules, one must guard against the dangers of the material mode of speech as it is ordinarily used in the word-language by keeping in mind the peculiar character of its sentences. Especially when important conclusions or philosophical problems are to be based on sentences of the material mode of speech, it is wise to make sure of their freedom from ambiguity by translating them into the formal mode. *It is not by any means suggested that the material mode of speech should be entirely eliminated.* For since it is established in general use, and is thus more readily understood, and is, moreover, often shorter and more obvious than the formal mode, *its use is frequently expedient.* Even in this book, and especially in this Part, the material mode of speech has often been employed; here are some examples:

Material mode of speech	*Formal mode of speech*
54 *a*. Philosophical questions are sometimes concerned with objects which do not occur in the object-domain of the empirical	54 *b*. In philosophical questions expressions sometimes occur which do not occur in the languages of the sciences; for

sciences. For example: the thing-in-itself, the transcendental, and the like (p. 278).

55 a. An object-question is concerned, for instance, with the properties of animals; on the other hand, a logical question is concerned with the sentences of zoology (p. 278).

•56 a. It is just as easy to construct sentences about the forms of linguistic expressions as it is to construct sentences about the geometrical forms of geometrical structures (pp. 282 f.).

example, the expressions: 'thing-in-itself', 'the transcendental', etc.

55 b. In an object-question, predicates of the language of zoology (designations of kinds of animals) occur; on the other hand, in a logical question, designations of sentences of the zoological language occur.

56 b. It is just as easy to construct sentences in which, as predicates, syntactical predicates occur, and, as arguments, syntactical designations of expressions, as it is to construct sentences in which, as predicates, predicates of the language of (pure) geometry occur, and, as arguments, object-designations of the language of geometry.

If a sentence of the material mode of speech is given, or, more generally, a sentence which is not a genuine object-sentence, then the translation into the formal mode of speech need not always be undertaken, but it must always be possible. *Translatability into the formal mode of speech constitutes the touchstone for all philosophical sentences*, or, more generally, for all sentences which do not belong to the language of any one of the empirical sciences. In investigating translatability, the ordinary use of language and the definitions which may have been given by the author must be taken into consideration. In order to find a translation, we attempt to use, wherever a universal word occurs (such as 'number' or 'property'), the corresponding syntactical expression (such as 'numerical expression' or 'property-word', respectively). Sentences which do not, at least to a certain extent, univocally determine their translation are thereby shown to be ambiguous and obscure. Sentences which do not give even a slight indication to determine their translation are outside the realm of the language of science and therefore incapable of discussion, no matter what depths or heights of feeling they may stir. Let us give a few warning examples of such sentences as they occur in the writings of our own circle or in those of closely allied authors. The majority of readers will scarcely, I think, succeed in finding a translation of these into the formal mode of speech that would satisfactorily represent the author's meaning. Even if the author himself is perhaps able to give such a translation—and in some cases even this seems doubtful —his readers will certainly fall into confusion and uncertainty. We shall see that the sentences in which the word 'inexpressible' or something similar occurs are especially dangerous. In the examples under heading I we find a *mythology of the inexpressible*, in the examples under II a *mythology of higher things*, and in Sentence 13 both of these.

I. 1. There is indeed the inexpressible. 2. The qualities which appear as content of the stream of consciousness can neither be asserted, described, expressed, nor communicated, but can only be manifested in experience. 3. What can be shown cannot be said. 4. The given experience possesses an utterable structure, but at the same time it possesses an unutterable content which is nevertheless very well known to us. 5. Human beings must verify psychological sentences by their own unutterable experience, which is nevertheless very well known to them; they must examine whether the sentence in question, the combination of symbols, is isomorphous (like in structure) with their unutterable experience. 6. The unutterable experience blue or bitter.... 7. The essence of individuality cannot be represented in words, and is indescribable, and therefore meaningless for science. 8. Philosophy will mean the unspeakable by clearly displaying the speakable. 9. The holding [subsistence] of [formal or] internal properties and relations cannot be asserted by propositions [sentences].

II. 10. The sense of the world must lie outside the world. 11. How the world is, is completely indifferent to what is higher. 12. If good or bad willing changes the world it can only change the limits of the world, not the facts. 13. Propositions [sentences] cannot express anything higher.

Let us suggest a few possibilities of translation which, however, probably do not correspond to the intentions of the authors. In the case of Sentence 1 it would be necessary to distinguish between two interpretations: 1 A. "There are unutterable objects", that is to say, "There are objects for which no object-designations exist"; *translation:* "There are object-designations which are not object-designations." 1 B. "There are unutterable facts", that is to say, "There are facts which are not described by any sentence"; *translation:* "There are sentences which are not sentences." Concerning 6: in other words, "The experience designated by the word 'blue' cannot be designated by any word"; *translation:* "The experience-designation 'blue' is not an experience-designation." Sentence 9 means: "The fact that a property of a certain kind appertains to an object cannot be asserted by means of a sentence"; *translation:* "A sentence in which a property-word of a certain kind occurs is not a sentence." Sentence 13 means: "The higher facts cannot be expressed by means of sentences"; *translation:* "The higher sentences are not sentences."

Let it be once more called to mind that the distinction between the formal and the material modes of speech does not refer to genuine object-sentences and therefore not to the sentences of the empirical sciences, or to sentences of this kind which occur in the discussions of the logic of science (or of philosophy). (See the three columns, on p. 286.) It is here a question of the sentences of the proper logic of science. According to the ordinary use of language it is customary to formulate these partly in the form of logical sentences and partly in the form of object-sentences. Our investigations have shown that the supposititious object-sentences of the logic of science are pseudo-object-sentences, or sentences which apparently speak about objects, like the real object-sentences, but which in reality are speaking about the designations of these objects. This implies that all the sentences of the logic of science are logical sentences; that is to say, sentences about language and linguistic expressions. And our investigations have further shown that all these sentences can be formulated in such a way as to refer not to sense and meaning but to the syntactical form of the sentences and other expressions—they can all be translated into the formal mode of speech, or, in other words, into syntactical sentences. *The logic of science is the syntax of the language of science.*

B. THE LOGIC OF SCIENCE AS SYNTAX

§ 82. THE PHYSICAL LANGUAGE

The logical analysis of physics—as a part of the logic of science —is the syntax of the physical language. All the so-called epistemological problems concerning physics (in so far as it is not a question of metaphysical pseudo-problems) are in part empirical questions, the majority of which belong to psychology, and in part logical questions which belong to syntax. A more exact exposition of the logical analysis of physics as the syntax of the physical language must be left for a special investigation. Here we shall only offer a few suggestions towards it.

The logical analysis of physics will have, in the first place, to formulate *rules of formation* for sentences and other kinds of expressions of the physical language (see § 40). The most important expressions which occur as arguments are the point-expressions (designations of a spatio-temporal point, consisting of four real-number expressions, namely, three space-co-ordinates and one time-co-ordinate) and the domain-expressions (designations of a limited space-time domain). The physical magnitudes are represented by descriptive functors. The descriptive functors and predicates can be divided into those having point-expressions and those having domain-expressions as arguments.

The sentences can be classified according to their degree of generality. We will here only discuss the two extreme kinds of sentences and, for the sake of simplicity, only those in which all the interior arguments are point- or domain-expressions: the *concrete sentences* contain no unrestricted variables; the *laws* contain no constants as interior arguments.

Either L-rules alone, or L-rules and P-rules, can be laid down as *transformation rules* of the physical language. If P-rules are desired, they will generally be stated in the form of P-primitive sentences. In the first place, certain most general laws will be formulated as P-primitive sentences; we will call these *primitive laws*. In addition, descriptive synthetic sentences of another form—even concrete ones—may be stated as P-primitive sentences. In the majority of cases, the primitive laws will have the form of a universal sentence of implication or of equivalence. The primitive laws and the other valid laws can be either deterministic or *laws of probability*; the latter can be formulated, for instance, with the help of a probability implication. Since the *concept of probability* is a very significant one for physics, particularly in view of the latest developments, the logical analysis of physics will have thoroughly to investigate the syntax of the sentences of probability; and it may be found possible to establish a connection with the concept of range in the general syntax.

We cannot go more fully into the concept of probability here. See the lectures and discussions of the Prague Congress (*Erkenntnis* I, 1930); further bibliographical references are given in *Erkenntnis*

II, 189 f., 1931; there are also investigations, as yet unpublished, by Reichenbach, Hempel, and Popper.* On the probability implication, see Reichenbach [*Wahrscheinlichkeitslogik*].

Syntactical rules will have to be stated concerning the forms which the *protocol-sentences*, by means of which the results of observation are expressed, may take. [On the other hand, it is not the task of syntax to determine which sentences of the established protocol form are to be actually laid down as protocol-sentences, for 'true' and 'false' are not syntactical terms; the statement of the protocol-sentences is the affair of the physicist who is observing and making protocols.]

A sentence of physics, whether it is a P-primitive sentence, some other valid sentence, or an indeterminate assumption (that is, a premiss whose consequences are in course of investigation), will be *tested* by deducing consequences on the basis of the transformation rules of the language, until finally sentences of the form of protocol-sentences are reached. These will then be compared with the protocol-sentences which have actually been stated and either confirmed or refuted by them. If a sentence which is an L-consequence of certain P-primitive sentences contradicts a sentence which has been stated as a protocol-sentence, then some change must be made in the system. For instance, the P-rules can be altered in such a way that those particular primitive sentences are no longer valid; or the protocol-sentence can be taken as being non-valid; or again the L-rules which have been used in the deduction can also be changed. There are no established rules for the kind of change which must be made.

Further, it is not possible to lay down any set rules as to how new primitive laws are to be established on the basis of actually stated protocol-sentences. One sometimes speaks in this connection of the method of so-called *induction*. Now this designation may be retained so long as it is clearly seen that it is not a matter of a regular method but only one of a practical procedure which can be investigated solely in relation to expedience and fruitfulness. That there can be no rules of induction is shown by the fact that the L-content of a law, by reason of its unrestricted universality, always goes beyond the L-content of every finite class of protocol-

---

* (*Note*, 1935.) These works have meantime appeared; see Bibliography.

sentences. On the other hand, exact rules for deduction can be laid down, namely, the L-rules of the physical language. Thus the laws have the character of *hypotheses* in relation to the protocol-sentences; sentences of the form of protocol-sentences may be L-consequences of the laws, but a law cannot be an L-consequence of any finite synthetic class of protocol-sentences. The laws are not inferred from protocol-sentences, but are selected and laid down on the grounds of the existing protocol-sentences, which are always being re-examined with the help of the ever-emerging new protocol-sentences. Not only laws, however, but also concrete sentences are formulated as hypotheses, that is to say, as P-primitive sentences—such as a sentence about an unobserved process by which certain observed processes can be explained. There is in the strict sense no refutation (falsification) of an hypothesis; for even when it proves to be L-incompatible with certain protocol-sentences, there always exists the possibility of maintaining the hypothesis and renouncing acknowledgment of the protocol-sentences. Still less is there in the strict sense a complete confirmation (verification) of an hypothesis. When an increasing number of L-consequences of the hypothesis agree with the already acknowledged protocol-sentences, then the hypothesis is increasingly confirmed; there is accordingly only a gradually increasing, but never a final, confirmation. Further, it is, in general, impossible to test even a singular hypothetical sentence. In the case of a single sentence of this kind, there are in general no suitable L-consequences of the form of protocol-sentences; hence for the deduction of sentences having the form of protocol-sentences the remaining hypotheses must also be used. Thus *the test applies, at bottom, not to a single hypothesis but to the whole system of physics as a system of hypotheses* (Duhem, Poincaré).

No rule of the physical language is definitive; all rules are laid down with the reservation that they may be altered as soon as it seems expedient to do so. This applies not only to the P-rules but also to the L-rules, including those of mathematics. In this respect, there are only differences in degree; certain rules are more difficult to renounce than others. [If, however, we assume that every new protocol-sentence which appears within a language is synthetic, there is this difference between an L-valid, and therefore analytic, sentence $\mathfrak{S}_1$ and a P-valid sentence $\mathfrak{S}_2$, namely, that such a new protocol-sentence—independently of whether it is acknowledged as valid or not—can be, at most, incompatible with $\mathfrak{S}_2$ but never with $\mathfrak{S}_1$. In spite of this, it may come about that, under the inducement of new protocol-sentences, we alter the language to such an extent that $\mathfrak{S}_1$ is no longer analytic.]

If a new P-*primitive sentence* $\mathfrak{S}_1$ is stated, but without sufficient transformation rules by which, from $\mathfrak{S}_1$ in conjunction with the other P-primitive sentences, sentences of the form of protocol-sentences could be deduced, then in principle $\mathfrak{S}_1$ *cannot be tested*, and is therefore useless from the scientific point of view. If, however, sentences of the form of protocol-sentences are deducible from $\mathfrak{S}_1$ in conjunction with the remainder of the P-primitive sentences, but only such as are deducible from the remaining P-primitive sentences alone, then $\mathfrak{S}_1$ as a primitive sentence is unproductive, and scientifically superfluous.

A *new descriptive symbol which is to be introduced* need not be reducible by means of a chain of definitions to symbols which occur in protocol-sentences. A symbol of this kind may also be introduced as a *primitive symbol* by means of new P-primitive sentences. If these primitive sentences are testable, i.e. if sentences of the form of protocol-sentences are deducible from them, then thereby the primitive symbols are reduced to symbols of the protocol-sentences.

Example: Let protocol-sentences be the observation sentences of the usual form. The electric field vector of classical physics is not definable by means of the symbols which occur in such protocol-sentences; it is introduced as a primitive symbol by the Maxwell equations which are formulated as P-primitive sentences. There is no sentence equipollent to such an equation, which contains only symbols of the protocol-sentences, although, of course, sentences of protocol form can be deduced from the Maxwell equations in conjunction with the other primitive sentences of classical physics; in this way, the Maxwell theory is empirically tested. *Counter-example.* The concept of "entelechy", employed by the neo-vitalists, must be rejected as a pseudo-concept. It is, however, not a sufficient justification for this rejection to point out that no definition of that concept is given by means of which it could be reduced to the terms of the observation sentences; for the same thing is also true of a number of abstract physical concepts. The decisive point is rather the fact that no laws which can be empirically tested are laid down for that concept.

The *explanation* of a single known physical process, the *deduction* of an unknown process in the past or in the present, from one that is known, and the *prediction* of a future event, are all operations of the same logical character. In all three cases it is, namely, a matter of deducing the concrete sentence which describes the process from valid laws and other concrete sentences. To explain a law (in the material mode of speech: a universal fact) means to deduce it from more general laws.

The construction of the physical system is not effected in accordance with fixed rules, but by means of conventions. These conventions, namely, the rules of formation, the L-rules, and the P-rules (hypotheses), are, however, not arbitrary. The choice of them is influenced, in the first place, by certain practical methodological considerations (for instance, whether they make for simplicity, expedience, and fruitfulness in certain tasks). This is the case for all conventions, including, for example, definitions. But in addition the hypotheses can and must be tested by experience, that is to say, by the protocol-sentences—both those that are already stated and the new ones that are constantly being added. Every hypothesis must be compatible with the total system of hypotheses to which the already recognized protocol-sentences also belong. That hypotheses, in spite of their subordination to empirical control by means of the protocol-sentences, nevertheless contain a conventional element is due to the fact that the system of hypotheses is never univocally determined by empirical material, however rich it may be.

Let us make brief mention of two theses held by us, upon which, however, the above view regarding the physical language does not depend. The thesis of *physicalism* maintains that the physical language is a universal language of science—that is to say, that every language of any sub-domain of science can be equipollently translated into the physical language. From this it follows that science is a unitary system within which there are no fundamentally diverse object-domains, and consequently no gulf, for example, between natural and psychological sciences. This is the thesis of the *unity of science*. We will not examine these theses in greater detail here. It is easy to see that both are theses of the syntax of the language of science.

On the view of the physical language here discussed and on the theses of physicalism and of the unity of science, see Neurath [*Physicalism*], [*Physikalismus*], [*Soziol. Phys.*], [*Protokollsätze*],

[*Psychol.*]; Carnap [*Phys. Sprache*], [*Psychol.*], [*Protokollsätze*]. In the discussions of the Vienna Circle, Neurath has been conspicuous for his early—often initiatory—and especially radical adoption of new theses. For this reason, although many of his formulations are not unobjectionable, he has had a very stimulating and fruitful influence upon its investigations; for instance, in his demand for a unified language which should not only include the domains of science but also the protocol-sentences and the sentences about sentences; in his emphasis on the fact that all rules of the physical language depend upon conventional decisions, and that none of its sentences—not even the protocol-sentences—can ever be definitive; and, finally, in his rejection of so-called pre-linguistic elucidations and of the metaphysics of Wittgenstein. It was Neurath who suggested the designations "Physicalism" and "Unity of science".— One of the most important problems of the logical analysis of physics is that of the form of the protocol-sentences and of the operation of testing (problem of verification); on this point, see also Popper.

On the view here expounded the domain of the scientific sentences is not so restricted as on the one formerly held by the Vienna Circle. It was originally maintained that every sentence, in order to be significant, must be *completely verifiable* (Wittgenstein; Waismann [*Wahrscheinlichkeit*] p. 229; and Schlick [*Kausalität*] p. 150); every sentence therefore must be a molecular sentence formed of concrete sentences (the so-called elementary sentences) (Wittgenstein [*Tractatus*] pp. 102, 118; Carnap [*Aufbau*]). On this view there was no place for the *laws of nature* amongst the sentences of the language. Either these laws had to be deprived of their unrestricted universality and be interpreted merely as report-sentences, or they were left their unrestricted universality, and regarded not as proper sentences of the object-language, but merely as directions for the construction of sentences (Ramsey [*Foundations*] pp. 237 ff.; Schlick [*Kausalität*] pp. 150 f., with references to Wittgenstein), and hence as a kind of syntactical rules. In accordance with the principle of tolerance, we will not say that a construction of the physical language corresponding to this earlier view is inadmissible; it is equally possible, however, to construct the language in such a way that the unrestrictedly universal laws are admitted as proper sentences. The important difference between laws and concrete sentences is not obliterated in this second form of language, but remains in force. It is taken into account in the fact that definitions are framed for both kinds of sentences, and their various syntactical properties are investigated. The choice between the two forms of language is to be made on the grounds of expedience. The second form, in which the laws are treated as equally privileged proper sentences of the object-language, is, as it appears, much simpler and better adapted to the ordinary use of language in the actual sciences than the first form. A detailed criticism of the view according to which laws are not sentences is given by Popper.

The view here presented allows great freedom in the introduction of new primitive concepts and new primitive sentences in the language of physics or of science in general; yet at the same time it retains the *possibility of differentiating pseudo-concepts and pseudo-sentences* from real scientific concepts and sentences, *and thus of eliminating the former.* [This elimination, however, is not so simple as it appeared to be on the basis of the earlier position of the Vienna Circle, which was in essentials that of Wittgenstein. On that view it was a question of "*the* language" in an absolute sense; it was thought possible to reject both concepts and sentences if they did not fit into *the* language.] A newly stated P-primitive sentence is shown to be a pseudo-sentence if either no sufficient rules of formation are given by means of which it can be seen to be a sentence or no sufficient rules of transformation by means of which it can, as previously indicated, be submitted to an empirical test. The rules need not be explicitly given; they may also be tacitly laid down, provided only that they are exhibited in the use of language. A newly stated descriptive term is shown to be a pseudo-concept if it is neither reduced to previous terms by means of a definition, nor introduced by means of P-primitive sentences that can be tested (see the example and counter-example on p. 319).

Like the individual sentences of the logic of science previously discussed, this presentation of a conception of the logic of science is intended only as an example. Its truth is not here in question. The example is only for the purpose of making it clear that the logical analysis of physics is the syntax of the physical language, and of further stimulating the formulation, within the domain of syntax, of views, questions, and investigations concerning the logic of science (in the ordinary mode of expression: epistemology) and thus making the subject more precise and more fruitful.

§ 83. THE SO-CALLED FOUNDATIONS OF THE SCIENCES

Much has been said in recent times about the problems of the so-called philosophical or logical foundations of the individual sciences, by which are understood (in our method of designation) certain problems of the logic of science in relation to the domains of the sciences. Taking the most important examples, we shall show briefly that these problems are questions of the syntax of the language of science.

The chief *problems of the foundations of physics* have already been spoken of in the previous section, and, earlier, in Examples 49 to 53 (on p. 307). We have seen that the problem of the structure of time and space is concerned with the syntax of the space and time co-ordinates. The problem of causality is concerned with the syntactical form of laws; and in particular the controversy regarding determinism with a certain property of completeness of the system of physical laws. The problem of empirical foundation (problem of verification) is an inquiry into the form of the protocol-sentences and the consequence-relations between the physical sentences—especially the laws—and the protocol-sentences. The question of the logical foundations of physical measurement is the question of the syntactical form of quantitative physical sentences (containing functors) and of the relations of derivation between these sentences and the non-quantitative sentences (containing predicates; for instance, sentences about pointer-coincidences). Further, such questions as those concerning the relation between macro- and micro-magnitudes or between macro- and micro-laws are to be formulated as syntactical questions; the elucidation of the concept of genidentity also belongs to syntax.

The problems of the foundations of biology refer mainly to the connection between biology and the physics of the inorganic, or, more exactly, to the possibility of translating the biological language S_1 into that sub-language S_2 of the physical language which contains the necessary terms for the purpose of describing the inorganic processes and the necessary laws for the explanation of these processes; in other words: to the relations between S_1 and S_2 on the basis of the total language S_3 which contains both as sub-languages. There are, most importantly, two questions which must be distinguished: (1) Can the *concepts* of biology be reduced to those of the physics of the inorganic? In syntactical form: Is every descriptive primitive symbol of S_1 synonymous in S_3 with a symbol which is definable in S_2? If this is the case, then there is in relation to S_3 an equipollent translation of the L-sub-language of S_1 into that of S_2. (2) Can the *laws* of biology be reduced to those of the physics of the inorganic? In syntactical form: is every primitive law of S_1 equipollent in S_3 to a law which is valid in S_2? If so, then there is, in relation to S_3, an equipollent translation of S_1 (as a P-language) into S_2. This second question constitutes the scientific core of the problem of *vitalism*, which is, however, often entangled with extra-scientific pseudo-problems.

The *problems of the foundations of psychology* contain analogues to those of biology just mentioned. (1) Can the *concepts* of psychology be reduced to those of physics in the narrower sense? (2) Can the *laws* of psychology be reduced to those of physics in the narrower sense? (Physicalism answers the first question in the affirmative, but leaves the second open.) The so-called *psychophysical problem* is usually formulated as a question concerning the relation of two object-domains: the domain of the psychical processes and the domain of the parallel physical processes in the central nervous system. But this formulation in the material mode of speech leads into a morass of pseudo-problems (for instance: "Are the parallel processes merely functionally correlated, or are they connected by a causal relation? Or is it the same process seen from two different sides?"). With the use of the formal mode of speech it becomes clear that we are here concerned only with the relation between two sub-languages, namely, the psychological and the physical language; the question is whether two parallel sentences are always, or only in certain cases, equipollent with one another, and, if so, whether they are L- or P-equipollent. This important problem can only be grappled with at all if it is formulated correctly, namely, as a syntactical problem—whether in the manner indicated or in some other. In the controversy regarding *behaviorism* there are two different kinds of question to be distinguished. The empirical questions which are answered by the behavioristic investigators on the basis of their observations do not belong here; they are object-questions of a special science. On the other hand, the fundamental question of behaviorism, which is sometimes designated as a methodological or an epistemological problem, is a problem of the logic of science. It is often formulated in the material mode of speech as a pseudo-object-question (e.g. "Do mental processes exist?", "Is psychology concerned only with physical behaviour?", and so on). If, however, instead of being formulated in this way it is formulated in the formal mode, it will be seen that here again the question is one of the reducibility of the psychological concepts; the fundamental thesis of behaviorism is thus closely allied to that of physicalism.

The *problems of the foundations of sociology* (in the widest sense, including the science of history) are for the most part analogous to those of biology and psychology.

§ 84. THE PROBLEM OF THE FOUNDATION OF MATHEMATICS

What should a logical foundation of mathematics achieve? On this question there are various views; the fundamental antithesis between them is particularly clearly brought out in two doctrines, *logicism*, which was founded by Frege (1884), and *formalism*, represented by Frege's opponents. (The designations 'logicism' and 'formalism' only appeared later.) Frege's opponents maintained that the logical foundation of mathematics is effected by the construction of a formal system, a calculus, a system of axioms, which makes possible the proof of the formulae of classical mathematics; in this the meaning of the symbols is not to be taken into consideration, the symbols are, so to speak, implicitly defined by the primitive sentences of the calculus; the question as to what numbers actually are—which goes beyond the domain of the calculus—must be rejected. Formalism today represents a view which is in essentials the same, but which has been improved upon in several important points, notably by Hilbert. According to this view, mathematics and logic are constructed together in a common calculus; the question of freedom from contradiction is made the centre of the investigations; the formal treatment (the so-called metamathematics) is carried out more strictly than before. As opposed to the formalist standpoint, Frege maintained that the logical foundation of mathematics has the task, not only of setting up a calculus, but also, and pre-eminently, of giving an account of the meaning of mathematical symbols and sentences. He tried to perform this task by reducing the symbols of mathematics to the symbols of logic by means of definitions, and proving the sentences of mathematics by means of the primitive sentences of logic with the help of the logical rules of inference ([*Grundgesetze*]). Later Russell and Whitehead, also representing the standpoint of logicism, carried out in an improved form the construction of mathematics on the basis of logic ([*Princ. Math.*]). We will not go into certain difficulties with which a structure of this kind is faced (see Carnap [*Logizismus*]), for we are here not so much concerned with the question whether mathematics can be derived from logic or must be constructed simultaneously with it, as with the question whether the construction is to be of a purely formal nature, or whether the meaning of the symbols must be determined. The apparently complete antithesis of the opposing views on this point can, however, be overcome. The formalist view is right in holding that the construction of the system can be effected purely formally, that is to say, without reference to the meaning of the symbols; that it is sufficient to lay down rules of transformation, from which the validity of certain sentences and the consequence relations between certain sentences follow; and that it is not necessary either to ask or to answer any questions of a material nature which go beyond the formal structure. But the task which is thus outlined is certainly not fulfilled by the construction of a logico-mathematical calculus alone. For this calculus does not contain all the sentences which contain mathematical symbols and which are relevant for science, namely those sentences which are concerned with the *application of mathematics*, i.e. synthetic descriptive sentences with mathematical symbols. For instance, the sentence "In this room there are now two people present" cannot be derived from the sentence "Charles and Peter are in this room now and no one else" with the help of the logico-mathematical calculus alone, as it is usually constructed by the formalists; but it can be derived with the help of the logicist system, namely on the basis of Frege's definition of '2'. A logical foundation of mathematics is only given when a system is built up which enables derivations of this kind to be made. The system must contain general rules of formation concerning the occurrence of the mathematical symbols in synthetic descriptive sentences also, together with consequence-rules for such sentences. Only in this way is the application of mathematics, i.e. calculation with numbers of empirical objects and with measures of empirical magnitudes, rendered possible and systematized. *A structure of this kind fulfils, simultaneously, the demands of both formalism and logicism.* For, on the one hand, the procedure is a purely formal one, and on the other, the meaning of the mathematical symbols is established and thereby the application of mathematics in actual science is made possible, namely, by *the inclusion of the mathematical calculus in the total language.* The logicist requirement only appears to be in contradiction with the formalist one; this apparent antithesis arises as a result of the ordinary formulation in the material mode of speech, namely, "an interpretation for mathematics must be given in order that it may be applied to reality". By translation into the formal mode of speech this relation is reversed: the interpretation of mathematics is effected by means of the rules of application. The *requirement of logicism* is then formulated in this way: *the task of the logical foundation of mathematics is not fulfilled by a metamathematics (that is, by a syntax of mathematics) alone, but only by a syntax of the total language, which contains both logico-mathematical and synthetic sentences.*

Whether, in the construction of a system of the kind described, only logical symbols in the narrower sense are to be included amongst the primitive symbols (as by both Frege and Russell) or also mathematical symbols (as by Hilbert), and whether only logical primitive sentences in the narrower sense are to be taken as L-primitive sentences, or also mathematical sentences, is not a question of philosophical significance, but only one of technical expedience. In the construction of Languages I and II we have followed Hilbert and selected the second method. Incidentally, the question is not even accurately formulated; we have in the general syntax made a formal distinction between logical and descriptive symbols, but a precise classification of the logical symbols in our sense into logical symbols in the narrower sense and mathematical symbols has so far not been given by anyone.

The logical analysis of geometry has shown that it is necessary to distinguish clearly between mathematical and physical geometry. The sentences belonging to the two domains, although they often have the same wording in the ordinary use of language, have a very different logical character. *Mathematical geometry* is a part of pure mathematics, whether it is constructed as an axiomatic system or in the form of analytical geometry. The questions of the foundation of mathematical geometry thus belong to the syntax of the geometrical axiom-systems, or to the syntax of the systems of co-ordinates respectively. *Physical geometry*, on the other hand, is a part of physics; it arises from a system of mathematical geometry by means of the construction of the so-called correlative definitions (see § 25). In the case of the problems of the foundation of physical geometry, the question is one of the syntax of the geometrical system as a sub-language of the physical language. The principal theses, for example, of the empiricist view of geometry: "The theorems of mathematical geometry are analytic", "The theorems of physical geometry are synthetic but P-valid", are obviously syntactical sentences.

§ 85. SYNTACTICAL SENTENCES IN THE LITERATURE OF THE SPECIAL SCIENCES

In all scientific discussions, object-questions and questions of the logic of science, i.e. syntactical questions, are bound up with one another. Even in treatises which have not a so-called epistemological problem or problem of foundation as their subject, but are concerned with specialized scientific questions, a considerable, perhaps even a preponderant, number of the sentences are syntactical. They speak, for instance, *about* certain definitions, about the sentences of the domain which have been hitherto accepted, about the statements or derivations of an opponent, about the compatibility or incompatibility of different assumptions, and so on.

It is easy to realize that a *mathematical* treatise is predominantly metamathematical, that is to say, that it contains, in addition to proper mathematical sentences (for instance: "Every even number is the sum of two prime numbers"), syntactical sentences (of such forms as: "From...it follows that...", "By substitution we get...", "We will transform the expression...", and the like). The same thing is equally true, however, of treatises of *empirical science*. We will illustrate this by an example from physics. In the following table the first column contains the initial sentences (abbreviated) of Einstein's *Zur Elektrodynamik bewegter Körper* (1905). The reformulation in the second column is merely for the purpose of making clear the character of the sentences. In the third column, the character of the individual sentences or descriptions is stated, and it is shown that the majority of these are syntactical.

Sentences from the original	*Paraphrase*	*Kinds of sentence* (p.s. = pure-syntactical. d.s. = descriptive - syntactical.)
That Maxwell's electro-dynamics ...	In the laws which are consequences of the Maxwell equations	p.s. description of sentences.
lead to asymmetries in their application to bodies in motion	certain asymmetries are shown	p.s. sentence about laws
which do not appear to appertain to the phenomena	which do not occur in the appertaining protocol-sentences.	and about protocol-sentences.
is well known.	Contemporary physicists know that	Historical d.s. sentence.
For example, if one thinks of ... reciprocal causation	*Example:* the reciprocal causation-sentences	p.s. description of sentences.
Here the observable phenomenon is dependent only upon the relative motion of conductor and magnet,	The protocol-sentences are dependent only upon such and such sentences of the system.	p.s. sentence.
while, according to the usual view, the case in which the one body is in motion must be strictly separated from the case in which the other is in motion.	In the ordinary form of the system the two concrete sentences '...' and '...' are not equipollent to each other.	p.s. sentence (with descriptions of two sentences).
If, namely, the magnet moves ..., then an electric field ... is the result,	If a magnet moves ..., then an electric field ... results.	Object-sentence (physical law).
which produces an electric current.	If an electric field ... arises, a current ... results.	As before.
But if the magnet does not move ... then no field ... results,	(Analogous.)	As before.
but on the other hand an electro-motive power results in the conductor ...,	(Analogous.)	As before.

Sentences from the original	Paraphrase	Kinds of sentence
which, however, ... causes ... electric currents.	(Analogous.)	As before.
Examples of a similar kind,	A 1. Sentences similar to the previous ones.	(Loose) p.s. description of sentences.
like the unsuccessful attempts to prove a motion of the earth relative to the "light medium",	A 2. Such and such protocol-sentences occurring in the history of physics. By means of these protocol-sentences such and such an hypothesis is refuted.	Historical d.s. description of sentences. p.s. sentence
lead to the supposition that	The sentences A suggest the tentative construction of a physical system S for which the sentences B are true (that is to say, S is a system of hypotheses which is confirmed by the sentences A).	p.s. sentence.
... in electro-dynamics no properties of the observable phenomena ... correspond to the concept of absolute rest,	B 1. There is no term in the appertaining protocol-sentences (of the system S) corresponding to the term 'absolute rest' in the sentences of electro-dynamics.	p.s. sentence.
but rather that ... the same electro-dynamic ... laws are valid for all co-ordinate systems	B 2. The ... laws (of the system S) have the same form in relation to all co-ordinate systems.	p.s. sentence (about certain transformations).
We will take this supposition		
(whose content will be called in what follows the "Principle of Relativity")	B 2 shall be called the "Principle of Relativity".	p.s. definition.
as an hypothesis.	B 2 is stated as a hypothetical P-rule.	p.s. convention (definition of 'P-valid in S').

§ 86. THE LOGIC OF SCIENCE IS SYNTAX

We have attempted to show by a brief examination of the problems of the logical analysis of physics and of the so-called problems of foundation of the different domains—which also belong to the logic of science—that these are, at bottom, syntactical, although the ordinary formulation of the problems often disguises their character. Metaphysical philosophy tries to go beyond the empirical scientific questions of a domain of science and to ask questions concerning the nature of the objects of the domain. These questions we hold to be pseudo-questions. The non-metaphysical logic of science, also, takes a different point of view from that of empirical science, not, however, because it assumes any metaphysical transcendency, but because it makes the language-forms themselves the objects of a new investigation. On this view, it is only possible, in any domain of science, to speak either *in* or *about* the sentences of this domain, and thus only object-sentences and syntactical sentences can be stated.

The fact that we differentiate these two kinds of sentences does not mean that the two investigations must always be kept separate. In the actual practice of scientific research, on the contrary, the two points of view and the two kinds of sentences are linked with one another. We have seen from the example of a treatise on physics that investigations in the domains of the special sciences contain many syntactical sentences. But it is also true, conversely, that researches in the logic of science always contain numerous object-sentences; these sentences are in part object-sentences of the domain to which logical analysis is being applied, and in part sentences concerning the psychological, sociological, and historical circumstances under which work is being done in that field. So although we can divide the concepts into logical and descriptive concepts, and the sentences of simpler form into sentences of the logic of science (that is to say, syntactical sentences) and object-sentences, on the other hand no strict classification of the investigations themselves and the treatises in which they are set forth is possible. Treatises in the domain of biology, for instance, contain in part biological, and in part syntactical, sentences; there are only differences of degree, according to which of the two sorts of question predominates; and on this basis one may, in practice, distinguish between specially biological treatises and treatises of the logic of science. He who wishes to investigate the questions of the logic of science must, therefore, renounce the proud claims of a philosophy that sits enthroned above the special sciences, and must realize that he is working in exactly the same field as the scientific specialist, only with a somewhat different emphasis: his attention is directed more to the logical, formal, syntactical connections. Our thesis that the logic of science is syntax must therefore not be misunderstood to mean that the task of the logic of science could be carried out independently of empirical science and without regard to its empirical results. The syntactical investigation of a system which is already given is indeed a purely mathematical task. But the language of science is not given to us in a syntactically established form; whoever desires to investigate it must accordingly take into consideration the language which is used in practice in the special sciences, and only lay down rules on the basis of this. In principle, certainly, a proposed new syntactical formulation of any particular point of the language of science is a convention, i.e. a matter of free choice. But such a convention can only be useful and productive in practice if it has regard to the available empirical findings of scientific investigation. [For instance, in physics the choice between deterministic laws and laws of probability, or between Euclidean and non-Euclidean geometry, although not univocally determined by empirical material, is yet made in consideration of this material.] All work in the logic of science, all philosophical work, is bound to be unproductive if it is not done in close co-operation with the special sciences.

Perhaps we may say that the researches of non-metaphysical philosophy, and especially those of the logic of science of the last decades, have all, at bottom, been syntactical researches, although unconsciously. This essential character of such investigations must now also be recognized in theory and systematically observed in practice. Only then will it be possible to replace traditional philosophy by a strict scientific discipline, namely, that of the logic of science as the syntax of the language of science. The step from the morass of subjectivist philosophical problems on to the firm ground of exact syntactical problems must be taken. Then only shall we have as our subject-matter exact terms and theses that can be clearly apprehended. Then only will there be any possibility of fruitful co-operative work on the part of the various investigators working on the same problems—work fruitful for the individual questions of the logic of science, for the scientific domain which is being investigated, and for science as a whole. In this book we have only created a first working-tool in the form of syntactical terms. The use of this instrument for dealing with the numerous and urgent contemporary problems of the logic of science, and the improvement of it which will follow from its use, demands the co-operation of many minds.

BIBLIOGRAPHY AND INDEX OF AUTHORS

The numbers immediately following an author's name indicate the pages of this book on which he is mentioned. The main references are printed in black type.

The shortened forms of titles which precede them in square brackets are those used in citation throughout the book.

* The publications marked with an asterisk have appeared since the writing of the German original, and hence are not mentioned in the text. The most important of these are: Hilbert and Bernays [Grundl. 1934]; Quine [System] (see the author's review in Erkenntnis, 5, 1935, p. 285); Tarski [Wahrh.] (cf. Kokoszynska [Wahrheit]).

Exhaustive bibliographies of the literature of logistics and logical syntax are to be found in: Fraenkel [Mengenlehre]; Jörgensen [Treatise]; and Lewis [Survey].

Ackermann, W.
Zum Hilbertschen Aufbau der reellen Zahlen. Math. Ann. **99**, 1928.
Über die Erfüllbarkeit gewisser Zählausdrücke. Math. Ann. **100**, 1928.
See also Hilbert.

Ajdukiewicz, K., **167**, **176**, 227.
[Sprache] Sprache und Sinn. Erk. **4**, 1934.
Das Weltbild und die Begriffsapparatur. Erk. **4**, 1934.
*Die syntaktische Konnexität. Studia Philos. **1**, 1935.

Ayer, A. J.
*Language, Truth and Logic. London, 1936.

Bachmann, F., see Carnap.

Becker, O., 46, 245, 246, **250**, **254**.
Mathematische Existenz. Jahrb. Phänom. 1927; also published separately.
[Modalitäten] Zur Logik der Modalitäten. Jahrb. Phänom. **11**, 1930.

Behmann, H., 49 f., **139**, 197, **246**.
Beiträge zur Algebra der Logik, insbesondere zum Entscheidungsproblem. Math. Ann. **86**, 1922.
[Logik] Mathematik und Logik, Leipzig, 1927.
Entscheidungsproblem und Logik der Beziehungen. Jber. Math. Ver. **36**, 1928.
Zu den Widersprüchen der Logik.... Jber. Math. Ver. **40**, 1931.
Sind die mathematischen Urteile analytisch oder synthetisch? Erk. **4**, 1934.

Bernays, P., 96, 97, 173.
[*Aussagenkalkül*] Axiomatische Untersuchungen des Aussagen-
kalküls der Principia Mathematica. *Math. ZS.* **25**, 1926.
With Schönfinkel: Zum Entscheidungsproblem der mathema-
tischen Logik. *Math. Ann.* **99**, 1928.
[*Philosophie*] Die Philosophie der Mathematik und die Hilbertsche
Beweistheorie. *Bl. f. dt. Philos.* **4**, 1930.
See also Hilbert.

Black, M.
The Nature of Mathematics. London, 1933.

Blumberg, A. E. and Feigl, H.
Logical Positivism. *Journ. of Philos.* **28**, 1931.

Borel, E.
Leçons sur la Théorie des Fonctions. 3rd ed. Paris, 1928.
(Appendix: Discussion between R. Wavre and P. Lévy on
intuitionist logic, reprinted from *Revue Métaphys.* **33**, 1926.)

Bréal, M., 9.

Bridgman, P. W.
The Logic of Modern Physics. New York, 1927.
*A Physicist's Second Reaction to Mengenlehre. *Scripta Math.*
2, 1934 (cf. Fraenkel [*Diagonalverfahren*]).

Brouwer, L. E. J., 46 ff., 148, 161, 222, 269, 281, 305. (See also
Intuitionism.)
[*Intuitionism*] Intuitionism and Formalism. *Bull. Amer. Math.
Soc.* **20**, 1913.
Intuitionistische Mengenlehre. *Jber. Math. Ver.* **28**, 1920.
Intuitionistische Zerlegung mathematischer Grundbegriffe. *Jber.
Math. Ver.* **33**, 1925.
Über die Bedeutung des Satzes vom ausgeschlossenen Dritten....
Journ. Math. **154**, 1925.
Intuitionistische Betrachtungen über den Formalismus. *Ber.
Akad. Berlin, Phys.-math. Kl.,* 1928.
[*Sprache*] Mathematik, Wissenschaft und Sprache. *Monatsh.
Math. Phys.* **36**, 1929.

Bühler, K., 9.

Cantor, G., 137 f., 267 f., 270.

Carnap, R.
[*Aufbau*] Der logische Aufbau der Welt. Berlin (now Meiner,
Leipzig), 1928.
[*Scheinprobleme*] Scheinprobleme in der Philosophie. Das Fremd-
psychische und der Realismusstreit. Berlin (now Leipzig), 1928.
[*Logistik*] Abriss der Logistik. (Schr. z. wiss. Weltauff.) Vienna,
1929.
Die alte und die neue Logik. *Erk.* **1**, 1930. (French transl.·
L'Ancienne et la Nouvelle Logique. Paris, 1933.)

Carnap, R.
[*Axiomatik*] Bericht über Untersuchungen zur allgemeinen Axiomatik. *Erk.* **1**, 1930.
Die Mathematik als Zweig der Logik. *Bl. f. dt. Philos.* **4**, 1930.
[*Logizismus*] Die logizistische Grundlegung der Mathematik. *Erk.* **2**, 1931.
[*Metaphysik*] Überwindung der Metaphysik durch logische Analyse der Sprache. *Erk.* **2**, 1932. (French transl.: *La Science et la Métaphysique.* Paris, 1934.)
[*Phys. Sprache*] Die physikalische Sprache als Universalsprache der Wissenschaft. *Erk.* **2**, 1932. (English transl.: *The Unity of Science.* (Psyche Min.) London, 1934.)
[*Psychol.*] Psychologie in physikalischer Sprache. Mit Erwiderungen. *Erk.* **3**, 1932.
[*Protokollsätze*] Über Protokollsätze. *Erk.* **3**, 1932.
On the Character of Philosophic Problems. *Philos. of Science*, **1**, 1934.
Logische Syntax der Sprache. (Schr. z. wiss. Weltauff.) Vienna, 1934. (The original of this book.)
Die Aufgabe der Wissenschaftslogik. (Einheitswiss.) Vienna, 1934. (French transl.: *Le Problème de la Logique de Science.* Paris, 1935.)
[*Antinomien*] Die Antinomien und die Unvollständigkeit der Mathematik. *Monatsh. Math. Phys.* **41**, 1934.
[*Gültigkeitskriterium*] Ein Gültigkeitskriterium für die Sätze der klassischen Mathematik. *Monatsh. Math. Phys.* **42**, 1935.
*Philosophy and Logical Syntax. (Psyche Min.) London, 1935.
*Formalwissenschaft und Realwissenschaft. *Erk.* **5**, 1935.
*Les Concepts Psychologiques.... *Rev. Synthèse*, **10**, 1935.
With Bachmann, F., *Über Extremalaxiome. Appearing in: *Erk.* **6**, 1936.
*Testability and Meaning. Appearing in: *Philos. of Science*, **3**, 1936.

Church, A., 160.
A Set of Postulates for the Foundation of Logic. *Ann. of Math.* **33**, 1932; **34**, 1933.
*The Richard Paradox. *Amer. Math. Monthly*, **41**, 1934.
*An Unsolvable Problem of Elementary Number Theory. *Amer. Journ. Math.* **58**, 1936.

Chwistek, L., 9, **213**, 245, 246, **249**.
Über die Antinomien der Prinzipien der Mathematik. *Math. ZS.* **14**, 1922.
Sur les Fondements de la Logique Moderne. *Atti V. Congr. Intern. Filos.* (1924), 1925.
Neue Grundlagen der Logik und Mathematik. I, *Math. ZS.* **30**, 1929; II, **34**, 1932.
[*Nom. Grundl.*] Die nominalistische Grundlegung der Mathematik. *Erk.* **3**, 1933.

Chwistek, L.
With W. Hetper and J. Herzberg: Fondements de la Méta-
mathématique rationelle. *Bull. Acad. Pol., Sér. A: Math.*, 1933.
As above: Remarques sur la...Métamathématique rationelle.
Loc. cit.

Curry, H. B.
An Analysis of Logical Substitution. *Amer. Journ. Math.* **51**, 1929.
Grundlagen der kombinatorischen Logik. *Amer. Journ. Math.*
52, 1930.
Apparent Variables from the Standpoint of Combinatory Logic.
Ann. of Math. **34**, 1933.
*Functionality in Combinatory Logic. *Proc. Nat. Acad. Sci.* **20**,
1934.

Dedekind, R., 137.
Was sind und was sollen die Zahlen? Brunswick, 1888.

Dubislav, W., 44.
[*Analyt.*] *Über die sog. analytischen und synthetischen Urteile.*
Berlin, 1926.
Zur kalkülmässigen Charakterisierung der Definitionen. *Ann.
Philos.* **7**, 1928.
Elementarer Nachweis der Widerspruchslosigkeit des Logik-
kalküls. *Journ. Math.* **161**, 1929.
Die Definition. Leipzig, 3rd ed., 1931.
Die Philosophie der Mathematik in der Gegenwart. Berlin, 1932.
Naturphilosophie. Berlin, 1933.

Duhem, P., 318.

Dürr, E.
[*Leibniz*] *Neue Beleuchtung einer Theorie von Leibniz.* Darmstadt,
1930.

Einstein, A., 178, **328**.

Feigl, H.
*The Logical Character of the Principle of Induction. *Philos. of
Sci.* **1**, 1934.
*Logical Analysis of the Psycho-Physical Problem. *Philos. of Sci.*
1, 1934.
See also Blumberg.

Fraenkel, A., **97** f., 162, 213, **267** ff., 270, 274, 275, 335.
[*Untersuchungen*] Untersuchungen über die Grundlagen der
Mengenlehre. *Math. ZS.* **22**, 1925.
Zehn Vorlesungen über die Grundlegung der Mengenlehre. Leipzig,
1927.
[*Mengenlehre*] *Einleitung in die Mengenlehre.* Berlin, 3rd ed., 1928.
Das Problem des Unendlichen in der neueren Mathematik.
Bl. f. dt. Philos. **4**, 1930.

Fraenkel, A.
Die heutigen Gegensätze in der Grundlegung der Mathematik.
Erk. **1**, 1930.
*Sur la Notion d'Existence dans les Mathématiques. *Enseign.*
Math. **34**, 1935.
*Sur l'Axiome du Choix. *Loc. cit.*
*[*Diagonalverfahren*] Zum Diagonalverfahren Cantors. *Fund.*
Math. **25**, 1935.

Frank, Ph., 280 f.
Was bedeuten die gegenwärtigen physikalischen Theorien für die
allgemeine Erkenntnislehre? *Naturwiss.* **17**, 1929; also in: *Erk.*
1, 1930.
[*Kausalgesetz*] *Das Kausalgesetz und seine Grenzen.* (Schr. z. wiss.
Weltauff.) Vienna, 1932.

Frege, G., 44, 49, 99, 134, **136** ff., 143, 144, 158, 197, 203, 259,
295, **325** ff.
Begriffsschrift. Halle, 1879.
[*Grundlagen*] *Die Grundlagen der Arithmetik.* Breslau, 1884. (New
ed. 1934.)
[*Grundgesetze*] *Grundgesetze der Arithmetik.* Jena, I, 1893; II,
1903.
[*Zahlen*] *Über die Zahlen des Herrn H. Schubert.* Jena, 1899.

Gätschenberger, R.
Symbola. Anfangsgründe einer Erkenntnistheorie. Karlsruhe, 1920.
*Zeichen, die Fundamente des Wissens. Eine Absage an die Philo-
sophie.* Stuttgart, 1932.

Gentzen, G.
*Die Widerspruchsfreiheit der reinen Zahlentheorie. *Math.*
Ann. **112**, 1936.
*Die Widerspruchsfreiheit der Stufenlogik. *Math. ZS.* **41**, 1936.

Glivenko, V., 227.

Gödel, K., 28, 55, **96** f., 99, **100**, **106** f., 129, **130**, **131** ff., 134, 139,
160, 173, 189, 197, 209, 211, **219**, 227, 250.
Die Vollständigkeit der Axiome des logischen Funktionenkalküls.
Monatsh. Math. Phys. **37**, 1930.
[*Unentscheidbare*] Über formal unentscheidbare Sätze der Prin-
cipia Mathematica und verwandter Systeme. I. *Monatsh.
Math. Phys.* **38**, 1931.
[*Kolloquium*] Various notes in: *Ergebn. e. math. Kolloquiums*
(K. Menger). Vols. 1–4, 1931–33.

Grelling, K. and Nelson, L., 211 ff.
Bemerkungen zu den Paradoxien von Russell und Burali-Forti.
Abh. d. Friesschen Schule, N.F. **2**, 1908.

Hahn, H., 280.
[*Wiss. Weltauff.*] Die Bedeutung der wissenschaftlichen Weltauffassung, insbes. für Mathematik und Physik. *Erk.* **1**, 1930.
Logik, Mathematik und Naturerkennen. (Einheitswiss.) Vienna,
1933.

Helmer, O.
Axiomatischer Aufbau der Geometrie in formalisierter Darstellung.
Diss., Berlin, 1935.

Hempel, C. G., 317.
Beiträge zur logischen Analyse des Wahrscheinlichkeitsbegriffes.
Diss., Berlin, 1934.
*Analyse Logique de la Psychologie. *Rev. Synthèse*, **10**, 1935.
*Über den Gehalt von Wahrscheinlichkeitsaussagen. *Erk.* **5**,
1935.
With P. Oppenheim. *Der Typusbegriff im Lichte der neuen
Logik.* Leyden, 1936.

Herbrand, J., 53, 134, 173.
Recherches sur la Théorie de la Démonstration. Thèse Fac. Sciences
Paris (Nr. 2121, série A, 1252), 1930. Also in: *Travaux Soc.
Sciences Varsovie*, Cl. III, Nr. 33, 1930.
[*Non-Contrad.*] Sur la Non-Contradiction de l'Arithmétique.
Journ. Math. **166**, 1931.
Sur le Problème fondamental de la Logique mathématique.
C.R. Soc. Sciences Varsovie, **24**, Cl. III, 1931.

Hertz, P., 275.
[*Axiom.*] Über Axiomensysteme für beliebige Satzsysteme. *Math.
Ann.* **101**, 1929.
Vom Wesen des Logischen.... *Erk.* **2**, 1932.

Herzberg, J. See Chwistek.

Hetper, W.
*Semantische Arithmetik. *C.R. Soc. Sciences Varsovie*, **27**, Cl. III.
1934,
See also Chwistek.

Heyting, A., 46 ff., 166, **203**, 222, **227**, 245, 246, 249 f.
[*Logik*] Die formalen Regeln der intuitionistischen Logik. *Ber.
Akad. Berlin*, 1930.
[*Math.*] Die formalen Regeln der intuitionistischen Mathematik.
I, II. *Loc. cit.*
[*Grundlegung*] Die intuitionistische Grundlegung der Mathe-
matik. *Erk.* **2**, 1931.
Anwendung der intuitionistischen Logik auf die Definition der
Vollständigkeit eines Kalküls. *Intern. Math.-Kongr.* Zürich,
1932.
*Mathematische Grundlagenforschung, Intuitionismus, Beweis-
theorie.* (Erg. d. Math., III, 4.) Berlin, 1934.

Hilbert, D., 9, 12, 19, 35, 36, 44 f., 48, 49, 79, 97, 99, 104, 128 f.,
    140, 147, 158, 160, 173, 189, 197, 203, 244, 259, 272, 274,
    281, 325, 327.
[Grundl. Geom.] Grundlagen der Geometrie. Leipzig, 1899.
    7th ed. 1930.
Axiomatisches Denken. Math. Ann. 78, 1918.
Neubegründung der Mathematik. Abh. Math. Sem. Hamburg, 1,
    1922.
[Grundl. 1923] Die logischen Grundlagen der Mathematik.
    Math. Ann. 88, 1923.
[Unendliche] Über das Unendliche. Math. Ann. 95, 1926.
Die Grundlagen der Mathematik. Mit Bemerkungen von Weyl
    und Bernays. Abh. Math. Sem. Hamburg, 6, 1928.
With Ackermann: [Logik] Grundzüge der theoretischen Logik.
    Berlin, 1928.
Probleme der Grundlegung der Mathematik. Math. Ann. 102,
    1930.
[Grundl. 1931] Grundlegung der elementaren Zahlenlehre.
    Math. Ann. 104, 1931.
[Tertium] Beweis des Tertium non datur. Nachr. Ges. Wiss.
    Göttingen, math.-phys. Kl., 1931.
With Bernays: *[Grundl. 1934] Grundlagen der Mathematik. I.
    Berlin, 1934.

Hume, D., 280.

Huntington, E. V.
Sets of Independent Postulates for the Algebra of Logic. Trans.
    Amer. Math. Soc. 5, 1904.
A New Set of Postulates for Betweenness, with Proof of Complete
    Independence. Trans. Amer. Math. Soc. 26, 1924.
A New Set of Independent Postulates for the Algebra of Logic,
    with Special Reference to Whitehead and Russell's Principia
    Mathematica. Proc. Nat. Acad. Sci. 18, 1932.

Husserl, E., 49.

Jaskowski, St.
*On the Rules of Suppositions in Formal Logic. (Studia Logica,
    Nr. 1.) Warsaw, 1934.

Jörgensen, J., 258, 335.
[Treatise] A Treatise of Formal Logic. Its Evolution and Main
    Branches with its Relation to Mathematics and Philosophy.
    3 vols. Copenhagen, 1931.
[Ziele] Über die Ziele und Probleme der Logistik. Erk. 3, 1932.

Kaufmann, Felix, 46, 51 f., 139, 161, 165.
[Unendliche] Das Unendliche in der Mathematik und seine Aus-
    schaltung. Vienna, 1930.
[Bemerkungen] Bemerkungen zum Grundlagenstreit in Logik und
    Mathematik. Erk. 2, 1931.

Mises, R. v., 149.
Wahrscheinlichkeit, Statistik und Wahrheit. (Schr. z. wiss. Weltauff.) Vienna, 1928.
Über das naturwissenschaftliche Weltbild der Gegenwart. *Naturwiss.* **19**, 1931.

Morris, C. W.
The Relation of Formal to Instrumental Logic. In: *Essays in Philosophy*, 1929.
*The Concept of Meaning in Pragmatism and Logical Positivism. *Proc. 8th Intern. Congr. Philos.* (1934). Prague, 1936.

Nagel, E.
*Impressions and Appraisals of Analytic Philosophy in Europe. *Journ. of Philos.* **33**, 1936.

Nelson, E. J., 254, **257**.
[Intensional] Intensional Relations. *Mind*, **39**, 1930.
Deductive Systems and the Absoluteness of Logic. *Mind*, **42**, 1933.
On Three Logical Principles in Intension. *Monist*, **43**, 1933.

Neumann, J. v., **96, 98**, 139, 147, 166, 173.
[Beweisth.] Zur Hilbertschen Beweistheorie. *Math. ZS.* **26**, 1927.
Die formalistische Grundlegung der Mathematik. *Erk.* **2**, 1931.

Neurath, O., **280**, 281, 283, 286, **320** f.
With others: *[Wiss. Weltauff.]* *Wissenschaftliche Weltauffassung. Der Wiener Kreis.* (Veröff. d. Vereins Ernst Mach.) Vienna, 1929.
[Wege] Wege der wissenschaftlichen Weltauffassung. *Erk.* **1**, 1930.
Empirische Soziologie. Der wissenschaftliche Gehalt der Geschichte und Nationalökonomie. (Schr. z. wiss. Weltauff.) Vienna, 1931.
[Physicalism] Physicalism. The Philosophy of the Viennese Circle. *Monist*, **41**, 1931.
[Physikalismus] Physikalismus. *Scientia*, **50**, 1931.
[Soziol. Phys.] Soziologie im Physikalismus. *Erk.* **2**, 1931.
[Protokollsätze] Protokollsätze. *Erk.* **3**, 1932.
[Psychol.] Einheitswissenschaft und Psychologie. (Einheitswiss.) Vienna, 1933.
*Radikaler Physikalismus und "wirkliche Welt". *Erk.* **4**, 1935.
Le Développement du Cercle de Vienne et l'Avenir de l'Empiricisme logique. Paris, 1935.

Nicod, J.
A Reduction in the Number of the Primitive Propositions of Logic. *Proc. Cambr. Phil. Soc.* **19**, 1917.

Ogden, C. K. and Richards, I. A.
The Meaning of Meaning. A Study of the Influence of Language upon Thought and of the Science of Symbolism. London, 1922.

Oppenheim, P. See Hempel.

Parry, W. T., 254, 257.
[*Koll.*] Notes in: *Erg. e. math. Kolloquiums* (ed. by Menger).
Heft 4, 1933.

Peano, G., 31 f., 44, **97**, 99, 144, 158, 166, 212.
Notations de Logique mathématique. Turin, 1894.
[*Formulaire*] *Formulaire de Mathématiques.* Turin (1895), 1908.

Peirce, Ch. S.
Collected Papers. Ed. by Ch. Hartshorne and P. Weiss. 5 vols.
Cambridge, Mass. 1931 ff. (Especially Vols. 2–4.)

Penttilä, A. and Saarnio, U.
*Einige grundlegende Tatsachen der Worttheorie.... *Erk.* 4,
1934.

Poincaré, H., 46, 161, 269, 318.
Wissenschaft und Hypothese. Leipzig (1904), 1914.
Wissenschaft und Methode. Leipzig, 1914.
[*Gedanken*] *Letzte Gedanken.* Leipzig, 1913.

Popper, K., 317, **321**.
Logik der Forschung. Zur Erkenntnistheorie der modernen Naturwissenschaft. (Schr. z. wiss. Weltauff.) Vienna, 1935.

Post, E. L., 208.
[*Introduction*] Introduction to a General Theory of Elementary
Propositions. *Amer. Journ. Math.* **43**, 1921.

Presburger, M.
Über die Vollständigkeit eines gewissen Systems der Arithmetik....
Congr. Math. Warschau (1929), 1930.

Quine, W. V., **190**.
*[*System*] A System of Logistic.* Cambridge, Mass., 1934.
*Ontological Remarks on the Propositional Calculus. *Mind*, **43**,
1934.
*Towards a Calculus of Concepts. *Journ. Symbol. Logic*, **1**, 1936.
*Truth by Convention. In: *Philosophical Essays for A. N.
Whitehead*, edited by O. H. Lee, 1936.
*A Theory of Classes Presupposing No Canons of Type. *Proc.
Nat. ..cad. Sci.* **22**, 1936.
*Definition of Substitution. *Bull. Amer. Math. Soc.* **42**, 1936.
*Set-Theoretic Foundations for Logic. *Journ. Symbol. Logic*, **1**,
1936.

Ramsey, F. P., 50, 86, 114, **211** f., 213, 283, **321**.
[*Foundations*] *The Foundations of Mathematics, and Other Logical
Essays.* London, 1931.

Reichenbach, H., 78, 281, 311, **317**.
[*Axiomatik*] *Axiomatik der relativistischen Raum-Zeit-Lehre.*
Brunswick, 1924.
[*Philosophie*] *Philosophie der Raum-Zeit-Lehre.* Berlin, 1928.

Reichenbach, H.
[*Wahrscheinlichkeitslogik*] Wahrscheinlichkeitslogik. *Ber. Akad. Berlin,* **29**, 1932.
*Wahrscheinlichkeitslehre. *Eine Untersuchung über die logischen und mathematischen Grundlagen der Wahrscheinlichkeitsrechnung.* Leyden, 1935.

Richard, J., **213, 219,** 222, 270.

Richards, I. A. See Ogden.

Rosser, J. B.
*A Mathematical Logic without Variables. I. *Ann. of Math.* **36**, 1935. II. *Duke Math. Journ.* **1**, 1935.
See also Kleene.

Rüstow, A., 213.
Der Lügner. Theorie, Geschichte und Auflösung. Diss. Erlangen, 1910.

Russell, B., 19, 22, 35, 44 f., 47 ff., **49** ff., 86, **96** f., 99, 134, **136** ff., 140, 143, **144** f., 158, 160, **162**, 164 f., 173, **189**, 192, 195, 197, 203, **211** f., **231**, **244**, **245** f., **249**, **253-255**, 257 f., 259 f., 261, 281, 291, 293, 295, **325** f., 327.
[*Principles*] *The Principles of Mathematics.* Cambridge, 1903.
The Theory of Implication. *Amer. Journ. Math.* **28**, 1906.
With Whitehead: [*Princ. Math.*] *Principia Mathematica,* I (1910), 1925; II (1912), 1927; III (1913), 1927.
Our Knowledge of the External World. New York, 1914.
[*Math. Phil.*] *Introduction to Mathematical Philosophy.* 1919.
[*Introd. Wittg.*] 1922. See Wittgenstein.

Schlick, M., 51, 101, 280 f., **284**, 310, **321**.
Allgemeine Erkenntnislehre. Berlin (1918), 2nd ed. 1925.
[*Metaphysik*] Erleben, Erkennen, Metaphysik. *Kantstud.* **31**, 1926.
[*Wende*] Die Wende der Philosophie. *Erk.* **1**, 1930.
[*Kausalität*] Die Kausalität in der gegenwärtigen Physik. *Naturwiss.* **19**, 1931.
[*Positivismus*] Positivismus und Realismus. *Erk.* **3**, 1932.
*[*Fundament*] Über das Fundament der Erkenntnis. *Erk.* **4**, 1934.
*Meaning and Verification. *Philos. Review,* **45**, 1936.

Scholz, H., 258, 260.
[*Geschichte*] *Geschichte der Logik.* Berlin, 1931.
With Schweitzer, H.: *Die sog. *Definitionen durch Abstraktion.* (Forsch. z. Logistik, No. 3.) Leipzig, 1935.

Schönfinkel, M.
Über die Bausteine der mathematischen Logik. *Math. Ann.* **92**, 1924.
See also Bernays.

Schröder, E., 44, 158.
Vorlesungen über die Algebra der Logik (exakte Logik). 3 vols.
Leipzig, 1890–1905.

Sheffer, H. M.
A Set of Five Independent Postulates for Boolean Algebras.
Trans. Amer. Math. Soc. **14**, 1913.
Mutually Prime Postulates. *Bull. Amer. Math. Soc.* **22**, 1916.

Skolem, Th., 270.
[*Erfüllbarkeit*] Logisch-kombinatorische Untersuchungen über
die Erfüllbarkeit oder Beweisbarkeit mathematischer Sätze.
Vidensk. Skr. Kristiania, 1920, No. 4.
Begründung der elementaren Arithmetik durch die rekurrierende
Denkweise.... *Vidensk. Skr. Kristiania*, 1923, No. 6.
Über einige Grundlagenfragen der Mathematik. *Skr. Norske
Vid.-Akad. Oslo.* I. *Mat. Nat. Kl.* 1929, No. 4.

Tarski, A., 32, 70, 89, **96** f., 160, 167, 172, **173**, 197, 200, **204**, 208,
209, 275.
Sur le Terme Primitive de la Logistique. *Fund. Math.* **4**, 1923.
Sur les Truth-Functions au Sens de MM. Whitehead and Russell.
Fund. Math. **5**, 1924.
Über einige fundamentale Begriffe der Metamathematik. *C.R.
Soc. Sciences Varsovie*, **23**, Cl. III, 1930.
[*Methodologie*] Fundamentale Begriffe der Methodologie der de-
duktiven Wissenschaften. I. *Monatsh. Math. Phys.* **37**, 1930.
Sur les Ensembles définissables de Nombres réels. I. *Fund.
Math.* **17**, 1931.
With Kuratowski, C.: Les Opérations logiques et les Ensembles
projectifs. *Fund. Math.* **17**, 1931.
[*Wahrheitsbegriff*] Der Wahrheitsbegriff in den Sprachen der
deduktiven Disziplinen. *Anzeiger Akad. Wien*, 1932, No. 2.
(Note on a Polish treatise; German translation: [*Wahrh.*])
[*Widerspruchsfr.*] Einige Betrachtungen über die Begriffe der
ω-Widerspruchsfreiheit und der ω-Vollständigkeit. *Monatsh.
Math. Phys.* **40**, 1933.
*Einige methodologische Untersuchungen über die Definier-
barkeit der Begriffe. *Erk.* **5**, 1935.
*Grundzüge des Systemenkalküls. I. *Fund. Math.* **25**, 1935.
*[*Wahrh.*] Der Wahrheitsbegriff in den formalisierten Sprachen.
Stud. Philos. **1**, 1936.
See also Lukasiewicz.

Vienna Circle, 7, 44, **280**, **282**, 309, **321** f. See also Carnap, Feigl,
Frank, Gödel, Hahn, Neurath, Schlick, Waismann.

Waismann, F., **321**.
Die Natur des Reduzibilitätsaxioms. *Monatsh. Math. Phys.* **35**,
1928.

Waismann, F.
[*Wahrscheinlichkeit*] Logische Analyse des Wahrscheinlichkeits-
begriffes. *Erk.* I, 1930.
*Über den Begriff der Identität. *Erk.* 6, 1936.

Wajsberg, M.
Über Axiomensysteme des Aussagenkalküls. *Monatsh. Math.
Phys.* 39, 1932.
Ein erweiterter Klassenkalkül. *Monatsh. Math. Phys.* 40, 1933.
Untersuchungen über den Funktionenkalkül für endliche Indi-
viduenbereiche. *Math. Ann.* 108, 1933.
Beitrag zur Metamathematik. *Math. Ann.* 109, 1933.
*Beiträge zum Metaaussagenkalkül. *Monatsh. Math. Phys.* 41,
1934.

Warsaw logicians, 9, 160, 281. See also Leśniewski, Lukasiewicz,
Tarski.

Wavre, R. See Borel.

Weiss, P., 258.
The Nature of Systems. (Reprinted from *Monist.*) 1928.
Two-Valued Logic, another Approach. *Erk.* 2, 1931.

Weyl, H., 46, 99, 148, 186, 305.
[*Kontinuum*] *Das Kontinuum.* Leipzig, 1918.
Über die neuere Grundlagenkrise der Mathematik. *Math. ZS.*
10, 1921.
Die heutige Erkenntnislage in der Mathematik. *Sympos.* I, 1925.
(Also published separately.)
Philosophie der Mathematik und Naturwissenschaft. Part I.
In: *Handb. d. Philos.*, ed. by Bäumler and Schröter, Munich,
1926. (Also published separately.)

Whitehead, A. N., 44, 99, 158.
See also Russell.

Wittgenstein, L., 44, 46, 49 ff., 51 f., 53, 101, 139, 140, 161, 186,
199, 245 f., 280, 282 ff., 295 f., 303, 304, 307, 321 f.
[*Tractatus*] *Tractatus Logico-Philosophicus.* With introd. by
B. Russell. London, 1922.

Zermelo, E., 93, 97.
Untersuchungen über die Grundlagen der Mengenlehre. *Math.
Ann.* 65, 1908.

INDEX OF SUBJECTS

The numbers refer to pages. The most important passages are indicated by black type.

Abbreviations: I = Syntax of Language I
II = Syntax of Language II
G = General Syntax

M

Material mode of speech, see *Mode*
Mathematics, see *Arithmetic, Number*
Mathematics, Classical, 83, 98, 128, **148**, 230, 325
Meaning, 189, **288** ff.
"Meaningless", 47, (82), 138, **162**, 163, **283**, 319, **321**, **322**
Metalogic, 9
Metamathematics, 9, 325 ff.
Metaphysics, 7 f., **278** f., 282–284, 309, 320

$\mathfrak{N}$, II: 84
Name, 12 f., 26, 189 f.
Name-language, 12, 189
Natural law, see *Law*
Negation, I: **19**, 20; G: **202** f.
Negation, Double, I: 34; G: 202
Non-contradictoriness, II:124,128; G: **207** ff., 211
Non-contradictoriness, Proof of, 128, **134**, **219**
Non-denumerable, 221, 267 ff.
 nu, see *Zero symbol*
Null, II: 134 f.; G: 262 f.

Object-language, **4**, 160
Object-sentence, 277 f., 284
Open, I: **21**, 66; G: **194**
Operable, G: **192**
Operand, I: 21; G: 192
Operator, I: 21, 23; II: 83 f.; G: **191**, 193

p, see *Predicate-variable*
P-, G: **180** ff., **184** f., 316
Perfect, G: 176
Phenomenology, 289, 305
"Philosophy", 8, 52, **277–281**, 332
Physicalism, 151, **320**, 325
Physical language, **149** f., 178, 307, **315** ff., 322, 328 ff.
rules, 178, **180** f.
syntax, 57, **79** ff.
Position, Positional symbols, 12, 45
Postulate, see *Axiomatic Method, Primitive Sentence, Principle*
pr, Predicate, 13; I: 16, 73; G: 188
$\mathfrak{Pr}$, Predicate-expression, II: 83, 87, 134 ff.; G: **188**, 191

Modalities, Logic of, G: 237, 246, **250–258**, 303
Mode of speech, Autonymous, 238, 247 ff.
Formal, 239, 286 f., 288 ff., 299 ff., 302 ff.
Indirect, 291 f.
Material, 237 f., **239**, 286, **287** ff., 297 ff., 302 ff., 308 ff.
Model, G: 272 f.
Molecular sentence, II: 88, 321

N

Null-content, 176
"Number", 285, 293 f., 295, **300**, **304** f., 311
Number, Cardinal, 139, **142** ff., 326
Real, II: 147 ff.; G: 207, 220, 305
Numerical expression, I: 14, **26**, 72; II: **87**; G: **205**
functor, G: 205
predicate, G: 205
symbol (Numeral), I: 14, 17, 24, 26, 59, 73; G: 205
variable, I: 17; II: 84; G: 205

O

Operator, Descriptional, 22; G: 193
Limited, I: 21; G: 191
Sentential, I: 30; II: 92
Universal, I: 21; II: 93; G: **193**, **196** f., 231
Ostension, ostensive definition, 80, 155

P

Predicate-variable, II: 84; G: 195
Premiss, 27
Premiss-class, G: 199
Principal expression, P-symbol, G: 177
Principle of: *Aussonderung*, 98, 268
Complete Induction, I: **32** f., 38; II: 92 f., 121
Comprehension, 98, 142
Contradiction, II: 125; G: 203
Double Negation, I: 34; II: 125
Excluded Middle, I: 34,48; II:125
Extensionality, II: 92, 98
Infinity, II: 81, 97, 140 f.
Limitation, 268 ff.
Reducibility, 86, 98, 142, 212

SYNTACTICAL SYMBOLS (used in connection with Gothic symbols):
{· ·}, 34; +, 34; () (··), 84; (::), see Substitution; [::], see Replacement.

International Library of Philosophy & Scientific Method

Editor: Ted Honderich

(Demy 8vo)

Allen, R. E. (Ed.), **Studies in Plato's Metaphysics** *464 pp. 1965.*
    Plato's 'Euthyphro' and the Earlier Theory of Forms *184 pp. 1970.*
Allen, R. E. and Furley, David J. (Eds.), **Studies in Presocratic Philosophy**
    326 pp. 197͡

Armstrong, D

  A Materi
Bambrough,
  184 pp. 1.
Barry, Brian,
Bird, Grahar
Bogen, Jam
Broad, C. D.
  (2nd Imp
Crombie, I. I
  I. Plato or
  II. Plato o
Day, John F
Dennett, D.
Dretske, Fre
Ducasse, C.
Edel, Abrahi
Farm, K. T. (
Flew, Anthc
Fogelin, Rol
Franklin, R.,
Gale, Richa
Glover, Jon
Goldman, L
Hamlyn, D.
  (3rd Impi
Husserl, Edi
Kemp, J., **R**

2.

Date Due

Körner, Step......., ...
Lazerowitz, Morris, **Studies in Metaphilosophy** *276 pp. 1964.*
Linsky, Leonard, **Referring** *152 pp. 1967.*
MacIntosh, J. J. and Coval, S. C. (Eds.), **Business of Reason** *280 pp. 1969.*
Meiland, Jack W., **Talking About Particulars** *192 pp. 1970.*
Merleau-Ponty, M., **Phenomenology of Perception** *487 pp. 1962.*
Naess, Arne, **Scepticism** *176 pp. 1969.*
Perelman, Chaim, **The Idea of Justice and the Problem of Argument**
    224 pp. 1963.
Ross, Alf, **Directives, Norms and their Logic** *192 pp. 1967.*
Schlesinger, G., **Method in the Physical Sciences** *148 pp. 1963.*
Sellars, W. F., **Science and Metaphysics** *248 pp. 1968.*
    Science, Perception and Reality *374 pp. 1963.*
Shwayder, D. S., **The Stratification of Behaviour** *428 pp. 1965.*